MODERN TOPICS IN BIOCHEMISTRY

Structure and Function of Biological Molecules

Thomas Peter Bennett The Rockefeller University

Earl Frieden The Florida State University

THE MACMILLAN COMPANY, NEW YORK
COLLIER-MACMILLAN LIMITED, LONDON

Fourth Printing 1967

Library of Congress catalog card number: 66-17380

The Macmillan Company, New York

Collier-Macmillan Canada, Ltd., Toronto, Ontario

Printed in the United States of America

Preface

Modern biochemistry has evolved into a massive and intriguing interdisciplinary field. As a liaison between chemistry and biology, it has become the subject which introduces chemists to biology and biologists to chemistry. The very nature of this science accounts for its steady introduction into both the biology and chemistry curricula during the past decade. Because of the usual arrangement of college programs, biochemistry has generally been reserved for students in their junior and senior years of study. However, significant reorganization of the biology and chemistry curricula now underway in most colleges and universities should permit—and often require—beginning undergraduates to study in some detail this fascinating subject. This book was written with these students in mind.

It is not our intention to make this book accessible to beginning undergraduates by limiting it to the simpler topics of biochemistry, since these simpler topics are excellently treated in high school textbooks and in popular paperbacks. Rather, our objective is to allow beginners to move into modern molecular biochemistry and to be carried on to more difficult areas without getting bogged down. We have thus emphasized the biologically important chemical compounds and reaction mechanisms which the cell uses again and again in widely diverse processes. For this reason this book may also serve advanced students as a valuable guidebook to biochemical principles.

Standard biochemical textbooks usually contain more than a thousand pages; even current "brief" texts number three to five hundred pages. Our objective is to offer an authoritative modern summary in less than two hundred pages. By its very nature, such a book as ours can only be an introduction to the topics of biochemistry, and consequently we have found it necessary to drastically condense some, and to omit many, of the peripheral areas of biochemistry. However, the material contained in the suggested readings for each chapter will considerably broaden the scope of the text proper.

Simplifications and generalizations are essential in presenting an introduction to any subject. We have tried to give due qualification when simplifying and presenting tentative, and often controversial, concepts. Of course the final word cannot be presented in this or any other text about the many fast-moving areas of biochemical research, and the beginning student must recognize this fact.

Finally, we hope that anyone with some knowledge of science and curiosity about biochemistry will find in this book stimulating discussions and appropriate answers to his questions about the chemistry of life.

We wish to express our sincerest appreciation to Professors Thomas Conway and Allen Vegotsky for their generous advice and counsel on the original manuscript, to Gudrun S. Bennett and David I. Hirsh for their many suggestions and helpful criticisms during the writing of this book, and to Nelda M. Hirsh for expert assistance in preparing the manuscript.

T. P. B.
E. F.

Contents

ONE

The Chemistry of Life: Biochemistry 1

The Organism—A Chemical Machine / Frontiers of Biochemistry

TWO

Unity and Diversity in the Biochemical Plan 5

The Atoms of Life and Their Importance / The Molecules of Life / Unity of the Biochemical Plan / Energy Transfer and Conversion / Biochemical Synthesis / Variability and Innovation in the Biochemical Plan

THREE

Proteins 14

Amino Acids—Building Blocks of Proteins / Peptide Linkage / Peptides / Proteins—General Features / Primary Structure of Proteins / Secondary Structure / Tertiary Structure / Quaternary Structure / Conjugated Proteins / Biochemical Functions of Proteins / Hormones

FOUR

Biological Catalysts: The Enzymes 43

Catalysis / Enzyme Structure / Enzyme Activity / Factors Influencing Enzyme Activity / Enzyme Specificity / Enzyme Inhibition / Enzyme Mechanisms

FIVE

Biochemical Energetics 57

Basic Thermodynamics / High Energy Compounds / Coupled Reactions

SIX

Adenosine Triphosphate Formation and Utilization 70

Substrate Level Phosphorylation / Oxidative Phosphorylation Linked to Electron Transport / Photosynthetic Phosphorylation / Biological Functions of Energy-Rich Compounds

SEVEN

Structure and Function of Carbohydrates 81

Monosaccharides / Chemical Representation of Sugars / Open Chain Formulation / Closed Ring Formulation / Oligosaccharides / Polysaccharides / Functions of Carbohydrates / Energy and Metabolite Production by Carbohydrates / Embden-Meyerhof Pathway / The Krebs Citric Acid Cycle / The Phosphogluconate Oxidative Pathway / Relationships of Pathways / Photosynthesis—Carbon Fixation

EIGHT

Lipids 102

Fatty Acids / Saturated Fatty Acids / Unsaturated Fatty Acids / Branched Chain Fatty Acids / Cyclic Acids / Simple Lipids / Compound Lipids / Steroids / Functions of Lipids / Fat Metabolism / Fatty Acid Oxidation / Energetics of Fatty Acid Oxidation / Glyoxylate Cycle

NINE

Nucleic Acids: Structure and Function 120

Pyrimidine Bases / Purine Bases / Sugar Group / Nucleosides / Nucleotides / Nucleic Acids / DNA Structure / RNA Structure / Biological Role of DNA / Biological Role of RNA

TEN

Principles of Biosynthesis 139

Introduction / The Energy Problem / Group Activation / Chain Elongation / Patternization / Biosynthesis of Several Micromolecules

ELEVEN

Macromolecular Biosynthesis 151

DNA Makes RNA Makes Protein / Replication—DNA Biosynthesis / Transcription and RNA Biosynthesis / Translation and Protein Biosynthesis / Polysaccharide Biosynthesis / Fatty Acid and Fat Biosynthesis

TWELVE

Biochemical Cytology 168

Intracellular Organization / Specialized Cells / Isolation of Cellular Components / Biochemical Properties of Cellular Components

Index 181

"Biochemistry is becoming, and will probably remain, our chief high-road in the analysis of the behavior of the living mechanism."

A. V. Hill, 1923

ONE

The Chemistry of Life: Biochemistry

Biochemistry—the science that provides molecular explanations for life processes—has become the wonder science of the mid-twentieth century.

The vast subject matter of biochemistry can be arbitrarily separated into two major divisions:

1. *Descriptive biochemistry:* the precise structural chemistry of animate matter.

2. *Dynamic biochemistry:* the chemical changes or metabolism occurring in living systems.

The descriptive chemistry of living systems is exceedingly complex since the composition of the cell is very heterogeneous. A single cell, even of the simplest type, consists of thousands of different chemical substances, both organic and inorganic. The separation and purification of these natural biological compounds, their identification, the determination of their composition and structure, were the initial tasks of biochemists. Originally, biochemistry dealt with the simplest substances, those molecules which were small and easy to crystallize, and substances that could be easily extracted from animal or plant tissues or obtained from the controlled decomposition of more complex molecules. Recently, more refined techniques have been introduced (e.g., chromatography, high speed centrifugation, X-ray diffraction) that permit the study of the fundamentally important macromolecules—starches, proteins, fats, and nucleic acids.

Such descriptive biochemical studies remain one of the main currents of biochemical research.

The dynamic aspects of biochemistry—the interactions and chemical conversions of intracellular substances—have, in recent years, become a well-documented phase of biochemistry. Whereas the physiologist has studied metabolism—the total exchanges of matter and energy in living organisms—the biochemist has been concerned with the chemical pathways and intermediates involved in metabolism. The result of the biochemists' preoccupation is a series of detailed metabolic maps for the biochemical degradation as well as synthesis of sugars, fats, proteins, and many other substances.

The Organism—A Chemical Machine

Contributions to our knowledge of biochemistry represent a coalescence of thought originating from contrasting scientific viewpoints. Observations on gross chemical changes in the whole animal or plant are frequently cited as the start of biochemistry. Thus, seventeen years before the French Revolution Antoine-Laurent Lavoisier demonstrated that living organisms utilize oxygen for combustion and heat production. His studies were the basis for the idea that every living organism is a thermochemical machine. This notion was extended by Julius Robert Mayer, James Prescott Joule, and Hermann von Helmholtz. Almost simultaneously (mid-1840's) these scientists asserted that the law of the conservation and conversion of energy is applicable to the activity of animate bodies and that, from the physical point of view, vital phenomena are indistinguishable from what occurs in the inorganic world.

Complementary to these discoveries was the demonstration by Marcelin Berthelot that mechanical energy can be derived from chemical processes. His work and that of others provided an essential link between physical interpretations of life processes and chemical interpretations.

The development of organic chemistry and the successful efforts to study biologically important substances occurred in the early part of the nineteenth century. Friedrich Wöhler, in 1828, stripped the veneer of mysticism from then-prevailing ideas about organic compounds by showing the ready convertability of ammonium cyanate, an inorganic salt, into urea, a compound found in urine,

$$\underset{\text{Ammonium cyanate}}{NH_4OCN} \xrightarrow{\text{heat}} \underset{\text{Urea}}{H_2NCONH_2}$$

Though his observation came about by chance, Wöhler correctly recognized his experiment as a telling argument against the so-called vital force which was said to be present in living matter. In a statement to Jöns Berzelius, one of the founders of modern chemistry, Wöhler wrote, "I can prepare urea without requiring a kidney, or an animal, either man or dog."

Louis Pasteur's research on the process of fermentation suggested that "ferments" might be a vital property inseparable from the structure and functions of the cell. Justus von Liebig, however, maintained that the "ferment" was a soluble material of proteinaceous nature which worked through catalytic action, and that structural or functional life was not essential to demonstrate its effects and properties. These conflicting ideas, which developed into the Pasteur-Liebig controversy, were resolved in 1897 by the research of Eduard Büchner. He and his brother prepared yeast extracts, totally cell-free, containing only soluble material and showed that the extracts were capable of carrying out the fermentation process. These findings undermined the ideas that a "vital force" inhabited organisms and that biological reactions were "vital properties" inseparable from the intact cell. The notion arose and became a tenuous conviction that living organisms were composed of defined chemical substances which interacted in understandable chemical ways. This can be considered the birth of biochemistry.

Frontiers of Biochemistry

Our optimistic presentation in the following chapters of the current status of biochemistry should not be construed to mean that this science will shortly become a completely documented area. In fact, the major problems of the chemistry of living systems are essentially unsolved. The precise proof of the chemical structures of many low molecular weight compounds has turned out to be much more difficult than anticipated. This is due to the many functional groups and high chemical reactivities of these compounds. We still do not know the structure of even a small fraction of the macromolecules of cells. Although we know the sequence of the subunit amino acids of several proteins, the total conformation of these and other macromolecules is still in doubt. The maps of intermediary metabolism are being developed but are far from complete. The detailed mechanism of action of even one enzyme is still undetermined. We have only a rudimentary knowledge of energy transduction in cells. The factors which control and regulate metabolic activities of living cells have only been glimpsed. How hormones function is still a biochemical riddle. Cellular development and differentiation are being explored, but certainly are not understood. The biochemical basis for such phenomena as memory and behavior are just now being approached. Indeed, perhaps completely new biochemical worlds will be uncovered by the exploration of space.

SUGGESTED READING

Fruton, J. S., and S. Simmonds, "Scope and History of Biochemistry" in *General Biochemistry,* 2nd ed., John Wiley & Sons, Inc., New York, 1960.

Gabriel, M. L., and S. Fogel (eds.), *Great Experiments in Biology,* Prentice-Hall, Inc., Englewood Cliffs, N.J., 1955.

Hill, A. V., *The Ethical Dilemma of Science,* Rockefeller Institute Press, New York, 1960, pp. 7–23.

Needham, J., and E. Baldwin (eds.), *Hopkins and Biochemistry,* Heffer and Son, Ltd., Cambridge, England, 1949.

Pi Sũner, A., *Classics of Biology,* C. M. Stern (trans.), Philosophical Library, New York, 1955.

"It is important, therefore, to establish a taxonomy of biochemical characteristics."

M. Florkin, 1949

TWO

Unity and Diversity in the Biochemical Plan

During biochemistry's early history, the notion emerged that there exists a *unity of biochemistry*—that all cells share the same biochemical processes. During recent years, however, extensive studies have revealed striking variability and biochemical individuality among organisms. This is an apparent contradiction of the unity of biochemistry principle. It is the purpose of this chapter to focus on both the broad similarities—the universalities—and the diversities in biochemical patterns in living matter and to reconcile these divergent views.

The Atoms of Life and Their Importance

Animals and plants are composed of only a fraction of the total known chemical elements. The four constituents hydrogen, oxygen, carbon, and nitrogen are the predominant chemical elements in living matter, and constitute about 99 per cent of the atoms of most organisms (see Table 2–1). Calcium, phosphorus, sodium, magnesium, potassium, chlorine, and sulfur are generally present in concentrations ranging from 0.05 per cent to 1 per cent. Additional elements are usually found in small but measurable amounts: iron, aluminum, copper, zinc, silicon, gallium, manganese, and cobalt. Occasionally other elements—iodine, molybdenum, and vanadium—have restricted roles in certain organisms.

The principal constituent atoms of organisms are, with the exception of iodine and molybdenum, members of the first four periods of the periodic table—all have atomic numbers less than 31. In fact, the four major constituents, H, C, O, N, have atomic numbers of 8 or below. Helium, neon, and argon, which are also in the first four periods, are inert elements and would not be expected to be utilized in biological compounds.

Recently, it has been suggested that the great preponderance of hydrogen, oxygen, nitrogen, and carbon among the atoms of living organisms is due to their being the smallest elements in the periodic system that can achieve stable electronic configurations by adding one, two, three, or four electrons respectively. Being able to add electrons by sharing them with other atoms is the first step in forming chemical bonds and thus molecules. Atomic smallness increases the stability of molecular bonds and also enhances the formation of stable multiple bonds.

Life on earth has evolved around the use of the much rarer element carbon than the relatively prevalent element silicon. Silicon is in fact 146 times as plentiful as carbon in the earth's crust. Silicon occupies the same position in the second period of the periodic table of the chemical elements as carbon does in the first period. It thus shares with carbon the property of tending to gain four electrons and form four covalent bonds. There are, however, significant differences which have resulted in a selective preference for carbon compounds over silicon compounds in organisms. Carbon to carbon, C—C, bonds are considerably more stable than silicon to silicon, Si—Si, bonds, especially in the presence of water or oxygen. Further, simple compounds of silicon, such as SiO_2, are not stable as monomers and aggregate to form huge, clumsy polymers of SiO_2. The corresponding carbon compound, CO_2, is unusually stable and remains as a single molecule.

The first thirty elements in the periodic table vary considerably in importance from organism to organism (Table 2–1). Some are essential to all life. For example, hydrogen, carbon, oxygen, nitrogen, phosphorus, and sulfur are fundamental atomic constituents of the cell's organic compounds. Calcium and magnesium are concentrated in bones and related tissues, and, in trace amounts, they are essential cofactors for many biochemical reactions. Sodium and chloride ions are respectively the principal extracellular cations and anions in animals. Potassium is the leading intracellular cation. These ions have more minor roles in higher plants. All the other elements in Table 2–1 are essential trace elements. Most of them are *transition* metals, and their biological importance is associated with their specific chemical properties. Certain other elements of the higher atomic numbers are frequently found in some plant species and occasionally in other organisms. These elements include: bromine, which is found in certain marine organisms; iodine, a constituent of thyroid hormone in higher animals; and strontium, barium, and silicon, which are found in plants.

TABLE 2-1

BIOLOGICAL SIGNIFICANCE OF SOME CHEMICAL ELEMENTS*

ELEMENT	SYMBOL	ATOMIC NUMBER	COMMENTS
Hydrogen	**H**	**1**	**Universally required for organic compounds and water**
Helium	*He*	*2*	*Inert and unused*
Lithium	*Li*	*3*	*Probably unimportant*
Beryllium	*Be*	*4*	*Unused*
Boron	B	5	An essential constituent of some plants; function not known
Carbon	**C**	**6**	**Universally required for organic compounds**
Nitrogen	**N**	**7**	**Universally required for organic compounds**
Oxygen	**O**	**8**	**Universally required for organic compounds**
Fluorine	F	9	Minor constituent of some bony structures, such as teeth
Neon	*Ne*	*10*	*Inert and unused*
Sodium	Na	11	Principal extracellular cation
Magnesium	Mg	12	Essential divalent cation required for the activity of many enzymes; present in chlorophyll and involved in photosynthesis
Aluminum	*Al*	*13*	*Importance not known and not likely*
Silicon	Si	14	Possible structural unit of diatoms and of possible importance to some plants
Phosphorus	P	15	Indispensable for biochemical synthesis and energy transfer as well as a structural component of many different macromolecules
Sulfur	S	16	Required constituent of proteins and many other important biological compounds
Chlorine	Cl	17	Principal intracellular and extracellular anion, particularly in animals
Argon	*A*	*18*	*Inert and unused*
Potassium	K	19	Principal intracellular cation
Calcium	Ca	20	Major structural component of bone and required for the activity of some enzymes
Scandium	*Sc*	*21*	*Probably unused*
Titanium	*Ti*	*22*	*Probably unused*
Vanadium	*V*	*23*	*Possibly essential in lower plants and tunicates, but unused otherwise*
Chromium	*Cr*	*24*	*Generally believed to be unused but may be essential to higher animals*
Manganese	Mn	25	Major trace element required for the activity of a limited number of enzymes
Iron	Fe	26	Most important metal ion; used in hemoglobin for oxygen transport and as an active site for many metalloenzymes in higher animals

* The relative predominance of the elements in life processes is indicated by the heaviness of type.

TABLE 2-1 (continued)

BIOLOGICAL SIGNIFICANCE OF SOME CHEMICAL ELEMENTS*

ELEMENT	SYMBOL	ATOMIC NUMBER	COMMENTS
Cobalt	Co	27	Structural component of vitamin B_{12}; may be required as trace element for the activity of a limited number of enzymes
Nickel	*Ni*	*28*	*Probably unused*
Copper	Cu	29	Comparable to iron as an essential constituent and vital oxidative enzyme; involved in oxygen transport of proteins in marine animals
Zinc	Zn	30	Trace element required for the activity of an appreciable number of enzymes
Molybdenum	Mo	42	Trace element required for several enzymes
Iodine	I	53	Required as an essential constituent of the thyroid hormone found in most higher animals
All other elements are either inert or toxic.			

* The relative predominance of the elements in life processes is indicated by the heaviness of type.

The Molecules of Life

The predominant atomic constituents of organisms—carbon, nitrogen, hydrogen, oxygen, phosphorus, and sulfur—go into making up the molecules of living matter. Table 2–2 shows the atomic make-up of biologically important small molecules—amino acids, sugars, fatty acids, and also purines, pyrimidines, and nucleotides. These molecules have independent biochemical roles and are also constituents, respectively, of the macromolecules: proteins, glycogen and starch, nucleic acids, and fats. The building blocks of all the macromolecules contain carbon, hydrogen, and oxygen. In addition some macromolecules contain phosphorus, nitrogen, and sulfur. Purines, pyrimidines, and amino acids contain, in addition, nitrogen. Several of the twenty different amino acids contain sulfur. Phosphorus occurs in nucleotides (which play a role in bioenergetics), and are also fundamental units of nucleic acids. Both phosphorus and sulfur are atomic constituents of many of the small accessory molecules called coenzymes.

Unity of the Biochemical Plan

The great variety of living organisms makes the problem of trying to summarize their chemical make-up and organization seem an impossible task. The difficulty is smaller than it appears to be, however, due to the existence of many underlying principles and patterns of biochemical structure and function. The generality of these principles and patterns has

TABLE 2–2

FUNDAMENTAL BIOLOGICAL MOLECULES

Small Molecules	Example (formula)	Atomic Constituents	Derived Macromolecules
Amino Acids	$CH_3CHCOOH$ (with NH_2 on the CH) Alanine	Carbon, nitrogen, oxygen (sulfur)	Protein
Sugars	CH_2OH, O, H, H, H, OH, H, HO, OH, H, OH (ring structure) Glucose	Carbon, hydrogen, oxygen	Glycogen, starch
Fatty acids	$CH_3(CH_2)_{14}COOH$ Palmitic Acid	Carbon, hydrogen, oxygen	Fats, oils
Purines	NH_2, C, N, C—N, CH, HC, C—N, N, H (ring structure) Adenine	Carbon, hydrogen, oxygen, nitrogen	(Nucleotides) Nucleic Acids, DNA and RNA
Pyrimidines	NH_2, C, N, CH, CH, C, O, N, H (ring structure) Cytosine		
Nucleotides	NH_2, C, N, CH, CH, C, O, N, O, $CH_2O—P—OH$ (with O and OH on P), H, H, H, H, HO, OH (ring structure) Cytidylic acid	Carbon, hydrogen, oxygen, nitrogen, phosphorus	Nucleic acids, DNA and RNA

given rise to the idea of the *unity of biochemistry,* a term which implies that there are broad and detailed similarities of composition and metabolic patterns among all living organisms.

The fundamental biochemical composition common throughout the animal and plant kingdoms can be briefly summarized. All living cells on this planet contain water as their predominant constituent. The remainder of the cell consists largely of proteins, nucleic acids, lipids, and carbohydrates along with a few common salts (see Tables 2–1 and 2–2). What must be more than an amazing coincidence is the repetition among plants and animals of the intimate chemical make-up of the two most important biological macromolecules, proteins and nucleic acids. Virtually the same twenty amino acids are found throughout all cells as protein constituents. The same two purine and three pyrimidine bases make up the nucleotide structures which when polymerized form the nucleic acids. A few smaller compounds are very ubiquitous and function universally in bioenergetics, e.g., adenosine triphosphate (ATP) for energy capture and transfer, and nicotinamide adenine dinucleotide (NAD or DPN) in biochemical dehydrogenation.

In addition to their similar chemical composition, all organisms share universal metabolic pathways. The breakdown of key metabolites such as sugars to lactic acid and pyruvic acid (Embden-Meyerhof pathway) and the subsequent oxidation of these acids (Krebs citric acid cycle) occurs via chemical reaction schemes general to most cells. There are in addition a limited number of mechanisms for nitrogen elimination with many compounds and metabolic pathways in common. The pathways for metabolic build-up of unique macromolecules and many simple compounds are of course varied, but the path for synthesis of a specific compound is essentially identical in a variety of plants and animals.

The ubiquity of many biochemical substances and processes is not too surprising when we realize that biochemical events are directed toward two principal objectives:

1. Energy transfer and conversion.
2. Synthesis of specific and patterned chemical structures.

Although we may have occasion to discuss these two basic activities separately, they are quite interrelated. Indeed, the production of discrete chemical entities is dependent upon energy-providing processes. Likewise, the energy conversion processes are dependent upon specific catalysts and other substances which must be synthesized and maintained. Let us explore these two major objectives of biochemical reactivity further.

Energy Transfer and Conversion

The reactions by which energy is made available and used form an impressive fraction of the total activities of living systems. This is true for both plants and animals despite the different directions of their metabolism. Green plants are autotrophic and construct organic substances such as carbohydrates, fats, nucleic acids, and proteins from water, carbon dioxide, simple nitrogen and phosphorus compounds, and other inorganic substances. The energy for these many syntheses comes from sunlight. Some bacteria are chemosynthetic autotrophs and make use of reducible inorganic substances, e.g., iron or sulfur, as an energy source rather than light energy. On the other hand, multicellular animals are heterotrophic and depend on preformed organic food as an energy source. There are also some bacteria, etiolated plants, some algae, and many fungi and protozoa which require complex compounds as a nutritional source of free energy. The contrasting orientation of these metabolisms may be pictured as shown in Figure 2–1.

Although the predominant directions of animal and plant metabolism may be different, it is important to remember that the inherent biochemical reactions are found to be remarkably similar. Thus many major reactions that we study in animals have their counterparts in plants. A conspicuous exception to this is the absence of photosynthetic reactions in animals.

Each biochemical reaction is concerned with some level of energy transfer and conversion, even if it does not produce or utilize energy-rich material. In autotrophic plant tissue, a large proportion of metabolism is devoted to biochemical mechanisms associated with the conversion of light energy into chemical energy and ultimately into energy-rich compounds. In animal tissues there are a variety of energy transformations, some of which are summarized in Table 2–3.

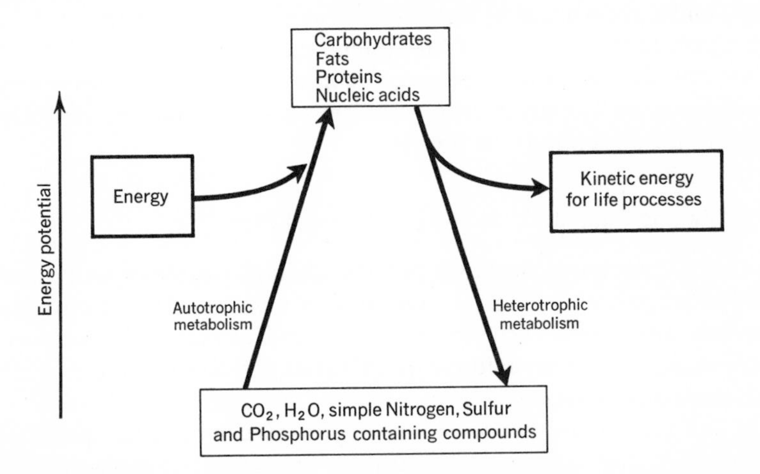

Figure 2–1. Autotrophic metabolism is an energy-consuming (endergonic) reduction reaction. The energy source may be light or a reducible substance as is the case for some bacteria. Heterotrophic metabolism is an energy-releasing (exergonic) oxidation reaction characteristic of all higher animals.

TABLE 2-3

ENERGY TRANSFORMATIONS

Transformation	Organ Transducer
Chemical to electrical energy	Brain, nerve, nose, tongue
Chemical to mechanical energy	Muscle
Chemical to osmotic energy	Kidney and all cell membranes
Chemical to radiant energy	Firefly luminescent organ
Light to chemical energy	Chloroplast
Light to electrical energy	Eye
Hydrostatic to electrical energy	Inner ear
Sound to electrical energy	Ear

Biochemical Synthesis

The production of specific and patterned chemical structures is perhaps much easier for us to appreciate. We know that, throughout the animal and plant kingdoms, nature is very repetitious as to the type of substances which are required for life. All organisms must synthesize deoxyribonucleic acid, the genetic material, and ribonucleic acids. Specific proteins, lipids, and carbohydrates must also be synthesized. In the case of the lower molecular weight compounds there is considerable difference in the biosynthetic capabilities of organisms. For example, humans are unable to biosynthesize eight amino acids and these are thus essential dietary components. Rats have less amino acid synthetic ability and require the same eight amino acids plus two additional ones, histidine and arginine, for optimal growth. Also there are individual fatty acids, vitamins, and sterols which can be synthesized by many organisms but not by others.

In regard to the biosynthesis of protein, it has recently been shown that the *genetic code,* which determines protein structure, is universal. Identical code characteristics exist in each organism's deoxyribonucleic acid (DNA) to specify the structure of its proteins.

Variability and Innovation in the Biochemical Plan

Although organisms display a remarkably high degree of unity in their biochemical patterns, detailed examination reveals that extensive variability and innovation occur in these biochemical plans. To mention the intense variety found in nature is to call attention to the manifestation of this biochemical diversity.

The biochemical differences among organisms can be either quantitative or qualitative. The same basic constituents are found in most cells, but the concentration of these substances may vary considerably from organism to organism. Small molecules and the subunits of macromolecules may be predominantly of one type in certain cells, and a different type in other cells. For example, the fat of aquatic animals contains mostly unsaturated fatty acid subunits, whereas saturated fatty acids predominate in fats of terrestrial animals. Some simple nitrogen-containing compounds are widely distributed among animals, but they are never found in certain insects.

There is also diversity in the metabolic functions and pathways in different organisms. For example, the transportation of oxygen throughout the organism is the function of macromolecules capable of loosely combining with oxygen. These may be copper proteins (hemocyanins) in crustaceans, or iron-containing proteins (hemoglobins) in vertebrates. The molecules differ in structure but perform similar tasks. Further, the end products of certain metabolic routes may vary from one organism to another because of the presence or absence of macromolecules capable of causing a particular reaction to occur. In yeast, for example, the product of the anaerobic breakdown of glucose is alcohol, whereas in muscle the product is lactic acid. Thus, the initial steps in the glucose degradative pathway (Embden-Meyerhof pathway) are identical, whereas the final stages differ.

The concepts of *unity* and *diversity* of biochemical architecture should be recognized as being non-contradictory and easily reconciled. This becomes apparent if one considers:

1. Unity of biochemical principle.
2. Diversity of cellular apparatus and methods.

Thus, there are general unitary concepts of cellular operation. There are energy, biosynthetic, and metabolic degradation problems that all cells have to solve. Superficially, the answers are the same for all organisms. More detailed investigation, however, has often shown that these solutions are brought about in different organisms by distinctive methods, by molecules which are analogous in function but unlike in their detailed structure.

SUGGESTED READING

Baldwin, E., *An Introduction to Comparative Biochemistry,* 3rd ed., Cambridge University Press, Cambridge, England, 1949.

Calvin, M., "The Origin of Life on Earth and Elsewhere" in *Advances in Biological and Medical Physics,* C. A. Tobias and J. H. Lawrence (eds.), Academic Press, Inc., New York, 1962.

Cohen, S., "On Biochemical Variability and Innovation," *Science, 139,* 1017 (1963).

Florkin, M., *Biochemical Evolution,* S. Morgulin (trans.), Academic Press, Inc., New York, 1949.

Florkin, M., *Unity and Diversity in Biochemistry,* T. Wood (trans.), Pergamon Press, Inc., New York, 1960.

Gaffron, H., "The Origin of Life," *Perspectives in Biology and Medicine, 3,* 163–212 (1960).

Oparin, A. J., *The Origin of Life on the Earth,* 3rd ed., Academic Press, Inc., New York, 1957.

Wald, G., "The Origin of Life," *Scientific American,* August, 1956.

"The X-ray analysis of myoglobin and hemoglobin have led to a great advance in our understanding of protein structure and have made it possible, for the first time, to construct three-dimensional models of protein molecules."

M. F. Perutz, 1962

"In determining the structures of only two proteins, we have reached, not an end, but a beginning; we have merely sighted the shore of a vast continent waiting to be explored."

J. C. Kendrew, 1962

THREE

Proteins

Proteins were named and their "first rank" (Greek, *protios,* of the first rank) importance was noted as early as 1838 by G. J. Mulder, a Dutch biochemist, who introduced the term protein:

> There is present in plants and animals a substance which . . . is without doubt the most important of the known substances in living matter, and without it, life would be impossible on our planet. This material has been named Protein.

During the intervening century and a quarter many biochemists have been occupied with determining the chemical make-up, physical properties, and biological function of this group of macromolecules. Their efforts have led to an understanding of the composition and arrangement of the amino acid—building blocks in proteins and the more complex structural features of protein chains. In addition, advances have been made in establishing the relationship between the physical-chemical properties of proteins and their biological roles.

Amino Acids—Building Blocks of Proteins

Amino acids are chemical compounds which contain both an acidic carboxyl (—COOH) and a basic amino (—NH_2) group. The common amino acids have the general structure

$$R\text{—}\overset{\displaystyle H}{\underset{\displaystyle NH_2}{C}}\text{—}COOH$$

in which the amino group, hydrogen, and R-group are attached to the carbon atom one position removed from the carboxyl group. The chemical and physical properties which amino acids have in common are caused by the presence and spatial arrangement of the carboxyl and amino groups. The unique properties of individual amino acids are established by the presence of different R-groups.

The history of the discovery of amino acids began in 1806 with the isolation of asparagine

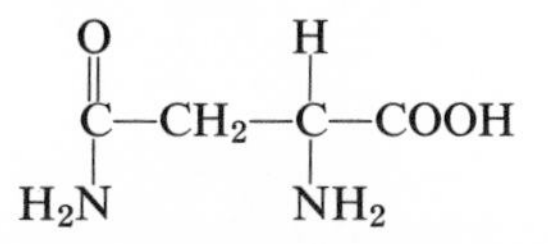

from asparagus juice. In 1820, the first amino acid was isolated from protein material. A high molecular weight protein, gelatin, was cleaved by digestion with dilute acid (hydrolysis). The cleavage products were separated and a major component of the product was identified as an amino acid with the structure

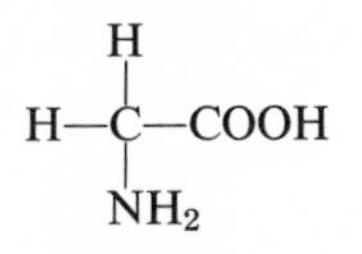

It was given the common name glycine because of its sweet taste. Between 1820 and 1935, the year that threonine

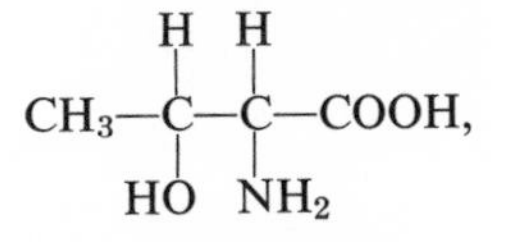

was isolated from the protein fibrin, eighteen individual amino acids were obtained from protein digests. The amino acids were frequently given trivial or common names by their discoverers. These names have survived and have greater usage in biochemical jargon than the more chemically descriptive terms. Although the finding of threonine marked the close of the period of discovery of the amino acid constituents of proteins, the list of naturally occurring amino acids has continued to increase. Many additional amino acids have been isolated from non-protein sources, such as antibiotics and bacterial cell walls, and also as biochemical metabolites in plant and animal cells. Figure 3–1 is a listing of the common names and

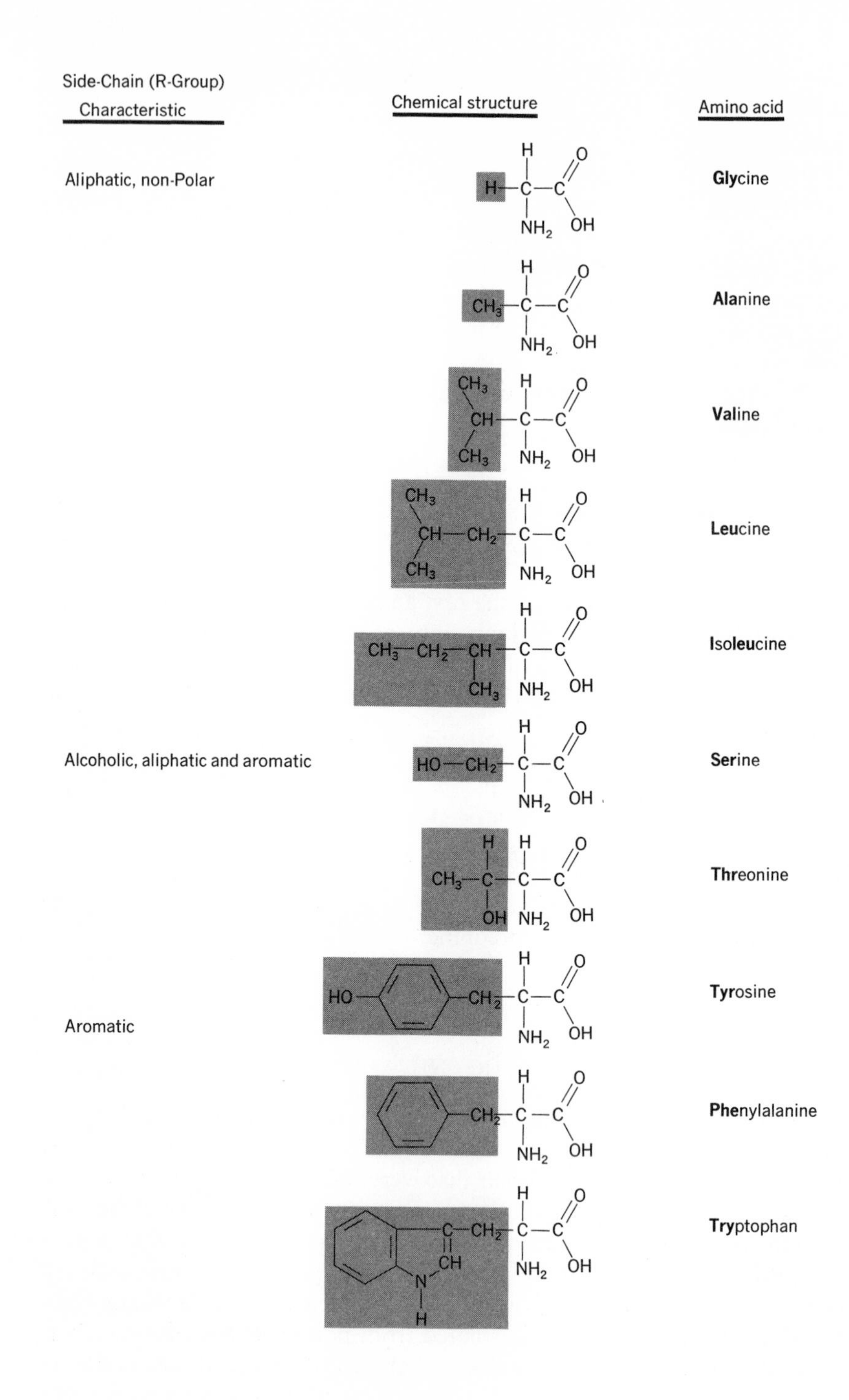
Side-Chain (R-Group)
Characteristic
Chemical structure
Amino acid
Aliphatic, non-Polar
Glycine
Alanine
Valine
Leucine
Isoleucine
Alcoholic, aliphatic and aromatic
Serine
Threonine
Aromatic
Tyrosine
Phenylalanine
Tryptophan

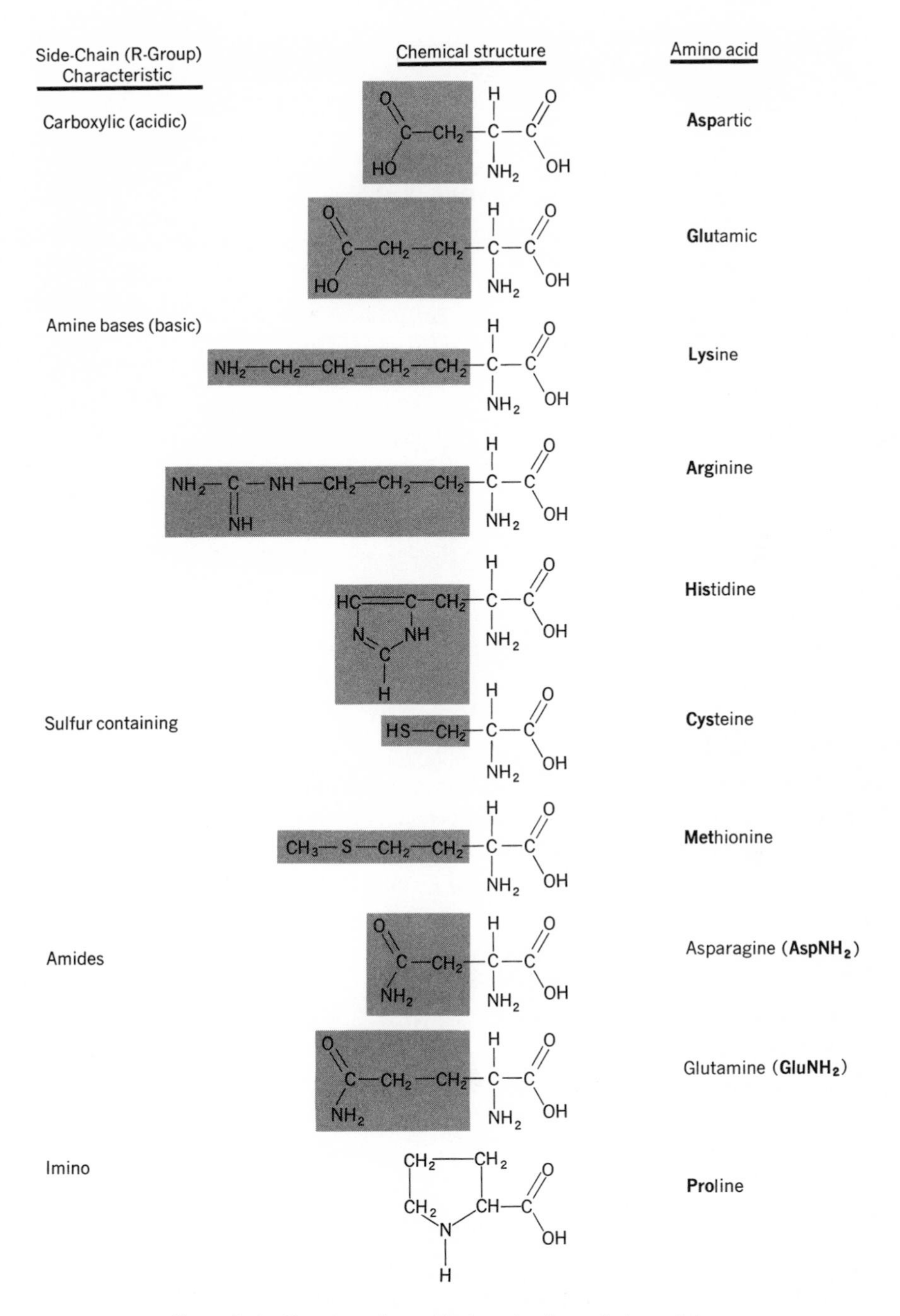

Figure 3–1. Twenty amino acids found universally in proteins.

structural formulae of the twenty common amino acids found universally in proteins. The three letter abbreviations for the amino acid residues are also indicated. Table 3–1 is a summary of the better known non-protein amino acids.

TABLE 3–1

SOME OTHER NATURALLY OCCURRING AMINO ACIDS

Amino Acid Name	Structural Formula	Biological Occurrence or Significance
γ-Aminobutyric	$H_2NCH_2CH_2CH_2COOH$	Present in the free state in the brain
Ornithine	$H_2NCH_2CH_2CH_2CH(NH_2)—COOH$	Intermediate in urea cycle
D-Glutamic acid	$HOOC—CH_2CH_2CH(NH_2)—COOH$	Bacterial capsule and spore wall constituent
Lanthionine	$HOOC—CH(NH_2)CH_2S—CH_2CH(NH_2)—COOH$	Present in the antibiotics subtilin and nisin
Alliin	$CH_2{=}CHCH_2—S(=O)—CH_2CH(NH_2)—COOH$	Garlic oil constituent

The chemical structures of the common amino acids can be written as derivatives of the glycine molecule, NH_2CH_2COOH. For example, alanine consists of the glycine basic structure with a substitution of a methyl group, $—CH_3$, for one of the two hydrogen groups in glycine; for valine

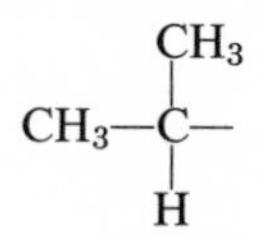

is substituted. These atomic groupings, attached to the unit

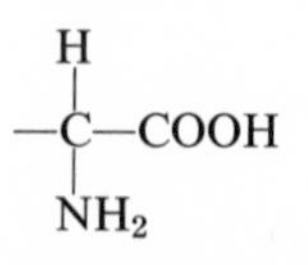

which is common to all amino acids, give individuality to each amino acid. A sampling of these groups, R-groups, is presented in Figure 3–1.

R-groups may be very reactive or chemically inert depending on the atoms they contain (Figure 3–2). The highly reactive sulfhydryl group,

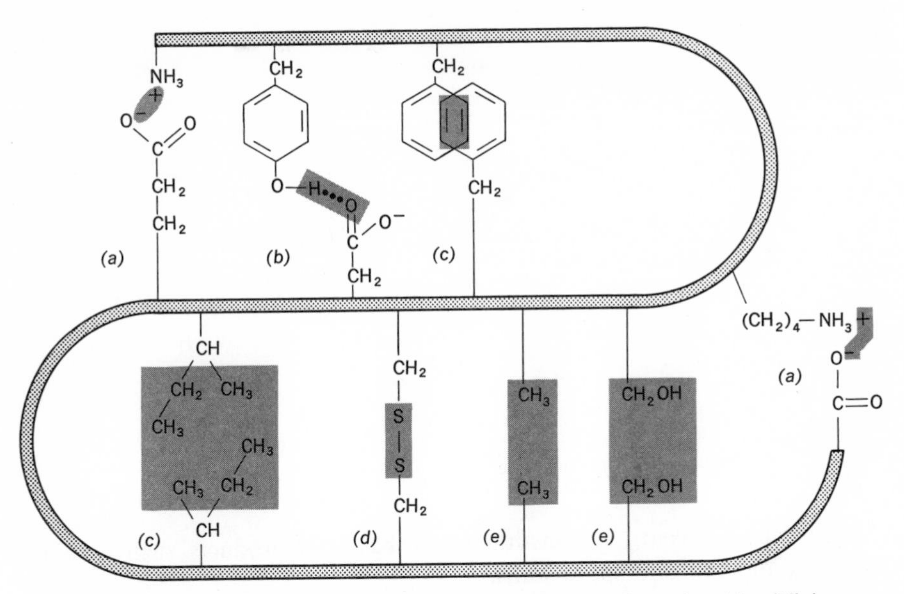

Figure 3–2. Bonds which stabilize 2° and 3° structural features of proteins: (*a*) salt linkages, electrostatic interactions; (*b*) hydrogen bonding; (*c*) interaction of non-polar side chains; (*d*) disulfide linkage between cysteine residues; (*e*) van der Waal's interactions. (Modified after Anfinsen, 1959.)

—SH, present in cysteine, is involved in the formation of disulfide bonds, S—S, found in proteins. The acidic carboxyl which occurs in glutamic and aspartic acid gives these amino acids more highly acid character in addition to the property of interacting with basic substances to form a salt linkage. Lysine and arginine owe their alkaline or basic nature to the second amino group which they contain. As free amino acids the acidic and alkaline amino acids undergo many reactions characteristic of simple acids and bases. One such reaction of biological importance is the interaction between the amino and carboxyl units contained in the R-group of basic and acidic amino acids. The shift of a proton (H^+) creates a strong salt linkage which is of importance in determining protein structure.

There are two possible arrangements in space of the atoms or chemical groups attached to the α-carbon atom of the natural amino acids (glycine is the exception because there are two hydrogen atoms attached to the α-carbon). This relationship is shown in Figure 3–3. The two structures (I) and (II) are mirror images and are designated by the letters L and D because their configurations correspond, respectively, to L- and D-glyceraldehyde (page 84). Technically they are referred to as isomers. Although there are two possible arrangements of the atoms attached to the α-carbon in amino acids, only one of the arrangements, the L structure, occurs in protein molecules. The mirror image of the L structure, the D isomer, occurs occasionally in nature but never in typical proteins. D-Amino acids, however,

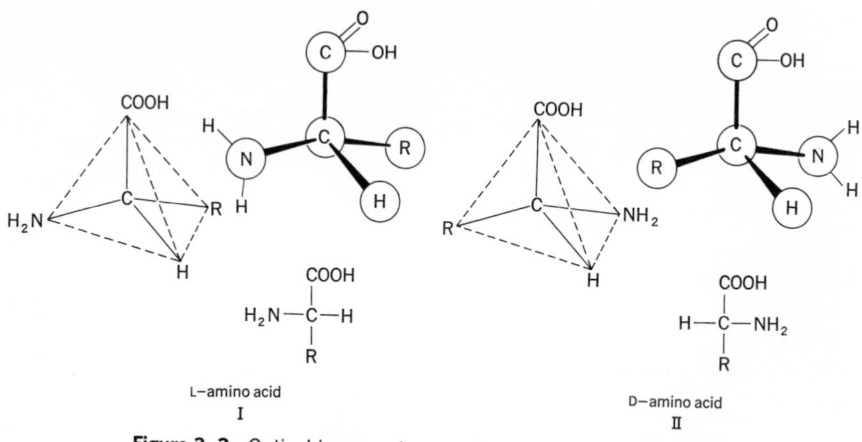

Figure 3–3. Optical isomers (or D and L forms) of an amino acid.

are naturally occurring constituents of bacterial products such as antibiotics and cell and spore walls.

Peptide Linkage

The chemical bond linking amino acids together to form protein molecules is called a *peptide linkage* or *peptide bond* (Figure 3–4). The peptide bond occurs when the amino group attached to the α-carbon of one amino acid is joined to the carboxyl group attached to the α-carbon of a second amino acid. This union is accompanied by the elimination of water from the molecules that unite. In Figure 3–4 the combination of a carbonyl and an amino group, is a peptide bond,

$$—\overset{\overset{\displaystyle O}{\|}}{C}—NH—$$

The repeating unit,

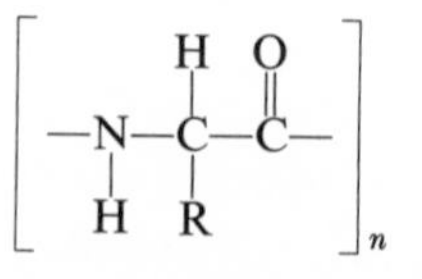

can be any amino acid unit and is called an amino acid residue. The product formed when two amino acids are joined is called a *dipeptide.* When additional amino acid units or residues are added, *tripeptides, tetrapeptides,* and higher polypeptides are formed.

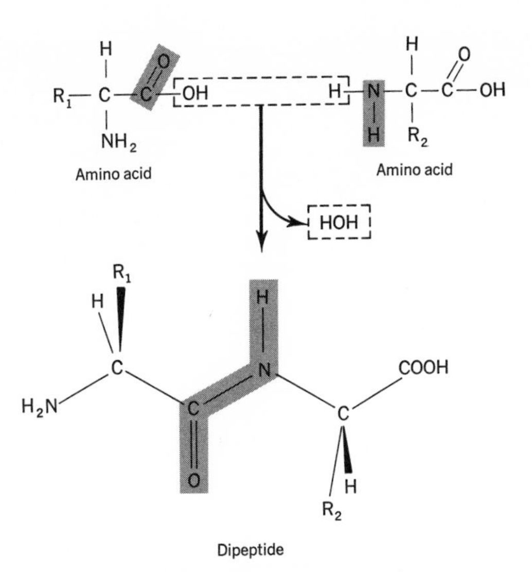

Figure 3–4. Formation of a peptide bond. Shading indicates the planarity of the bond.

Peptides

There are many naturally occurring peptides having known biological significance. These include mammalian peptide hormones, accessory growth factors, and bacterial products (see Figure 3-5). A summary of

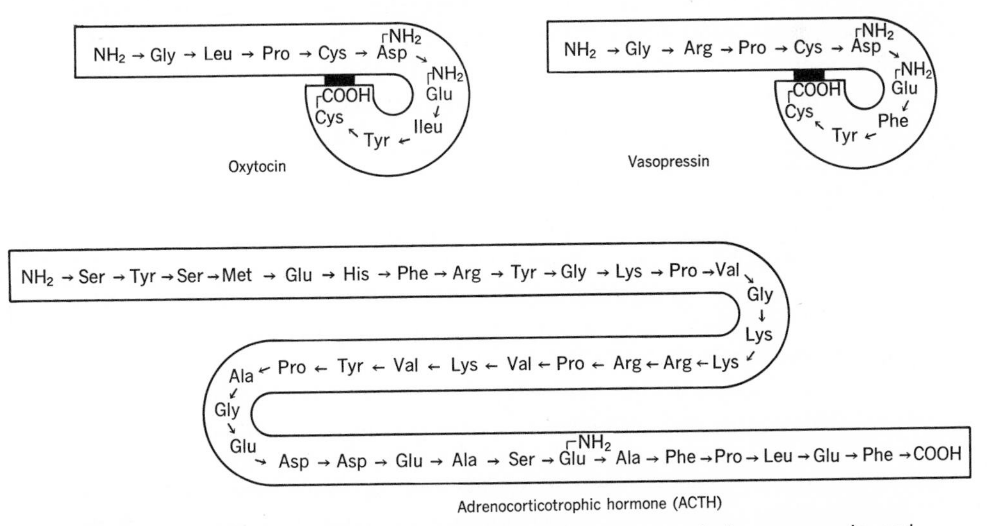

Figure 3–5. The primary structure of the pituitary hormones: oxytocin, vasopressin, and adrenocorticotrophic hormone (ACTH). (S—S bonds in this figure and in Figures 3–10 and 3–11 are represented by black "cement" between chains, or between folds of a chain.)

some biologically important peptides is given in Table 3–2. All except the smallest peptides are generally referred to as polypeptides. As the peptide size increases, a point is reached when general usage suggests that the term *protein* be used instead of *polypeptide*. The distinction between the terms protein and polypeptide is not clear-cut, but, in general, a peptide larger than seventy amino acid units and containing the amino acids of Figure 3–1 is referred to as a protein.

TABLE 3–2

POLYPEPTIDES OF BIOLOGICAL SIGNIFICANCE

Peptide	Amino Acid Residues	Biological Significance
Glutathione	3	Biological reducing agent
Vasopressin	9	Water balance hormone
Oxytocin	9	Stimulates uterine contraction
Gramicidin A	10	Antibiotic
Bacitracin	12	Antibiotic
Melanocyte stimulating hormone (MSH)	18	Stimulates pigment cell production
Glucagon	29	Increases sugar in blood
Adrenocorticotropic hormone (ACTH)	39	Stimulates cortex of adrenal gland

Proteins—General Features

The multitude of different proteins have the common feature of being composed of amino acid residues joined consecutively by peptide bonds. Each protein gets its unique features from: (1) the sequential arrangement of the amino acid units; (2) linkages between the amino acid R-groups; (3) the presence of non-amino acid units or atoms and molecules known as *prosthetic* groups (e.g. Fe^{III}, Co^{II}).

Proteins differ considerably in shape, size, and molecular weight. The smallest known protein is about 6000 times as heavy as a hydrogen atom, i.e., its molecular weight is about 6000. The largest known proteins have molecular weights of the order of 7,000,000. The determination of molecular weight has been made possible by the development of the ultra-high speed centrifuge aided by light-scattering techniques and osmotic pressure measurements. The ultracentrifuge is capable of speed up to 60,000 revolutions per minute and developing centrifugal forces as much as 200,000 times that of gravity. By whirling proteins in an ultracentrifuge and by determining the rate at which they sediment or move outward from the center of rotation—the larger the molecule the faster it moves—biochemists have determined the relative dimensions of many proteins (Figure 3–6).

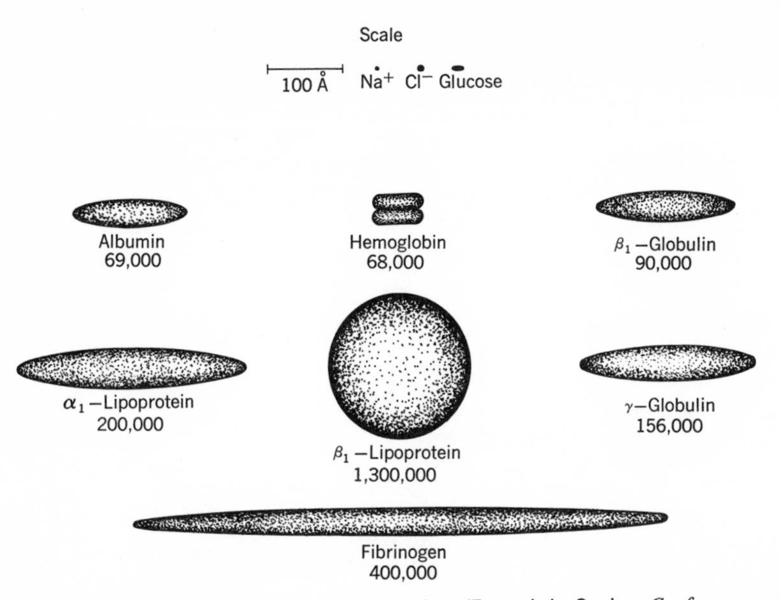

Figure 3–6. Relative dimensions of various proteins. (From J. L. Oncley, *Conference on the Preservation of the Cellular and Protein Components of Blood*, American National Red Cross, Washington, 1949.)

There are four levels of structural organization in protein molecules (Figure 3–7). The primary (1°) structural features are established by the peptide bond linkage between successive amino acid residues. Coiling of the amino acid chain into characteristic patterns—generally spirals or more properly helices—accounts for the secondary (2°) level of structural organization. Folding over and bending of these helices results in the tertiary (3°) structural features. Quaternary (4°) structural features arise from the arrangement of polypeptide or protein subunits to form superprotein structures. The characteristics of these structural levels will be illustrated for the protein molecule hemoglobin.

Primary Structure of Proteins

The fixed amino acid sequence of the polypeptide chain or chains of a protein molecule is the basis for primary structural features and in a sense establishes possibilities for other structural effects, sometimes described as the *conformation* of the protein. Early studies on the acid hydrolysis (cleavage) products, directed toward establishing the amino acid content of proteins, were a first step toward understanding the primary structure of proteins. The amino acid composition of many purified proteins was established by hydrolyzing the protein and analyzing the amino acid composition of the hydrolysis product. For example, ribonuclease, upon

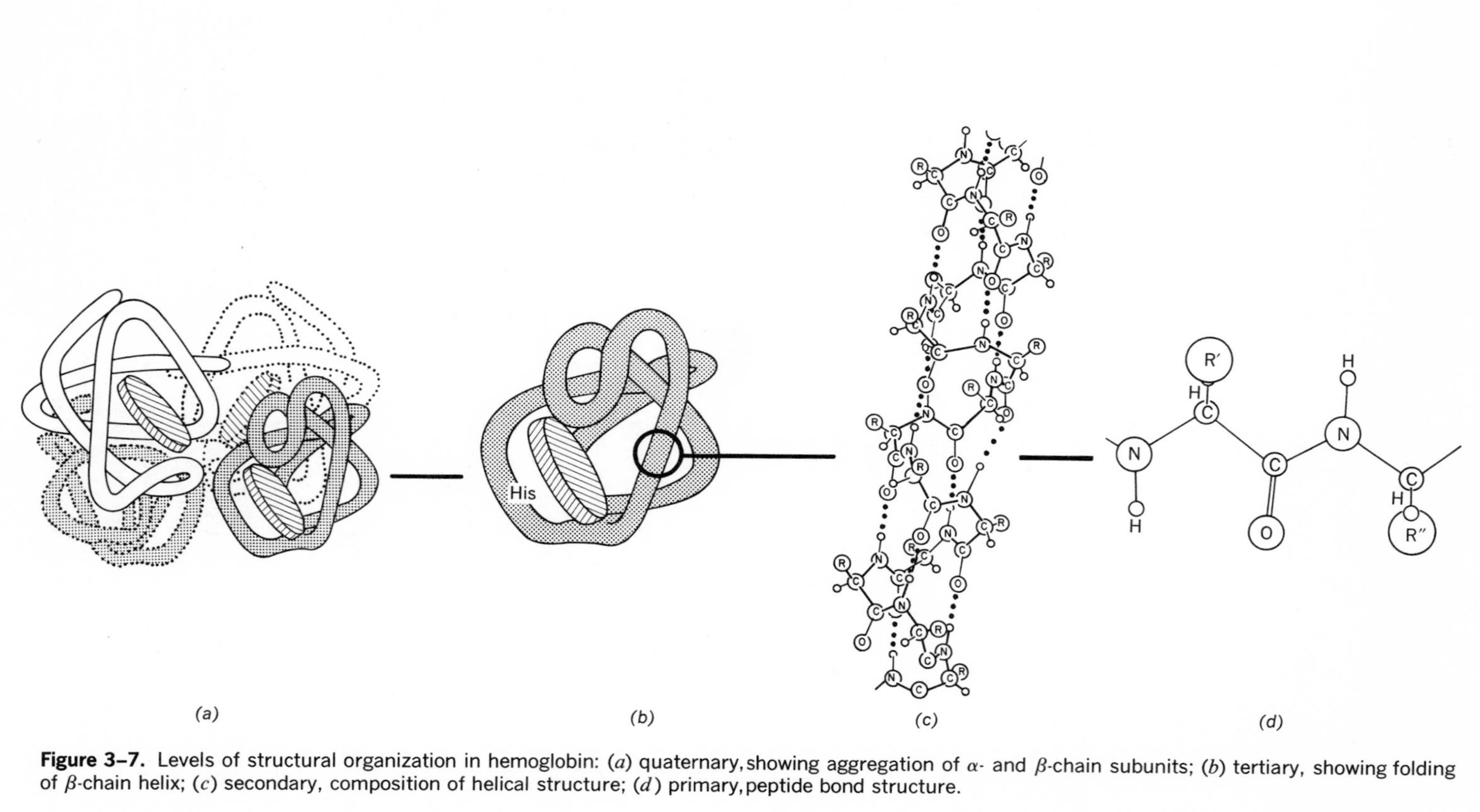

Figure 3–7. Levels of structural organization in hemoglobin: (*a*) quaternary, showing aggregation of α- and β-chain subunits; (*b*) tertiary, showing folding of β-chain helix; (*c*) secondary, composition of helical structure; (*d*) primary, peptide bond structure.

hydrolysis, was found to yield the following number of amino acid units: 10 $AspNH_2$, 7 $GluNH_2$, 5 Asp, 5 Glu, 3 Gly, 12 Ala, 9 Val, 2 Leu, 3 Ileu, 15 Ser, 10 Thr, 8 Cys, 4 Met, 4 Pro, 3 Phe, 6 Tyr, 4 His, 10 Lys, and 4 Arg. To establish the sequential arrangement of amino acids in peptide linkage was a more difficult problem.

Sequence studies were first made on peptides because they are simpler than proteins. As techniques were improved and new methods discovered, the size of amino acid chains for which the sequence was known became longer. Today the complete amino acid sequence is known for thirty or more large polypeptides. These polypeptides are mammalian hormones and bacterial products. In addition, the complete primary structure is known for a small protein hormone insulin, several enzymes, e.g., ribonuclease A (RNAse), lysozyme, and chymotrypsin, the protein coat of the tobacco mosaic virus (TMV), the blood protein (hemoglobin), cytochrome c, and the muscle protein (myoglobin). Partial sequences are known for many other proteins, several virus coat proteins, and a number of enzymes.

Methods for determining the primary structure of peptides have been available for decades. Progress, however, in elucidating the structure of high molecular weight polypeptides and small proteins has been slow. The lack of highly purified peptides and proteins was one hindrance, but the rather widespread lack of conviction that a sequence study was possible, perhaps, was the limiting factor. Improved analytical techniques and isolated, successful sequence studies ushered in a period of optimism in the 1950's which has yielded the results of the past few years.

The questions about primary structure which can be asked and which must be answered to provide an understanding of protein structure are:

1. What is the amino acid at the N-terminal end of the polypeptide chain (i.e., NH_2-terminal)? (See Figure 3–8).
2. What amino acid is at the C-terminal (i.e., COOH-terminal) end of the chain?
3. What amino acids occur between the amino acids in (1) and (2)? How are they sequentially arranged?

A method which has been indispensable in answering the first question was first used in 1918 in studies on the dipeptide anserine, and has been

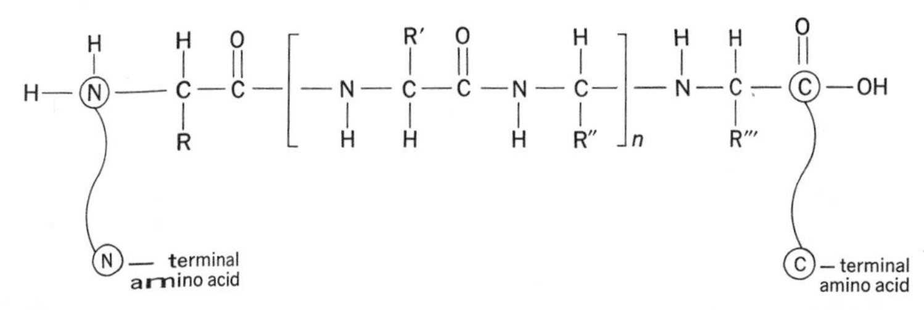

Figure 3–8. Diagram showing the N- and C-terminal amino acids of a polypeptide.

advances in protein biochemistry. Because of the pivotal position Sanger's studies on insulin occupy in primary structural studies, we have chosen to outline in some detail his achievement. The first step was the separation of the so-called A and B polypeptide chains of insulin; chains which are joined by disulfide linkages. This was accomplished by performic acid oxidation of the disulfide linkage to cysteic acid residues ($CySO_3H$). The isolated chains were broken up to intermediate-sized peptides of two to five amino acid units. These peptides were separated and further broken down, and then characterized according to their amino acid composition. Larger peptide fragments were obtained by enzymic digestion of the chain. By knowledge of the amino acid composition of the peptide fragments, Sanger was able to deduce the correct arrangement of amino acids in the entire insulin molecule (Figure 3–10). For example, the peptides containing (1) Phe, Val, Asp, Glu, (2) Val, Asp, (3) Asp, Glu, (4) Phe, Val could have come only from the sequence:

Phe · Val · Asp · Glu

if phenylalanine is established to be the N-terminal amino acid.

The technique of fragmentation has further been developed, extended, and successfully applied to the elucidation of the structure of the enzyme protein RNAse (Figure 3–11), which catalyzes the hydrolysis (or water splitting) of ribonucleic acid (RNA). RNAse sequence studies have centered around the question of the nature of the enzyme's "active site." That is to say, an attempt has been made to understand which amino acids are involved in the binding of RNA to the protein. Biochemists are hopeful that the detailed picture of exactly how RNAse works can be obtained

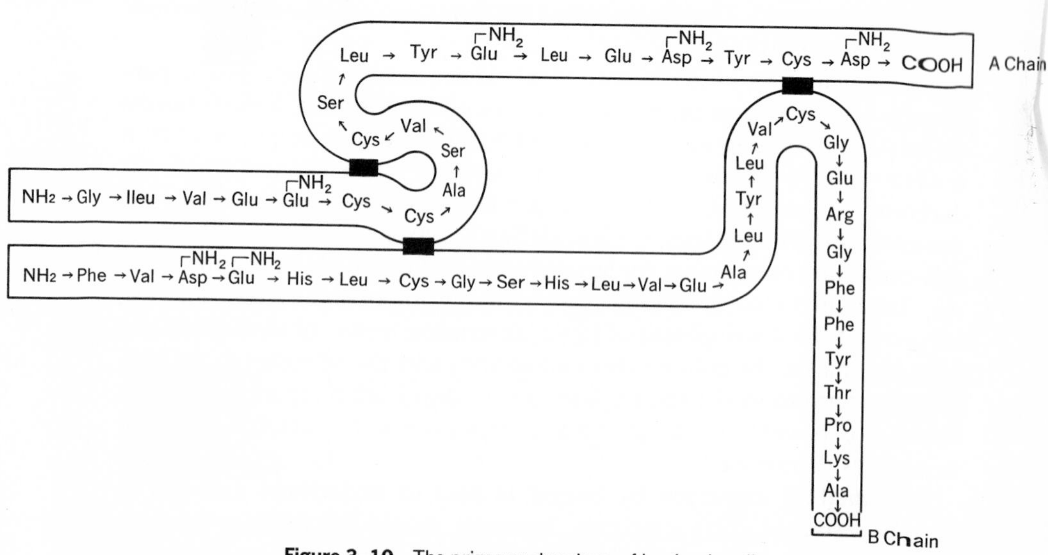

Figure 3–10. The primary structure of bovine insulin.

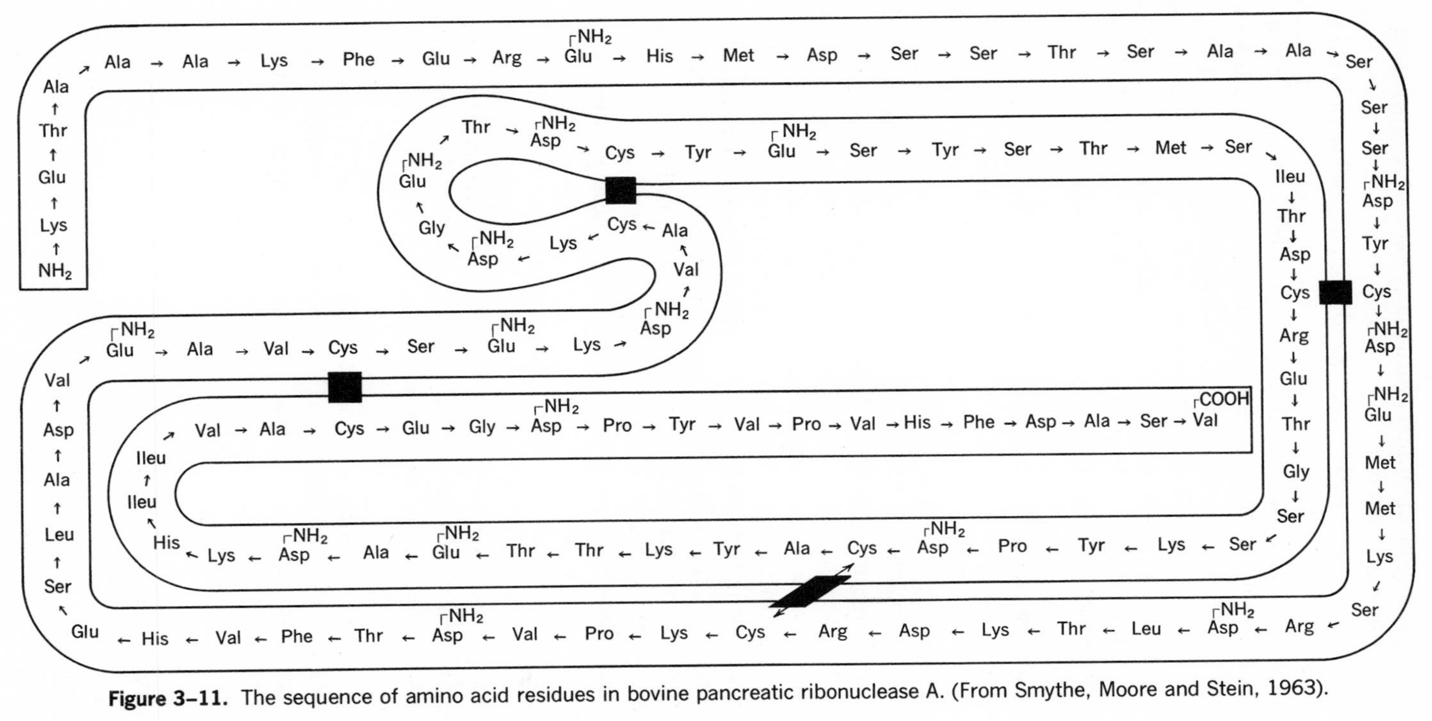

Figure 3–11. The sequence of amino acid residues in bovine pancreatic ribonuclease A. (From Smythe, Moore and Stein, 1963).

through a correlation of primary structural data with other information available about the enzyme.

Several laboratories, working independently, have determined the complete amino acid sequence of the protein subunits composing the coat of the tobacco mosaic virus. This protein coat is made up of 2200 identical subunits of protein arranged to form the rod-shaped virus. Early interest in the amino acid sequence of the protein subunits focused on two points: (1) whether there are intrinsic differences which distinguish viral proteins from other natural proteins, and (2) whether there are demonstrable chemical differences in viral strains which might result in different biological properties. Only partial answers to these questions have been obtained.

The complete amino acid sequences of myoglobin, the muscle protein, and also hemoglobin are known. Myoglobin is a relatively simple protein molecule with a single peptide chain and a single heme (a combination of iron and protoporphyrin) unit. The role of myoglobin in muscle is similar to that of hemoglobin in the red blood cell. It stores oxygen in muscle, particularly in marine animals such as whales and seals, and thus prolongs the time these animals can spend under water. The structure of sperm whale myoglobin has been elucidated by a combined approach involving chemical fragmentation methods and X-ray diffraction analysis. Not only the sequence of the 151 amino acid residues but also the secondary and tertiary aspects of the structure of myoglobin are known. Vertebrate hemoglobin is a protein with a molecular weight of approximately 65,000, or four times the molecular weight of myoglobin. Four of its 10,000 atoms are iron atoms which are combined with protoporphyrin to form four heme groups, the red pigment material of the blood. The remaining atoms are in four polypeptide chains of roughly equal size and identical in pairs (Figure 3–15). Human hemoglobin comprises two identical so-called α-chains (141 residues) and two β-chains (146 amino acid residues). The primary structure of these chains has been determined by the technique of chemical fragmentation. Secondary and tertiary structural features are also known for hemoglobin.

There is a twofold purpose in enumerating the several proteins for which complete structures are known: (1) to illustrate that biological macromolecules are organic compounds with definite chemical structures and (2) to indicate the progress made toward elucidating these complex structures.

Secondary Structure

The secondary structural features of proteins have two aspects. The first aspect is the way in which the protein chain is folded and bent; the second is the nature of the linkages and bonds which stabilize this structure. The

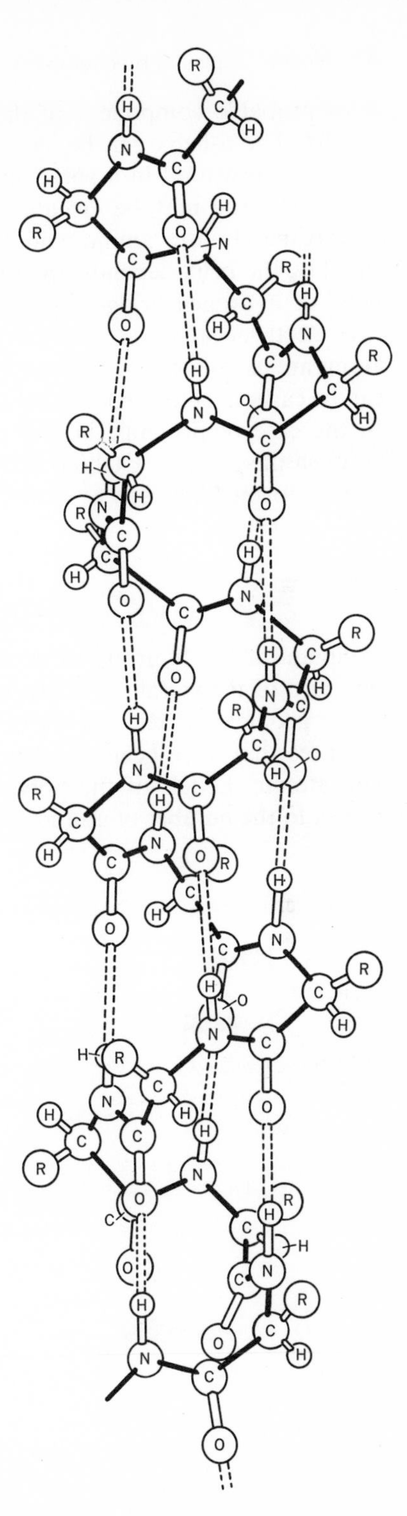

Figure 3–12. Model of an α helix, a configuration of the polypeptide chain believed to occur in proteins. The backbone of the chain consists of repeating sequences of C, C, N. R represents side groups of the different amino acids. The broken lines represent hydrogen bonds that stabilize the helix.

most probable component of the secondary structure of proteins is the α-helix. The α-helix can be easily visualized by imagining a polypeptide chain being wound in a spiral manner the length of a small rod (Figure 3–12). The rod may be visualized as small enough in diameter to allow approximately four amino acid residues to make one complete turn. For stability, the helix depends upon so-called hydrogen bonds. The hydrogen bond or hydrogen bridge consists of a hydrogen atom bridging, usually, two electronegative atoms. In biological systems, the electronegative atoms are usually nitrogen or oxygen, and under special circumstances one can be carbon, chlorine, or another element. This is shown in Figure 3–13. In the case of proteins, helical coiling is stabilized by hydrogen bonds between the peptide (CONH) linkages of the protein chain. The hydrogen bond is formed between a

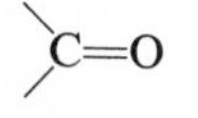

group and a H—N group three amino acid units along the chain, in the next turn of the spiral. Actually, a number of helical arrangements which fit the geometrical restrictions imposed by bond angles and interatomic distances that have been determined experimentally may be constructed with atomic models of the polypeptide chain. These models differ with respect to the number of amino acid residues per turn of helix, in the pitch

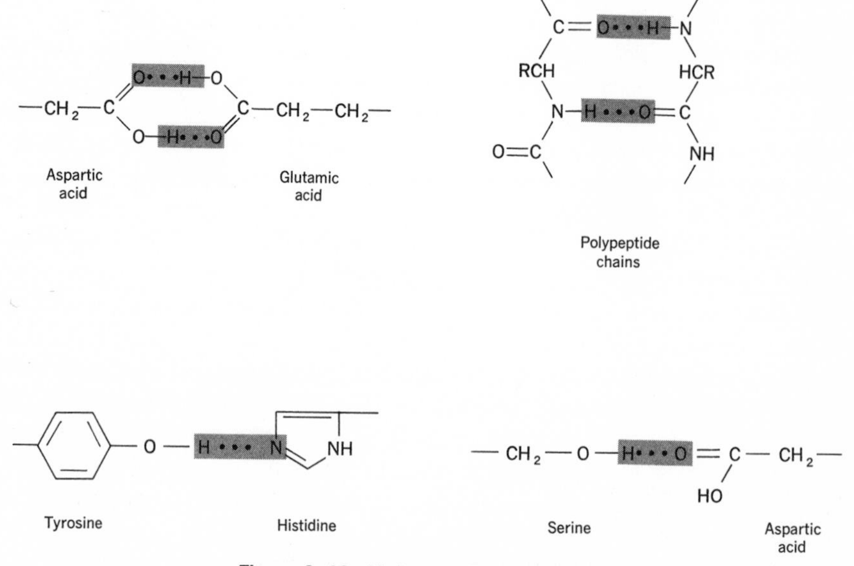

Figure 3–13. Hydrogen bond formation.

of the helical screw, and in the amount of unfilled space left within the helical center. In the α-helix, however, the maximum number of intra-helical hydrogen bonds are formed between the —CONH linkages, and the structure is consequently a fairly stable one. Another important factor is that the atoms comprising the peptide bond fall in one plane without strain. The α-helix is a completely general structure that will accommodate any amino acid side chain.

Tertiary Structure

In spite of the stabilization given by the internal hydrogen bonds, the helical structure is not sufficiently stable to exist in water solutions, but can unfold into a random, disoriented strand. Stabilization of helical coiling and the folding and bending of the helical coil which give the characteristic tertiary structure of proteins require linkages and bonds in addition to hydrogen bonds. Some of the linkages giving tertiary structural effects are shown in Figure 3–2. These linkages are formed between the side chains or R-groups of amino acids in the polypeptide chain. Several of these amino acid to amino acid bonds were mentioned on page 19 of this chapter.

Bonds involved in tertiary structure include hydrogen, ionic, non-polar (hydrophobic), covalent, and van der Waals linkages. Hydrogen bonds can be expected to form between two amino acids, one of which has a hydrogen donor group, such as the hydroxyl (OH) group in tyrosine, the other having a hydrogen acceptor group (very likely a carboxyl group (COOH) as in glutamic acid). Ionic bonds or salt linkages within proteins may be expected to form between amino acid side groups that are capable of ionizing to form electrically charged species. R-groups with unlike charges, such as the COO^- of glutamic acid and the NH_3^+ of lysine would be attracted to each other, whereas groups with similar charges would repel each other. Non-polar bonds which form between amino acids (Leu, Ileu, Phe, Val, etc.) with hydrocarbon side chains contribute to the tertiary structure of proteins in a way which is not well understood. One general interpretation is that hydrocarbons are relatively insoluble in water, and, if the polypeptide chain can roll up into a ball with most of its hydrocarbon chains tucked inside, it will do so. Covalent linkages such as disulfide bonds between cysteine residues and peptide bonds between glutamic acid and lysine, have been discussed on page 19. The distinction between van der Waals type of linkages and non-polar links is not well defined. This is due in the main to a lack of understanding of the nature and significance of these bonds in determining the tertiary structural features of peptides and proteins.

A landmark in the elucidation of the tertiary structure of proteins is the elegant work of J. C. Kendrew, M. Perutz, and their coworkers on myoglobin and hemoglobin. Using the techniques of X-ray crystallography and mathematical analysis (Fourier syntheses), Kendrew and his coworkers have determined the structure of myoglobin at 1.4 Ångstrom resolution. Their information has been correlated with chemical data to give a complete picture of the primary, secondary, and tertiary structure of myoglobin. Kendrew has written:

> What is the nature of the molecule which has emerged with progressively increasing clarity from successive Fourier syntheses? Some 118 out of the total of 151 amino acid residues make up eight segments of right-handed α-helix, seven to 24 residues long. These segments are joined by two sharp corners (containing no nonhelical residues) and five nonhelical segments (of one to eight residues); there is also a nonhelical tail of five residues at the carboxyl end of the chain. The whole is folded in a complex and unsymmetrical manner to form a flattened, roughly triangular prism with dimensions about 45 by 35 by 25 angstroms. The whole structure is extremely compact; there is no water inside the molecule, except for a very small number (less than five) of single water molecules presumably trapped at the time the molecule was folded up; there are no channels through it, and the volume of internal empty space is small. The heme group is disposed almost normally to the surface of the molecule, one of its edges (that containing the polar propionic acid groups) being at the surface and the rest buried deeply within.
>
> Turning now to the side chains, we find that almost all those containing polar groups are on the surface. Thus, with very few exceptions, all the lysine, arginine, glutamic acid, aspartic acid, histidine, serine, threonine, tyrosine, and tryptophan residues have their polar groups on the outside (the rare exceptions appear to have some special function within the molecule—for example, the heme-linked histidine). The interior of the molecule, on the other hand, is almost entirely made up of nonpolar residues, generally close packed and in van der Waals contact with their neighbors.

Hemoglobin has been the subject of similar studies by Perutz and his coworkers. Because of certain technical limitations, the X-ray results on hemoglobin have not yet reached the same high degree of resolution and show less detail than do the myoglobin studies. They are sufficient, however, to see the general layout of the polypeptide chains and the positions of the heme groups. In agreement with the chemical evidence, the electron density maps obtained by X-ray diffraction show four separate chains which are identical in pairs. They are very similar in structure, and each chain bears a strong resemblance to myoglobin.

The hemoglobin molecule is easily assembled from models based on the X-ray data. Each chain is matched with its symmetrically related partner (Figure 3–14); then the pair of white chains—the α-chains—are inverted and placed over the top of the pair of black ones—the β-chains.

The models shown in Figures 3–15 and 3–16 clarify the relations between hemoglobin and myoglobin.

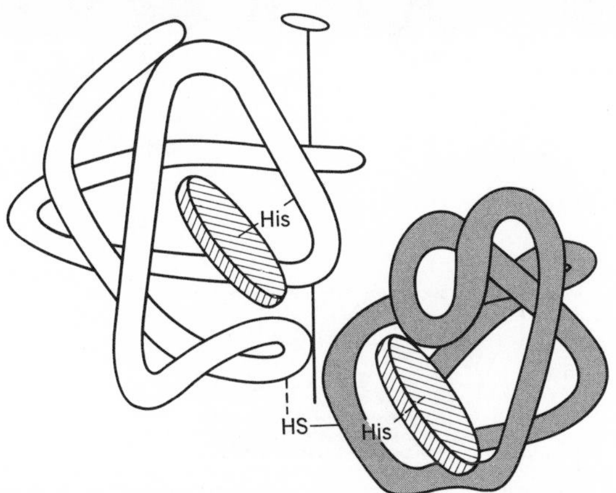

Figure 3–14. Hemoglobin molecule as deduced from X-ray diffraction studies showing tertiary and quaternary structure. The hemoglobin molecule is made up of two identical α-chains (light blocks) and two identical β-chains (dark blocks). Each chain enfolds a heme prosthetic group, and the oxygen-binding site on this group is marked by O_2. The photograph shows how closely these chains fit together in approximately tetrahedral arrangement. The model in the photograph is built up from irregular blocks which represent electron density patterns at various levels in the molecule. (From Perutz *et al.,* 1960.)

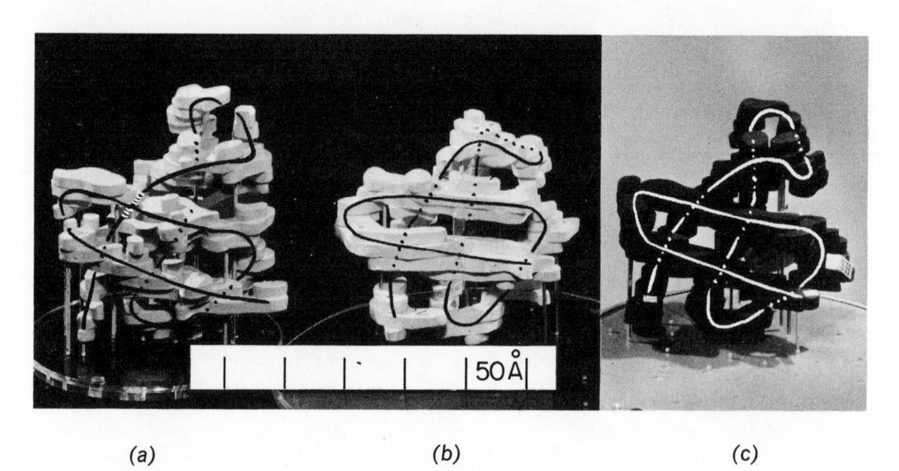

Figure 3–15. Comparison of myoglobin (*a*) with the white and black units of hemoglobin, (*b*) and (*c*). The white hemoglobin unit corresponds to the α- and the black to the β-chain of the chemical sequence. The N-terminal end of each chain is at the bottom left (Cullis *et al.*, 1962).

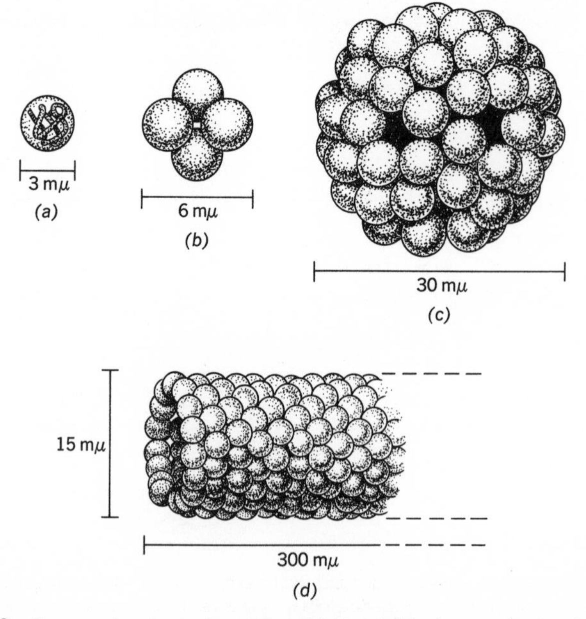

Figure 3–16. Quaternary structure of proteins: (*a*) Myoglobin, has no 4° structure; (*b*) hemoglobin, four similar subunits in tetrahedral arrangement; (*c*) polio virus, 60 identical subunits arranged in rings of five to form a hollow sphere, with each subunit built up of two or three smaller subunits comparable in size with (*a*); (*d*) tobacco mosaic virus, hollow tube formed by a spiral of subunits, with 16 units per turn, approximately. (After Haggis, 1961.)

Quaternary Structure

The arrangement of polypeptide subunits to form superstructures results in so-called quaternary structural features (Figure 3–16). The quaternary structure of hemoglobin has been shown to be four compact chains, each similar to myoglobin, closely packed together. The protein coats of several viruses have been studied and shown to be essentially protein subunits arranged in an ordered array. In the case of spherical viruses, identical subunits are arranged in rings of five to form a hollow sphere. Each of the composition's subunits is built up of two or three smaller units more comparable in size with the subunits of hemoglobin. The protein coat of tobacco mosaic virus appears to be a hollow tube formed from a spiral of some 2000 subunits, approximately 16 to a turn. The question, "Why do these subunits aggregate?" has received two general answers. Since the surface of the subunit carries a distribution of positive and negative charges, owing to the charged groups on many of the amino acid side groups, subunits may be held together by electrostatic attraction. Second, the folding of the tertiary structure may not have brought all the hydrocarbon chains out of contact with water. If a region of the subunit outer surface is hydrocarbon, then subunits will tend to come together and make contact with water, since this will reduce the area of hydrocarbon-water interface. The same factors are involved when an oil-water mixture is allowed to stand for a while; small oil droplets group together to form larger and larger droplets.

Conjugated Proteins

Proteins in the living organism are frequently associated with one of many biochemical metabolites. When a protein is associated with nonprotein material (prosthetic group), it is called a conjugated protein. Two conjugated metalloproteins (metal containing) have been mentioned in this chapter, i.e., hemoglobin and myoglobin. In these proteins the heme moiety is the so-called prosthetic group. Lipoproteins (lipid containing) and mucoproteins (carbohydrate containing) are important structural material for cell membranes and the cellular particulates. The nucleoproteins, which contain a nucleic acid moiety, are integral parts of the genetic apparatus of the organism.

Biochemical Functions of Proteins

Two broad functions (Table 3–3) of proteins are as: (1) *structural materials,* and (2) *metabolic mediators and regulators.*

The structural materials of animals consist in large part of protein, whereas in plants such structures are principally made up of polysaccharides. The structural proteins are *fibrous* proteins, or chains of proteins

TABLE 3-3

BIOCHEMICAL FUNCTIONS OF SOME PROTEINS

General Protein Groups	Biochemical Roles
Enzymes	Metabolic catalysts, hydrolysis, oxidation and synthesis, etc.
Structural proteins	Keratins, e.g., proteins of hair, wool, feathers; collagen-connective tissue fibers; muscle proteins; silk and chitin
Respiratory proteins	Hemoglobin, cytochromes, myoglobin, hemocyanin
Antibodies	Proteins formed in response to antigens; protection against foreign proteins
Hormones	Regulation of metabolism, e.g., insulin controls carbohydrate and fat metabolism
Nucleoproteins	Chromosomal proteins, control of hereditary transmission; ribosomal proteins, involved in protein synthesis

arranged parallel to each other to form fibers. Collagen, the material composing the tendons and developing bones, is one of the most prevalent fibrous proteins. Keratin, the primary constituent of skin, hair, and nails, is another fibrous structural protein. Myosin and actin, structural components of muscle, are special contractile proteins.

The role of proteins in biochemical and physiological metabolism is enormous. These proteins are generally spheroidal in shape and are termed globular proteins. Chapter Four will deal with the function of proteins as biological catalysts, or enzymes.

There are many metalloproteins, most of which function in oxidation-reduction reactions (e.g., cytochromes). The heme proteins, hemoglobin and myoglobin, which function in oxygen transport and storage, are usually restricted to animals.

Antibodies are proteins which defend the organism against foreign agents and attack by bacteria and viruses. Many hormones are amino acid derivatives, peptides or protein molecules, or have proteins associated with them in their functional state. The blood volume and water balance of higher animals depends upon the osmotic effect of plasma proteins, serum albumin in particular. Proteins in the diet of animals and certain bacteria provide amino acids which the organism is unable to synthesize itself.

Hormones

Hormones are highly active biological substances which are produced by specialized cells of endocrine tissues, secreted into the blood stream, and transported to a different target organ or tissue. Once at the target site the hormone exerts a profound metabolic control on the function of the target organ or tissue. Physiologists have long pictured hormones as being involved in the adaptation of organisms to both chemical and physical stress. For example, when the animal is confronted with a physical stress, there is an increased secretion of epinephrine, a derivative of tyrosine, from the adrenal medulla and this results in a variety of metabolic changes designed to prepare the animal to resist the emergency. Blood sugar and heart rate increase, and the blood is diverted from the abdominal area into the limbs for more effective muscle response. The response to epinephrine is fast and dramatic in contrast to the slower response of the higher animals to chemical stress, which is mediated by the steroid hormones (page 112) of the adrenal cortex. The ability of a protein hormone of the pancreas, insulin, to lower the blood sugar is a relatively rapid reaction compared to the effect of the thyroid hormone on respiration which takes several days for the maximum effect.

Although most of the interest in the hormones has centered around their action in mammals, corresponding substances, but generally not of protein nature, have been found in lower vertebrates, invertebrates, and plants. Biological systems in which widespread differentiation is taking place are usually under hormonal control. The classic example of differentiation in vertebrates, the metamorphosis of the tadpole to the frog, is under the direct control of the thyroid hormones and is indirectly controlled by hypothalmic and pituitary factors. Invertebrate hormones play a major role in insect metamorphosis. The prothoracic gland produces ecdysone, which stimulates molting and transforms the caterpillar to the pupa and the pupa to the butterfly. Larval shedding is effected by another lipid-like substance, the juvenile hormone, which is secreted by the corpora allata, a neural tissue. Plants employ a group of growth-modifying substances known as phytohormones. Auxins such as β-indoleacetic acid and gibberellic acid stimulate the elongation of plant cells. Gibberellic acid and kinetin (6-furfurylaminopurine) also stimulate cell division in plants.

The hormones represent the classic example of intercellular feedback inhibition, a major device employed for the control of the rates of metabolic reaction in all cells. The principle is relatively simple and is depicted in Figure 3–17. A group of substances with a similar hormonal function, e.g., the glucocorticosteroids (page 110 and Table 8–3) is manufactured by certain cells of the adrenal cortex and secreted into the blood stream. Eventually these hormones make contact with the hypothalmus, in the midbrain, which transmits appropriate information, probably through the pituitary stalk, to the anterior lobe of the pituitary gland, indicating that an adequate supply of the corticosteroids is now present in the blood. This information results in a temporary cessation of the output of a protein hormone, the adrenocorticotrophic hormone (ACTH), by the pituitary. It is this hormone, ACTH, which stimulates the adrenal cortex to make and

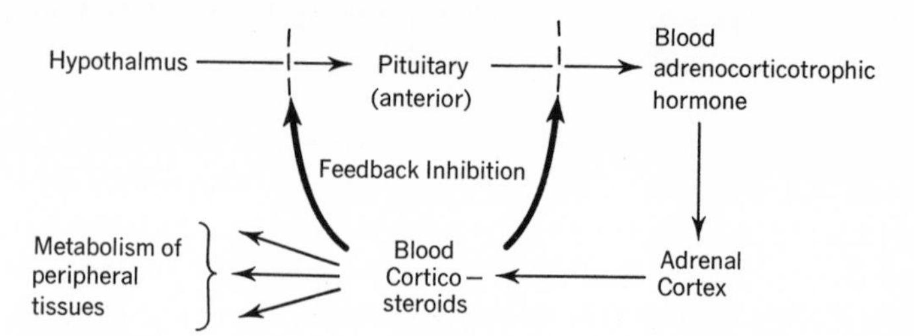

Figure 3–17. Feedback control of a hormone secretion. High levels of blood corticosteroids cause an inhibition or block (---) in the pathway leading to their production.

secrete more corticosteroids. As time passes, the circulating steroids fall, releasing the inhibition of ACTH formation and secretion, and more steroid is produced by the adrenals as a result.

The pituitary gland is involved in so many feedback control systems that it occupies the role of a master gland in most mammals. It is a polypeptide factory under the sensitive control of the hypothalmus and the circulating peripheral hormones. All of its hormones (listed in Table 3–4) are peptides or derived from proteins. Its targets are scattered all over the body and include the thyroid, the ovaries, the testes, and the mammary glands. One hormone, the growth hormone, exerts a general positive or anabolic

TABLE 3–4

PEPTIDE AND PROTEIN HORMONES OF THE PITUITARY GLAND

Hormone	Target Tissue	Principle Effect
Anterior lobe:		
Growth (GH, somatotropin)	Many tissues	Growth of bone and muscle
Adrenocorticotrophic (ACTH)	Adrenal cortex	Synthesis and secretion of glucocorticoids
Thyroid stimulating (TSH)	Thyroid	Synthesis and secretion of thyroxine and triiodothyronine
Follicle stimulating (FSH)	Ovary	Synthesis of estrogens
Luteinizing (LH, gonadotropin)	Ovary	Synthesis of progesterone series
Interstitial cell stimulating (ICSH)	Testis	Synthesis of androgens
Prolactin	Mammary, ovary	Stimulation of milk secretion, ovarian function
Posterior lobe:		
Oxytocin	Uterus, mammary	Contraction of smooth muscle, milk ejection
Vasopressin	Kidney, arterioles	Water reabsorption, contraction of smooth muscles
Intermediate lobe:		
Melanocyte stimulating (MSH)	Melanophores	Dilation leading to pigment dispersal

effect on growth and metabolic processes in virtually every tissue. Several important peptide hormones, including oxytocin and vasopressin, are secreted by the posterior part of the pituitary. Their precise structure has been determined and is included in Figure 3–5.

Most of the vertebrate hormones are peptides or proteins. At least four other hormones are derived from the two amino acids tyrosine and tryptophan. A third major group of hormones, non-protein in nature, consists of members of four different groups of steroids (page 112) which are synthesized from cholesterol, and the chemical structures of these hormones are given in Table 8–3. A summary of the better known amino acid and derived hormones of the vertebrates, their tissues of origin, and their principal biological functions is presented in Tables 3–4 and 3–5.

TABLE 3–5

NON-PITUITARY HORMONES OF MAN*

Hormone	Endocrine Gland	Major Function
Peptides or proteins:		
Insulin	Pancreas	Carbohydrate metabolism; lower blood sugar
Glucagon	Pancreas	Increase blood sugar
Relaxin	Ovary, placenta	Relaxation of pelvic muscles
Parathyroid	Parathyroid	Metabolism of calcium
Secretin	Pancreas	Secretion of salt and water
Pancreozymin	Pancreas	Secretion of digestive enzymes
Cholecystokinin	Gall bladder	Contraction of gall bladder
Enterogastrine	Stomach	Stomach mobility
Gastrin	Stomach	Acid secretion of stomach
Erythropoietin	Kidney	Red blood cell formation
Amino acid derivatives:		
Thyroxine	Thyroid	Metabolic rate; growth and development
Epinephrine	Adrenal medulla	Breakdown of glycogen; increase of heart rate, blood pressure
Melatonin	Pineal	Contraction of melanophores
Serotonin	Blood platelets, brain	Vasoconstriction

* This table excludes steroid hormones.

SUGGESTED READING

Anfinsen, C. B., *The Molecular Basis of Evolution,* John Wiley & Sons, Inc., New York, 1959.

Kendrew, J. C., "Three-Dimensional Study of a Protein," *Scientific American,* December, 1961.

Kendrew, J. C., "Myoglobin and the Structure of Proteins," *Science, 139,* 1259–1266 (1963).

Oncley, J. L., "Chemical Characterization of Proteins, Carbohydrates, and Lipids" in *Biophysical Science: A Study Program,* J. L. Oncley (ed.), John Wiley & Sons, Inc., New York, 1959.

Perutz, M. F., *Proteins and Nucleic Acids,* Elsevier Publishing Co., New York, 1962.

Perutz, M. F., "The Hemoglobin Molecule," *Scientific American,* November, 1964.

Sanger, F., "The Structure of Insulin" in *Currents in Biochemical Research,* D. Green (ed.), Interscience Publishers, Inc., New York, 1956.

Stein, W. H., and S. Moore, "The Chemical Structure of Proteins," *Scientific American,* March, 1961.

"... I discovered on the 29th of April a means of obtaining from the Jack Bean a new protein which crystallizes beautifully ...."

James B. Sumner, 1926

FOUR

Biological Catalysts: The Enzymes

Enzymes are biological catalysts that accelerate the myriads of reactions which occur in the living organism. Many of these reactions are not only accelerated by enzymes but would not occur to any appreciable extent at body temperature. Although enzymes become intimately involved in the reactions they catalyze, they emerge essentially unchanged at the end of the reaction.

The systematic study of enzymes began in 1835 when the Swedish chemist, Jön Jakob Berzelius included biological reactions among the chemical changes he termed *catalytic.* The fact that a mixture of enzymes from potatoes breaks down starch faster than does sulfuric acid made a great impression on Berzelius. With remarkable insight he predicted that it would eventually be found that all substances in living organisms are made under the influence of catalysts. A century later biochemists are still making discoveries that confirm his prediction.

The brilliant studies of James B. Sumner, which culminated in his crystallizing the enzyme urease, made clear that enzymes were protein molecules. Prior to Sumner's findings, the consensus was that the catalyst was an inorganic constituent or metal ion associated with protein. It is now accepted that all enzymes are proteins. Indeed, the amino acid sequence occurring in many enzymes, has been determined (page 25).

During the past several decades, increasing emphasis has been placed on the role of enzymes as chemical reactants. This emphasis has come about because of studies which have shown that enzymes are more than mysterious catalysts for a reaction. Enzymes, in fact, have been shown to interact with substances (substrates) whose reactions they catalyze according to established principles of organic chemistry. This interaction results in a definite intermediate, the enzyme-substrate complex (ES), which frequently can be experimentally observed.

Catalysis

Catalysis is a good starting point for a discussion of enzymes and their mechanism of action. The defining characteristic of catalysts is that they modify the speed of a chemical reaction without being used up or appearing as one of the reaction products. The acid hydrolysis of esters is a familiar example from organic chemistry. It is characteristic of catalytic reactions that the amount of catalyst bears no stoichiometric relationship to the quantity of substance altered. Whereas some catalysts may transform only a small number of molecules per unit time, others have very high efficiencies.

Before the end of the nineteenth century, chemists understood that molecules must obtain extra energy—the energy of activation—before they can interact. This energy may be provided when one molecule collides with another or from an external source of energy, for example, heat. Thus, as shown in Figure 4–1, it is the magnitude of this energy requirement, the energy of activation (E_A), that determines the rate at which the reaction will go; the higher the energy barrier, the fewer the molecules which pass over it in unit time. In 1888, Svante Arrhenius, the Swedish

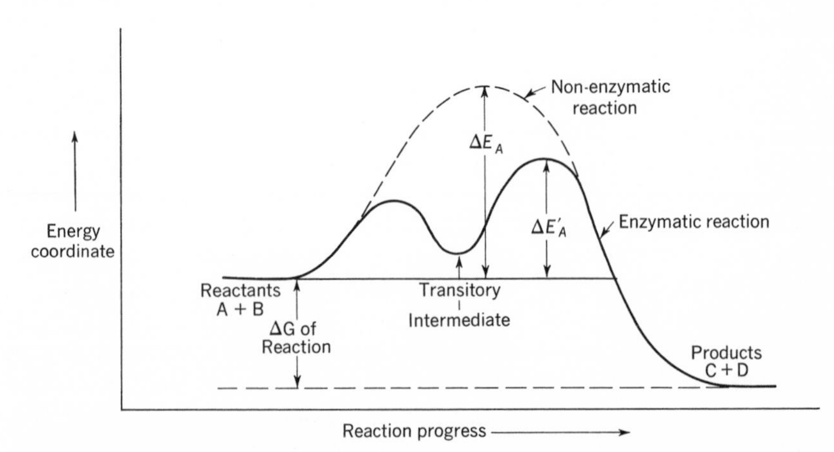

Figure 4–1. The energy barrier in enzymatic and uncatalyzed reactions of A + B → C + D. E_A represents the activation energy for the uncatalyzed reaction, E'_A for the enzymatic reaction.

chemist, suggested that a way to explain the action of any catalyst (C) is to suppose that it forms an intermediate compound (CS) with the reactant (S):

$$C + S \longrightarrow CS$$

From this intermediate the reaction proceeds at a lower energy of activation ($\Delta E'_A$). In this case, the catalyst contributes no energy, but alters the reaction path so that S is converted to product (P) via a different route with a lower activation energy, as is shown in Eq. (1). As this equation shows,

$$C + S \rightleftharpoons CS \longrightarrow C + P \tag{1}$$

the catalyst is regenerated unchanged and can participate in the reaction again and again. If we replace the word catalyst by the word enzyme and change Eq. (1) to Eq. (2), we arrive at the fundamental equation of enzymology, usually attributed to Michaelis and Menten.

$$\underset{\text{Enzyme}}{E} + \underset{\text{Substrate}}{S} \rightleftharpoons \underset{\substack{\text{Enzyme}\\\text{substrate}\\\text{complex}}}{ES} \longrightarrow \underset{\text{Enzyme}}{E} + \underset{\text{Products}}{P} \tag{2}$$

Enzymes generally reduce the activation energies far more effectively than inorganic catalysts and thus permit reactions to take place at lower temperatures. For example, to decompose hydrogen peroxide into water and oxygen requires an activation energy of 18 kilocalories per mole of hydrogen peroxide. Catalytic iron brings this value down to 13 kilocalories; platinum, to 12 kilocalories. Catalase, the liver enzyme, reduces the activation energy to less than 5 kilocalories!

Enzyme Structure

The important advance made in 1926 by James Sumner in crystallizing the enzyme urease ushered in a new era of concepts about enzyme structure. The studies of Sumner and later investigators provided compelling evidence that enzymes are protein in nature. Certain enzymes were shown to be solely protein; the digestive enzymes pepsin and trypsin are of this type. Subsequently, however, other enzymes have been found to consist of a non-protein part plus the protein and are therefore conjugated proteins. If the non-protein portion is an organic moiety and is readily separated from the enzyme, this fragment is generally called a *coenzyme.* It is usually called a *prosthetic group* if it is firmly attached to the protein portion of the enzyme.

The complete amino acid sequence has been determined for several enzymes (page 25) and partial sequences established for many others. The chemical nature of prosthetic groups and coenzymes for conjugated protein enzymes has been determined in many instances (Table 4–1). It

TABLE 4-1

COMMON COENZYMES AND PROSTHETIC GROUPS

	Corresponding vitamin	See page
Flavine adenine dinucleotide (FAD)	Riboflavin	76
Nicotinamide adenine dinucleotide (NAD)	Nicotinamide	76
Coenzyme A	Pantothenic acid	144
Tetrahydrofolic acid	Folic acid	144
Biotin	Biotin	144
Thiamine pyrophosphate	Thiamine	144
Pyridoxal phosphate	Pyridoxine	
Copper	—	8
Zinc	—	8
Iron heme	—	7

should be noted that many coenzymes are closely related to vitamins, the active compounds which must be ingested in food. Since the role of these vitamins is essentially catalytic, as are the enzymes with which they function, the amounts that must be ingested daily are relatively minute.

Enzyme Activity

The activities of enzymes can be studied in cell-free systems under controlled conditions. By adding an enzyme (E) to a substrate (S), the rate of appearance of a product (P) can be greatly increased (Figure 4–2). That is, for every time interval, a proportionally larger amount of P will form if the enzyme is present. Increased amounts of enzyme will result in a greater initial rate if sufficient S is present in the reaction mixture and the forma-

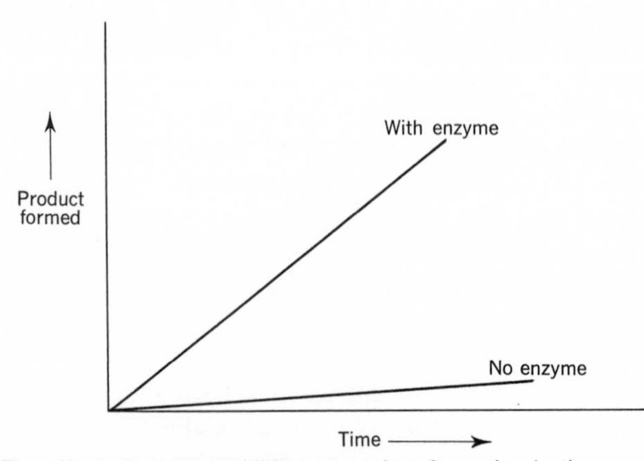

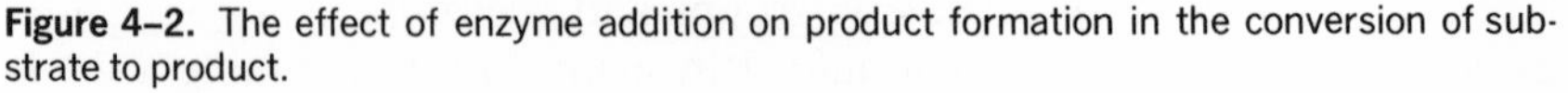

Figure 4–2. The effect of enzyme addition on product formation in the conversion of substrate to product.

tion of P does not adversely affect the reaction. For metabolic reactions, the rate of the non-catalyzed reaction is almost imperceptible. Two well-known exceptions to this are the decomposition of H_2O_2 to O_2 and water and that of H_2CO_3 to CO_2 and water.

Factors Influencing Enzyme Activity

There are several physical and chemical factors other than the amount of enzyme present which affect the rate of enzyme catalyzed reactions (Figure 4–3): (*a*) pH, (*b*) *temperature,* (*c*) *substrate concentration,* (*d*) *concentration of any activators present,* (*e*) *concentration of any inhibitors present.*

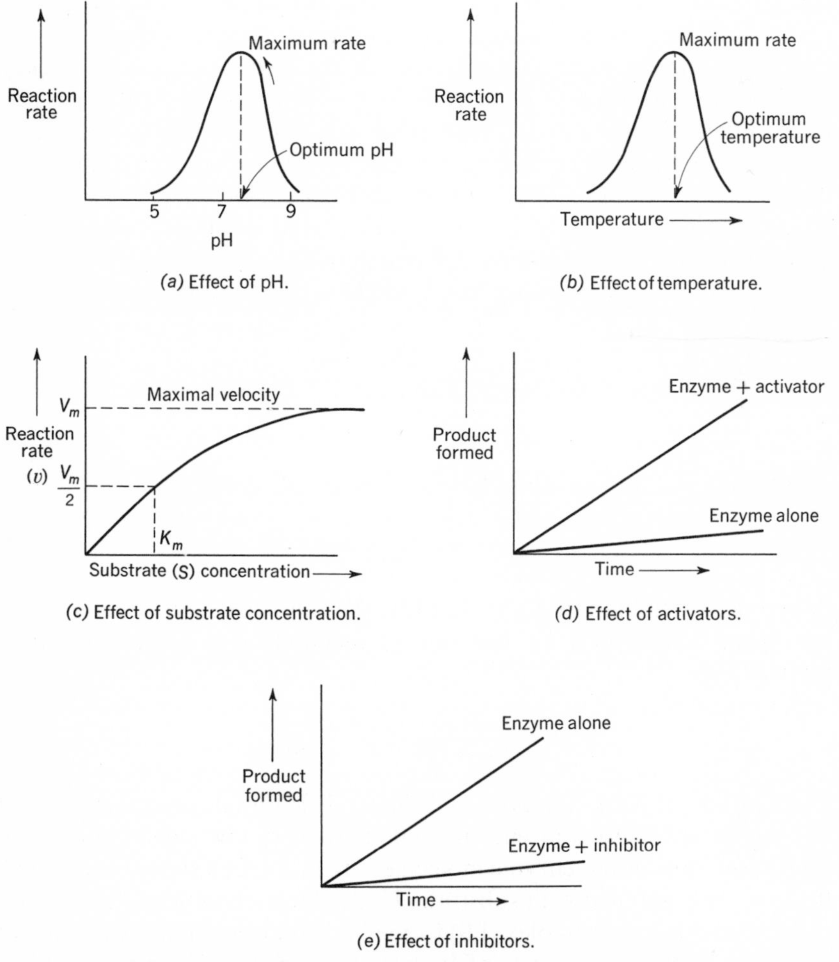

Figure 4–3. Physical and chemical effects on enzyme activity.

The hydrogen ion concentration (pH) has a rather complicated effect on the rate of enzyme reactions; different types of behavior are obtained with different enzymes, and indeed with different substrates for the same enzyme. In most cases, the rate is found to pass through a maximum as the pH is varied (Figure 4–3*a*). Extreme changes in pH cause irreversible destruction of most enzymes.

The effect of temperature on many enzyme reactions is well documented. As in the case of pH, enzymes for different substrates vary greatly in their *temperature optimum* (Figure 4–3*b*). For most mammalian enzymes this optimum is around 37°C. Much above this temperature, they usually lose activity rapidly and are destroyed. Bacteria and algae that live in hot springs, however, have enzymes which are occasionally active at temperatures considerably above 40°C. At the other extreme are enzymes from certain arctic bacteria that have a temperature optimum as low as 0°C!

If the concentration of the reactant or substrate is increased and all other conditions are kept constant, the rate of the enzyme-catalyzed reaction increases to a maximum; further increase in substrate concentration produces no additional effect. Presumably this occurs because the rate of formation of an enzyme-substrate complex (ES) becomes limited by the enzyme concentration. This is shown in Figure 4–3*c*. Here the rate of a typical enzyme reaction is shown as a function of substrate concentration.

In 1913, L. Michaelis and M. Menten derived equations which interpret Figure 4–3*c*. Their analysis is based on the scheme shown in Eq. (3).

$$\underset{\text{Enzyme}}{E} + \underset{\text{Substrate}}{S} \underset{k_{-1}}{\overset{k_{+1}}{\rightleftharpoons}} \underset{\substack{\text{Enzyme}\\\text{substrate}\\\text{complex}}}{ES} \xrightarrow{k_{+2}} \underset{\text{Enzyme}}{E} + \underset{\text{Product}}{P} \tag{3}$$

A constant, K_m, the so-called Michaelis constant, is defined as:

$$K_m = \frac{k_{+2} + k_{-1}}{k_{+1}} \tag{4}$$

A practical definition of K_m is that it is the *substrate concentration at half maximum velocity* ($V_m/2$). The rate of reaction, v, is expressed mathematically as:

$$v = \frac{k_{+2}(E)(S)}{K_m + (S)} = \frac{V_m(S)}{K_m + (S)} \tag{5}$$

Examination of these equations and Figure 4–3*c* reveals several interesting and significant aspects of enzyme action. At very low substrate (S) concentration most of the enzyme molecules are in the free state; only a small fraction are combined with substrate. Under these conditions, the amount of enzyme-substrate complex (ES) formed is proportional to the amount of substrate. Therefore, the rate of formation of products, v, is proportional to the concentration of substrate. At high substrate concentration, however, the enzyme becomes saturated with substrate; practically all enzyme is in the form of ES complex. An increase in substrate concentration can therefore cause no further increase in the concentration of ES. Thus the rate, v, which is proportional to the concentration of ES, is now independent of S concentration.

Certain substances activate enzyme reactions, Figure 4–3*d*. This activation may be the effect of an inorganic ion, such as sodium or potassium, on the rate of the reaction. Another example would be the effect of a reagent that converts the enzyme into a more active form by a subtle chemical change (e.g., —S—S— to —SH). Many coenzymes and prosthetic groups are of course *activators.*

The kinetic effect of *inhibitors* is the opposite of activators. They slow down the reaction rate (Figure 4–3*e*). For obvious reasons, inhibition studies are of great practical interest in pharmacology and medicine. The subject of inhibition has also received major consideration by enzymologists. In the main, this has resulted from interest in the wealth of information which can be obtained about enzyme action and mechanisms through such studies.

The most potent poisons of living organisms exert their action by inhibiting enzymes (Table 4–2). The action of many drugs has been explained through their inhibition of a particular enzyme reaction. For example, antibiotics are effective inhibitors of a variety of enzymes essential for bacterial growth. Penicillin prevents cell wall formation in sensitive microbes. The nerve gases produce paralysis by inhibiting the enzyme that catalyzes the hydrolysis of acetylcholine, which is involved in the transmission of the nerves impulse.

Before we can understand the various types of inhibition in more detail, we must consider the phenomenon of enzyme specificity.

TABLE 4–2

POISONS AS ENZYME INHIBITORS

Poison	Formula	Enzyme Inhibited	Site of Action
Cyanide	CN^-	Cytochrome oxidase	Binds metal coenzymes or prosthetic groups
Arsenate	$AsO_4^=$	Phosphotransacetylase	Substitutes for phosphate
Fluoride	F^-	Enolase	Binds metal cofactor
Silver	Ag^+	Glutamic dehydrogenase	Salt formation with —SH groups
Nerve gases (substituted alkyl phosphates)	$F{-}\overset{O}{\overset{\|\|}{P}}{-}(OR)_2$	Acetylcholine esterase, chymotrypsin	Serine OH groups

Enzyme Specificity

Some enzymes exhibit an intense specificity for their substrates, a remarkable fact in view of their common protein nature. This characteristic sharply distinguishes them from inorganic catalysts, which are far less selective and discriminating in their specificity requirements.

There is a wide range of enzyme specificity from urease, which has only one substrate, urea, to some esterases which act on the esters of many different fatty acids. The following arbitrary cases provide a useful grouping for specificities:

1. Absolute specificity.
2. Group specificity.
3. Reaction, or linkage, specificity.
4. Stereochemical specificity.

Absolute specificity exists when an enzyme will catalyze a reaction for only one substrate. Certain enzymes exhibit a lower degree of specificity and act on molecules that have specific functional groups (group specificity) and are thus very structurally similar. A low degree of specificity is shown by certain *reaction specific* enzymes, that is, they catalyze a certain type of reaction or act on a particular chemical bond irrespective of the type of chemical groups present in the vicinity of this bond linkage. Most enzymes show a high degree of stereochemical specificity. Only a particular steric or optical isomer is acted on by enzymes with this kind of specificity.

Enzyme Inhibition

Inhibition of enzyme action has been mentioned (page 49 of this chapter). Competitive inhibition is best explained with reference to enzyme specificity, since it depends on the lack of absolute specificity of the chemical reactivity on the *active site,* or locus of enzyme activity. This active site combines more or less loosely with the inhibitor, which is usually structurally related to the substrate, thus preventing access of the substrate to the enzyme surface. If an inhibitor is present in sufficient quantity, complete inhibition of activity results. On the other hand, if the substrate concentration is increased, the substrate is able to compete more effectively for enzyme sites; the rate of its transformation to product thus increases (Figure 4–4). Two classic examples of competitive inhibitors are given in Figure 4–5. Malonate competes with succinate as a substrate for the important enzyme of the Krebs cycle, succinate dehydrogenase. The famous antibacterial agent sulfanilamide interferes with the synthesis of folic acid coenzyme by competing with *p*-aminobenzoic acid.

Noncompetitive inhibition cannot be reversed by simply raising the substrate (S) concentration. Regardless of the amount of substrate present the fractional decrease of velocity with noncompetitive inhibitors depends only on the amount of inhibitor present. For these inhibitions the substrate and inhibitor do not compete for the active site on the enzyme. The inhibitor binds the enzyme at a locus other than the substrate attachment site and is able to exert an effect on the active site. This may occur by a change in the conformation of the enzyme protein so that the active site cannot operate on the substrate (Figure 4–4).

There is a third important group of enzyme inhibitors which do not form readily reversible complexes with enzymes. These are compounds which form covalent bonds with key enzyme structures near or at the active site of the enzyme. In several instances, it has even been possible to crystallize these enzyme-inhibitor compounds. The nerve gases are believed to affect biological systems by forming an enzyme-inhibitor compound with the

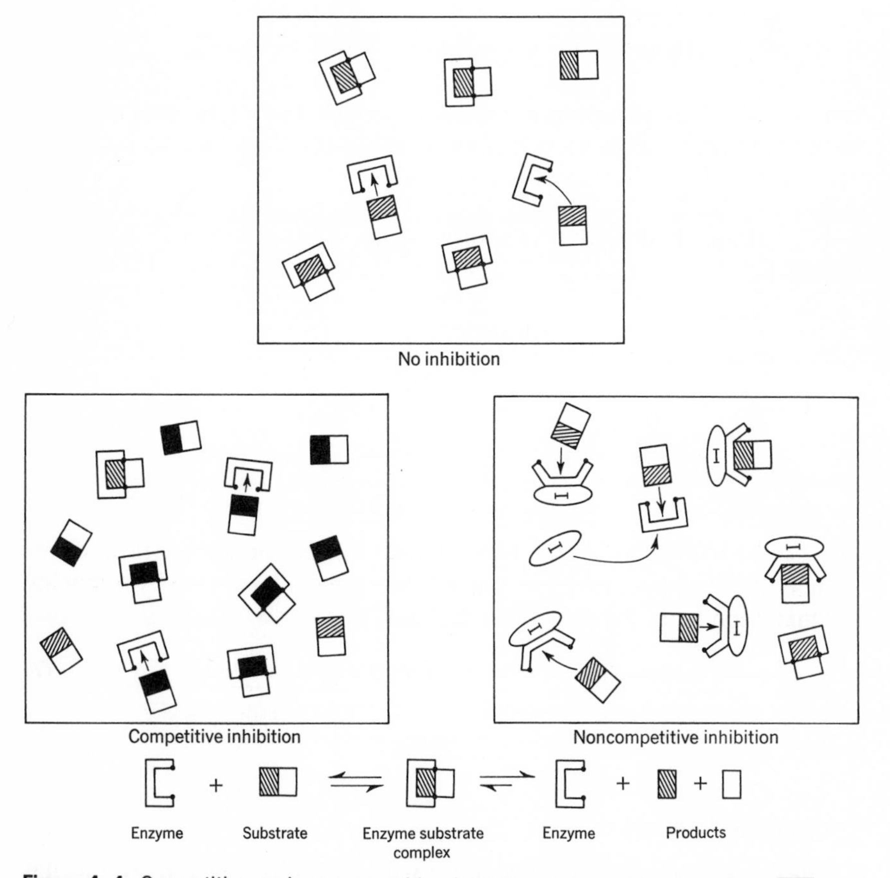

Figure 4–4. Competitive and noncompetitive inhibition. Competitive inhibitors, ■□, are bound to enzyme at the substrate site. Non-competitive inhibitors, (I), influence the catalytic activity of an enzyme although they are not bound to the active site.

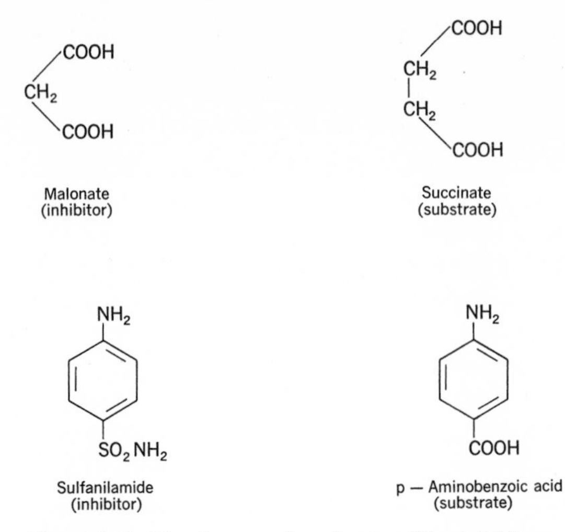

Figure 4–5. Classic examples of competitive inhibitors.

enzyme acetylcholine esterase (and many other hydrolytic enzymes such as chymotrypsin, trypsin) as is shown in Eq. (6). This kind of inhibition

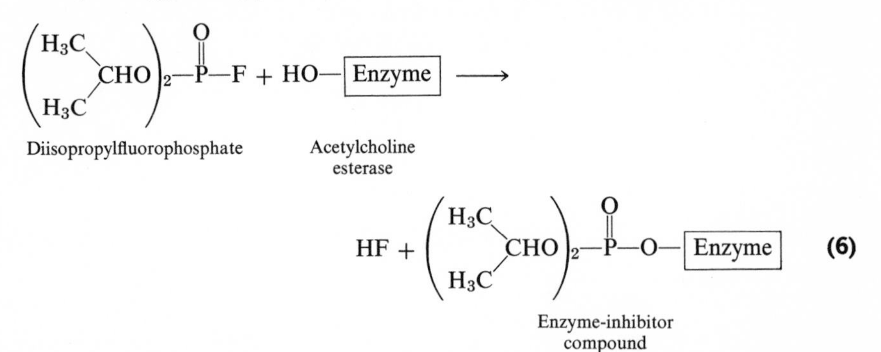

also occurs when a metal ion reagent such as CN^- or a powerful chelator such as ethylenediaminetetracetate inhibits a metalloenzyme by removing the metal ion from the enzyme as in Eq. (7).

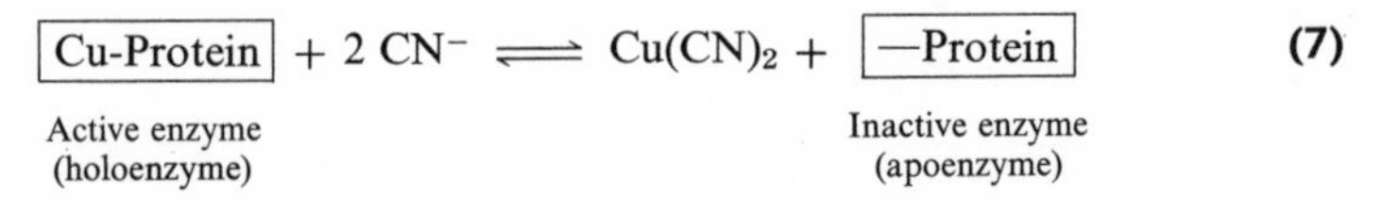

(7)

Enzyme Mechanisms

The detailed way that an enzyme transforms a substrate into product has been extensively studied during the last decade, but as yet the intricacies of the reaction are not understood.

Central to an understanding of enzyme mechanisms is knowledge of the concept of the enzyme-substrate complex (ES), which occurs in enzyme-catalyzed reactions as in Eq. (8).

$$E + S \underset{k_{-1}}{\overset{k_{+1}}{\rightleftharpoons}} ES \xrightarrow{k_{+2}} P + E \tag{8}$$

The idea that such a complex exists, an intermediate combination of enzyme with substrate, originated in 1913 from kinetic evidence. The first direct evidence for the ES complex came in 1936 when several investigators simultaneously reported that the mixing of certain enzymes with their substrates in solution brought a change of color in the solution. For example, the enzyme solution was brown, but when its substrate was added to the solution it turned green. Then, a few seconds later, it turned red. Both the green and red colors were attributed to the ES complex. Agents which reverse the enzyme reaction were shown to regenerate the brown color of the enzyme.

In 1940 the ES complex gained further respectability when it was measured quantitatively by the use of very rapid mixing and flow techniques and a highly sensitive spectrophotometer. The growth and decay of the enzyme-substrate complex was followed by determining the changes in the color of the solution (Figure 4–6). It was found that, as the ES complex

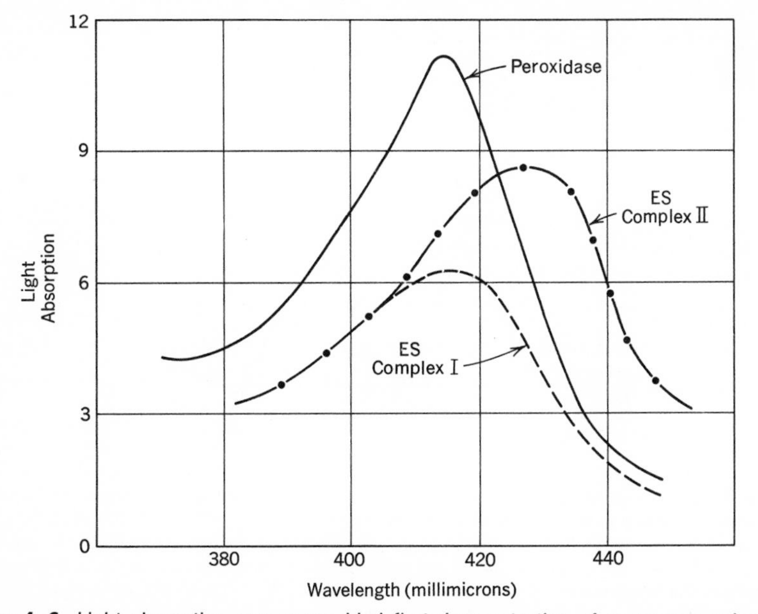

Figure 4–6. Light absorption curves provided first demonstration of an enzyme-substrate (ES) complex. Absorption by the enzyme peroxidase gives rise to brown color (solid line), but the primary complex of the enzyme and the substrate hydrogen peroxide is green (broken line). A secondary ES complex then forms and a change to red color quickly follows. The complete visible spectrum of these compounds is not shown.

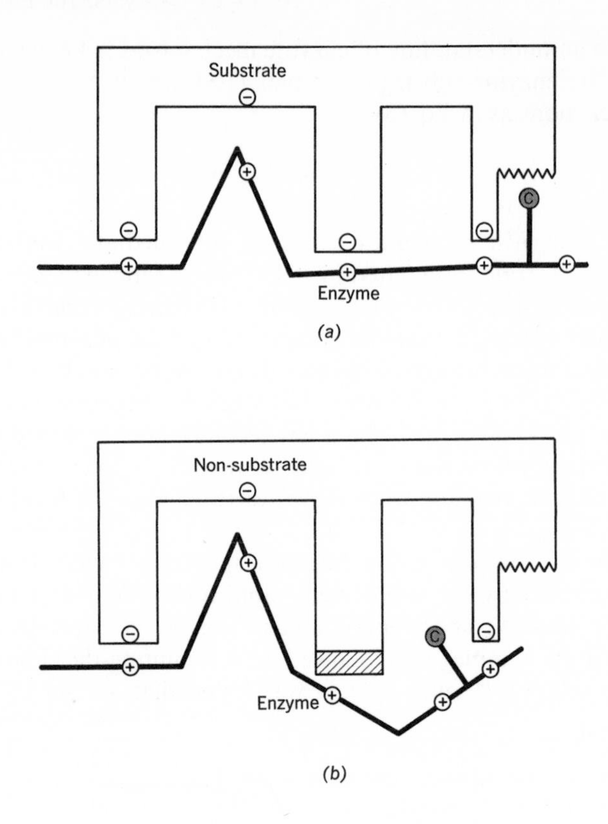

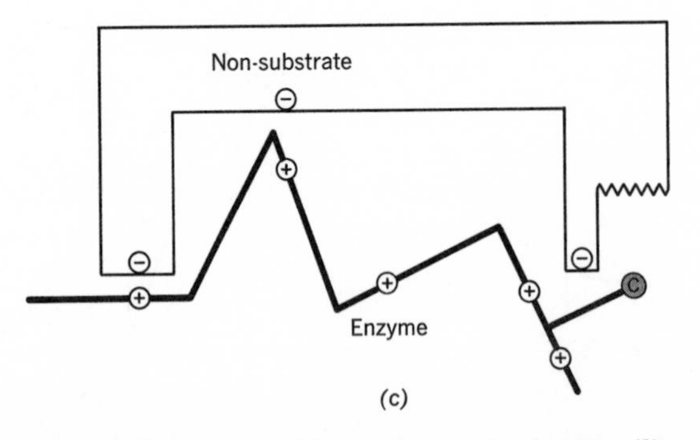

Figure 4–7. Induced-fit theory of specificity: (*a*) normal substrate; (*b*) compound in which one attractive group in substrate has been replaced by a larger group; (*c*) compound in which one attractive group in substrate has been deleted. Ⓒ designates catalytic group; jagged line, bond to be broken. In (*a*) the substrate approaches the enzyme surface at a site that has the requisite attractive groups but is subject to a certain amount of bond rotation and translation. As the substrate comes into close contact, as it forms the ES complex, the attractive groups and buttressing groups form a complementary structure so that the catalytic site Ⓒ is in proximity of the bond to be broken (ʌʌʌʌ). When a group is too large (*b*), a disorientation occurs so that the catalytic group is not in juxtaposition with the bond to be broken. This compound could act as an inhibitor for the substrate. (Redrawn after Koshland.)

rapidly forms, it reaches a maximum and a steady state for a brief period and then declines slowly to zero. The measurements of the kinetics agree so closely with theoretical predictions that at present we accept this work as the most convincing proof of the existence of the union of enzyme and substrate. Other investigations, which have made use of similar or strikingly different techniques, have strengthened these earlier findings and established the ES as a definite intermediate in enzyme reactions. It is now customary to write the enzyme into the reaction as a full-fledged reactant.

The binding of the substrate with enzyme and the catalytic action occurs at the so-called *active site* of the enzyme. Although the theory that enzymes function by means of an active site is now supported by considerable experimental evidence, we still do not know whether the full catalytic activity of an enzyme resides in the protein structure as a whole or in a small part associated with the active site. The molecules of certain enzymes have been trimmed down to somewhat smaller size without appreciable loss in catalytic activity. For example, the enzyme ribonuclease (page 29) loses little of its activity when it is partially degraded. The molecule has also been broken into a large part and a small part that are inactive separately but become active when they are put into solution together.

For many enzymes, the extraordinary success of proteins as selective catalysts may depend on much more than the simple order of the amino acid units of which they are made. The chains of these units are often arranged in helices and generally are folded in various and intricate ways. The geometrical relationship of one helix to others may be crucial to catalytic activity. It has been suggested, for example, that, when the enzyme and substrate form their complex, the enzyme structure changes extensively before it exerts any catalytic activity. After catalysis the original structure is resumed by the enzyme. In addition to pointing out the necessity of gross spatial changes for catalytic activity, this theory suggests an explanation for enzyme specificity. The *induced-fit theory,* proposed by D. Koshland and depicted in Figure 4–7, is more compatible with current experimental findings than the similar but older *lock and key theory,* which assigned a less flexible structure to the enzyme.

Although we have discussed in some detail the physical and chemical properties of enzymes, we have yet to present representative enzymes to the reader. In future chapters many different enzymes will be mentioned and their biological roles considered. For a comprehensive classification and listing of enzymes, the reader is referred to *The Report of the Commission on Enzymes of the International Union of Biochemistry,* 1961.

SUGGESTED READING

Chance, B., "Enzyme Substrate Compounds," *Advances in Enzymology, 12,* 153–190 (1951).

Dixon, M., and E. C. Webb, *Enzymes,* Academic Press, Inc., New York, 1958.

Koshland, D. E., "Mechanisms of Transfer Enzymes," in *The Enzymes,* P. D. Boyer, H. Lardy and K. Myrbäck (eds.), vol. I, Academic Press, Inc., New York, 1959.

Nielands, J. B., and P. K. Stumpf, *Outlines of Enzyme Chemistry,* 2nd ed., John Wiley & Sons, Inc., New York, 1958.

Northrop, J. H., M. Kunitz, and R. M. Herriott, *Crystalline Enzymes,* 2nd ed., Columbia University Press, New York, 1948.

Report of the Commission on Enzymes of the International Union of Biochemistry, 1961, Pergamon Press, Inc., New York, 1961.

Sumner, J. B., "The Story of Urease," *Journal of Chemical Education, 14,* 255 (1937).

"The problem is: how does energy drive life?"

Albert Szent-Györgyi, 1957

FIVE

Biochemical Energetics

Energy for biological processes comes ultimately from the sun. Light is absorbed by chlorophyll pigments in plant cells and is eventually transformed through photosynthetic phosphorylation into the chemical energy needed for cellular functions. The carbohyrdrates and other substances produced by plants are ingested by animals and then metabolically broken down. At several stages in this metabolic degradation process, utilizable energy is produced in the form of *energy-rich* or *high energy* compounds. The terminal stage is an oxidative series of reactions which occur in the cell's mitochondria (page 171) and account for the major portion of energy-rich compounds produced. These energy-rich substances, which are usually phosphate compounds, are the negotiable energy for the many processes (biosynthesis, nerve conduction, movement) that are characteristic of life (Figure 5–1).

Adenosine triphosphate or ATP (Figure 5–2) is the key energy-rich compound for cellular functions. This chapter will deal with the nature of this and other energy-rich substances, whereas their formation and utilization will be considered in Chapter Six.

Biological energetics are like ordinary physicochemical energetics in theory. The major differences, however, reside in the chemical nature of the molecules involved and in the complexity of the system in which they operate. In general, molecules involved in biochemical energetics are more

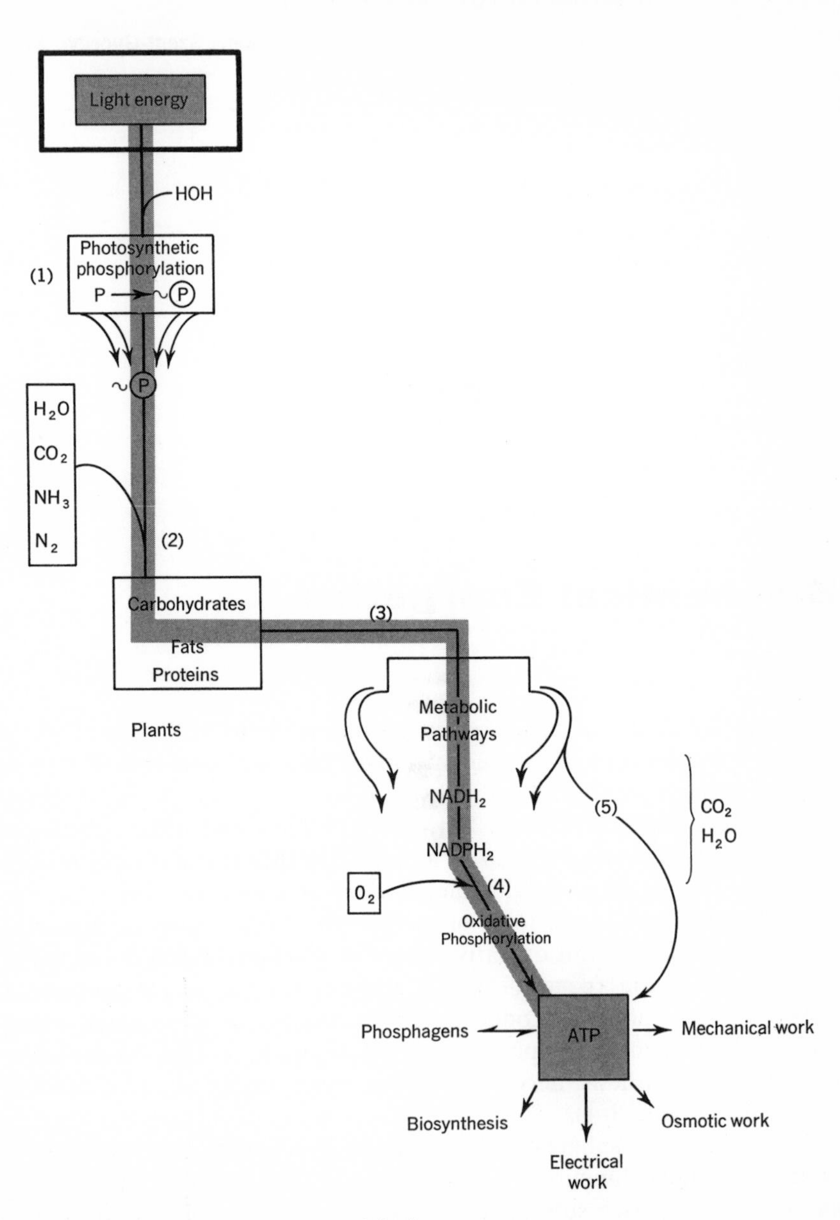

Figure 5–1. Energy flow through living systems. Photosynthetic phosphorylation (1) provides energy-rich phosphate compounds, ~Ⓟ, which are usable energy for carbon fixation and biosynthesis (2) in plants. The plant products are ingested (3) by animals, and through metabolic degradation they eventually result in ATP energy, (4) and (5), for cellular functions.

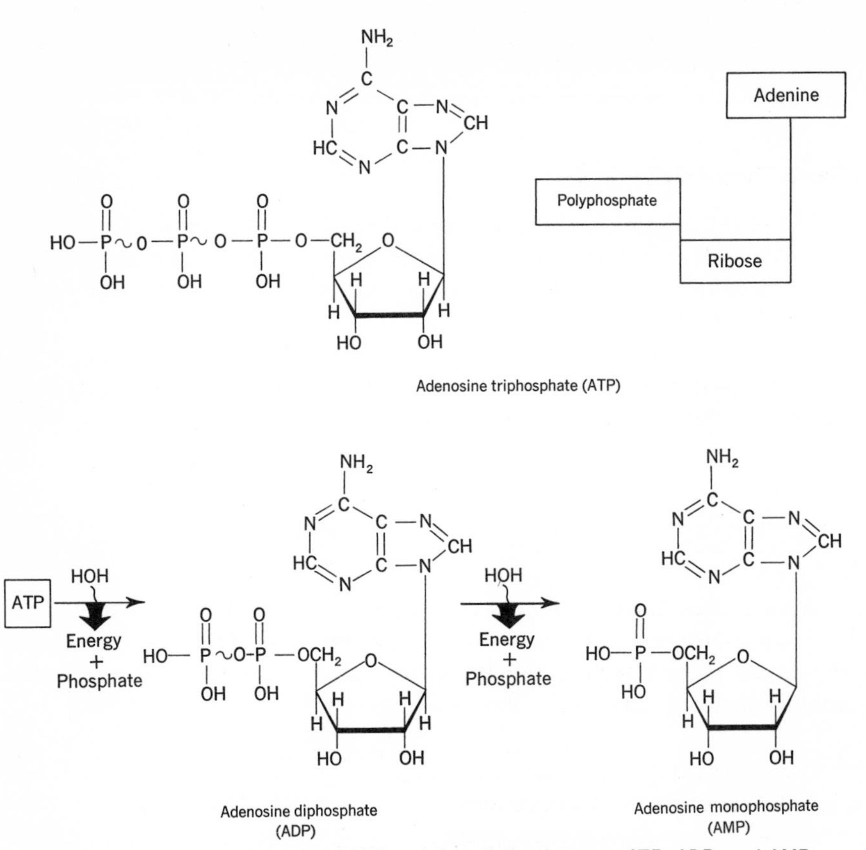

Figure 5–2. Chemical formula of ATP and the relation between ATP, ADP, and AMP.

complex than those studied by the physical chemist. The system, protoplasm, in which these molecules interact is more complicated than the systems of the physical chemist. Although these differences have hindered biochemists when they have attempted to formulate cellular energetics according to the laws of physics and chemistry, and have demanded that certain assumptions be made, progress has been made in expressing bioenergetics in thermodynamic terms.*

As a prelude to a discussion of biochemical energetics, the basic rules of thermodynamics will be stated, for they are directly pertinent to this subject. In the following section, these rules will be expressed in the form of

* In discussing this problem of expressing biological energetics in chemical terms, Fritz Lipmann has written: "Chemical and biological definitions are becoming more and more confluent. In this situation, terminologies occasionally need a mutual adjustment for which some common sense has to be used. Cellular chemistry is part of a technology of a very special kind and this aspect often deviates from interests of pure chemistry. Thus, the term "energy-rich" bond and the ~ sign in the biological sense describe energy units in cellular metabolism. Their acceptance and wide use by biologically minded chemists show the need for this type of description in the context of cellular chemistry."

equations which are a direct consequence of the three laws of thermodynamics. A more complete development of the equations and their significance can be found in any physical chemistry textbook.

Basic Thermodynamics

The physicochemical state of chemical reactants at a temperature (T) is completely described in terms of the Gibbs free energy (G),* enthalpy (H), and entropy (S). These thermodynamic functions are related as follows:

$$G = H - T \times S \tag{1}$$

When molecules A + B interact to form products C + D, the amount of energy and arrangement of molecules in a unit system changes as in Eq. (2).

$$\begin{array}{ccc} A + B & \longrightarrow & C + D \\ (G_A + G_B) & = & (G_C + G_D) \\ \text{Initial} & & \text{Final} \end{array} \tag{2}$$

We are interested in the change (Δ) that occurs in these energy and molecular-ordering functions during this reaction. This change can be expressed by subtracting the thermodynamic expression for the initial conditions from that for the final situation, or:

$$\Delta G = (G_C + G_D) - (G_A + G_B) \tag{3}$$

A similar expression can be obtained for ΔH and ΔS. Thus we may write

$$\Delta G = \Delta H - T \times \Delta S \tag{4}$$

at constant temperature.

These terms are helpful in evaluating the possibility that a particular reaction can occur. This is shown as follows:

ΔH, the heat of reaction, is equal to the

$$\Sigma H \text{ (products)} - \Sigma H \text{ (reactants)}$$

A negative value for ΔH ($\Delta H < 0$) means that during a chemical reaction heat is given off. For example, the burning of sugar has a negative heat of reaction. This is called an *exothermic* reaction. The converse, $\Delta H > 0$, is an *endothermic* reaction.

ΔS is the difference in entropy or disorder of products and reactants. Solids represent the most orderly state of matter, whereas liquid solutions and gases are less ordered and are said to possess more entropy.

ΔG, the difference in free energy of products and reactants, is the thermodynamic function pertinent to biological energetics. Free energy is defined

* Formerly the Gibbs free energy was denoted by F; this symbol will be found for it in many of the books in the list of suggested readings.

as the maximum useful work that can be obtained from a chemical reaction. The magnitude of the free energy change, ΔG, indicates the amount of useful work obtainable during the course of a chemical transformation and the potential ability of a substance to undergo such a transformation. Equation (4) states that the sign and magnitude of ΔG will reflect contributions from the change in heat content (ΔH) and the change in entropy (ΔS) during a chemical reaction. Under most circumstances ΔG and ΔH are so close in value that they can generally be regarded as equal.

Consider the reaction:

$$A + B \rightleftharpoons C + D \quad (5)$$

for which

$$\Delta G = \Delta H - T \times \Delta S \quad (6)$$

If $\Delta G > 0$, then the chemical reaction cannot occur except with external aid and energy must be supplied. The reverse reaction, however, will occur spontaneously.

If $\Delta G < 0$, the reaction tends to proceed spontaneously with the release of usable energy.

If $\Delta G = 0$, a state of equilibrium exists and no net chemical change will occur.

Processes which are attended by a decrease of free energy (i.e., $\Delta G < 0$) are said to be *exergonic,* whereas those which involve an increase of free energy ($\Delta G > 0$) are known as *endergonic* changes (Figure 5–3).

It is important to realize that ΔG is a thermodynamic function which refers to the potential of a reaction's occurring and, thus, to the final equilibrium point. ΔG gives no information about the rate at which this equilibrium point can be attained. The rate, but not the equilibrium point itself, can be influenced by catalysts (enzymes in biological systems).

The relationship between the thermodynamic concept of ΔG and metabolism becomes clear when the biochemistry of organisms is considered as myriads of exergonic and endergonic chemical reactions, catalyzed by enzymes. First, consider endergonic reactions or processes such as active transport, cellular motility, bioluminescence, or synthesis of macromolecules and low molecular weight metabolites. These are partial thermodynamic reactions with $\Delta G > 0$. Exergonic reactions include the breakdown and oxidation of fats, carbohydrates, and proteins and, in addition, the hydrolysis of energy-rich compounds. These partial thermodynamic reactions have $\Delta G < 0$.

We may ask: (1) "What happens to the energy made available in exergonic reactions? Is it lost as heat?" (2) "How can reactions occur which are thermodynamically unfavored in their simplest form? Where do these reactions obtain their supply of energy?" The answers to these questions can be found in the concepts of *high energy compounds* and *coupled reactions.*

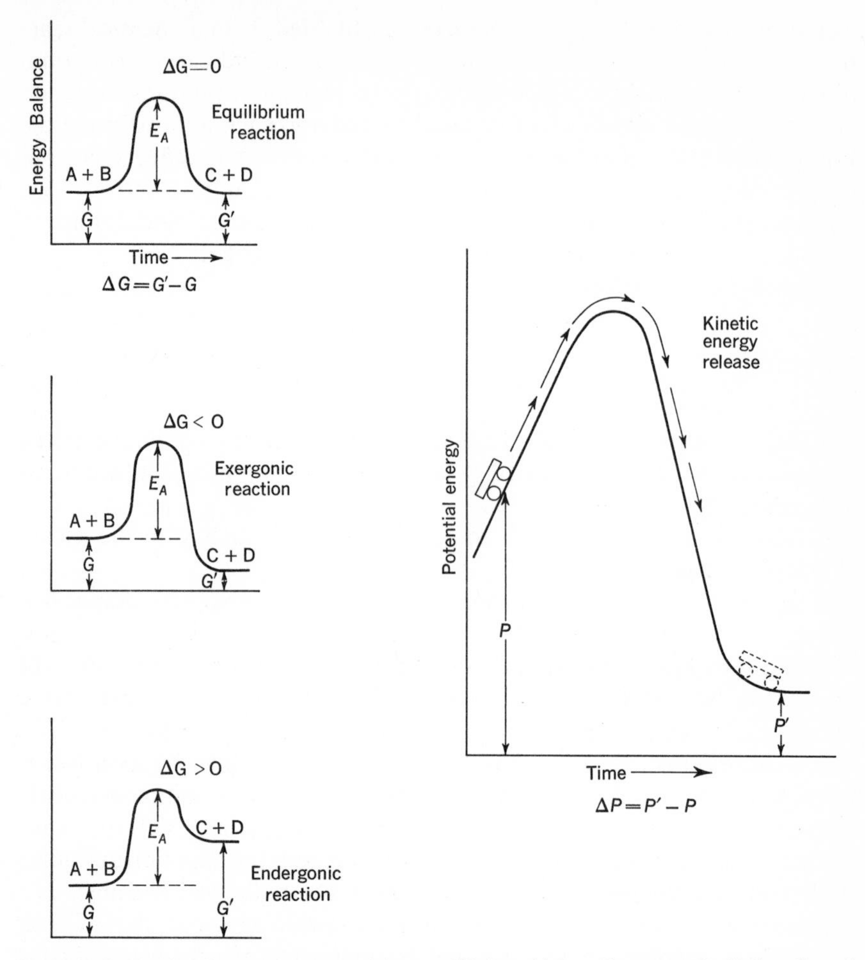

Figure 5–3. Energy diagrams summarizing equilibrium ($\Delta G = 0$), exergonic ($\Delta G < 0$) and endergonic ($\Delta G > 0$) reactions of A + B → C + D. Energy of activation is represented by E_A, free energy, G and G', potential energy, P.

High Energy Compounds

The concept of *high energy compounds* or *phosphate bond energy,* as developed by Fritz Lipmann and his contemporaries, has enormously contributed to our understanding of the chemical basis of bioenergetics. In this formulation, high energy compounds are characterized by one or more high energy bonds, bonds which have a large free energy of hydrolysis. These energy-rich bonds are symbolized by a *wriggle bond* (∼). In this system high and low energy bonds are distinguished on the basis of the free energy change (ΔG) that accompanies hydrolysis of the particular bond. A ΔG of -1 to -5 kilocalories per mole (kcal/mole) characterizes a low, and from -5 to -15 kcal/mole a high, energy bond. For example, in the reaction,*

$$\text{R—O—Ⓟ} \xrightarrow[\text{hydrolysis}]{+\text{HOH}} \text{ROH} + \text{HO—Ⓟ} \qquad \Delta G = -2 \text{ kcal/mole}$$

the O—Ⓟ bond is a low energy bond. In the hydrolysis of ATP, however,

$$\underset{\text{ATP}}{\text{Adenosine—Ⓟ—O}\sim\text{Ⓟ—O}\sim\text{Ⓟ}} \xrightarrow[\text{hydrolysis}]{+\text{HOH}} \underset{\text{ADP}}{\text{Adenosine—Ⓟ—O}\sim\text{Ⓟ}} + \text{HO—Ⓟ}$$

$$\Delta G = -8 \text{ kcal/mole}$$

a high energy bond is broken; that is, the ΔG of hydrolysis is about -8 kcal/mole. The location, however, of the wriggle bond (~) in a particular compound, for example, between phosphorus and oxygen in ATP, will depend on the reaction under consideration and will refer to the bond cleavage point.

The bond energy in these biochemical formulations has a special meaning and should not be confused with the terminology of the physical chemist. When a biochemist talks of a high energy bond, he is not referring to the bond energy which is usually referred to in physical chemistry as ε, the energy needed to disrupt a covalent linkage and separate two atoms. In particular, the biochemist is talking about the ΔG of the *reaction* of a particular compound at about pH 7.0, a reaction that involves the bond or chemical change under consideration. This ΔG is unusually large in the high energy compound, although the bond strengths, ε, of the specific linkages are not unusual. In an energy-rich compound the linkage that is called the high energy bond is that bond which is broken during the course of chemical reaction even though the high potential energy that is made available is a property of the entire reaction. For comparing the ΔG of such compounds, it has become conventional to refer to one common reaction partner, namely, water.

It is unfortunate that occasionally the term high energy bond and the symbol ~ have been used indiscriminately, and have obscured the fact that the free energy changes that give rise to high energy bonds must occur as reactions between complete molecules. A wriggle bond (~) in a biochemical formula means only that a *particular compound* can be expected, under the proper conditions, to enter into reactions which may involve a free energy change greater than 5 kilocalories per mole when the linkage is cleaved. High energy compounds are not wonder molecules supercharged

* P_i represents HO—P(=O)(OH)—OH, —Ⓟ terminally represents —P(=O)(OH)—OH, internally —P(=O)(OH)—

with mysterious energy. They are simply molecules with particular structures that give high energies of hydrolysis, and for this reason they are well suited to supply energy for biochemical processes.

Figure 5–1 illustrates several points about high energy bonds and the involvement of ATP in animal metabolism. Food, potential energy for the cell, is assimilated and enters one of many metabolic pathways. These metabolic processes include mechanisms for the breakdown of sugars (aerobic and anaerobic glycolysis), fats, proteins, and other materials and eventually result in CO_2 and water (waste products). Energy-rich phosphate bonds (~Ⓟ) primarily are generated during these processes in the form of ATP. The phosphate bond energy is transferred in this form to sites of utilization. Energy-rich ATP may then be used directly or it may be converted to another high energy form, e.g., uridine triphosphate (UTP), which functions in energy-consuming reactions. The excess ~Ⓟ that is formed can be stored as creatine phosphate or arginine phosphate. Creatine phosphate is the phosphagen, or storage form of ~Ⓟ, in most vertebrate animals; arginine phosphate is the storage form in invertebrates.

There are innumerable energy-rich compounds involved in the operation of the biological machinery. When these energy-rich compounds undergo metabolic reactions, there is a free energy change which can be marshaled to drive endergonic reactions. Examples of energy-rich compounds are summarized in Table 5–1. Primarily, these are phosphate com-

TABLE 5–1

ENERGY-RICH COMPOUNDS

Characteristic Linkage	General Formula	General Designation	Biochemical Example	$\Delta G°$ (kcal/mole)
—C(=)—N(H)~	RC(=NH)—N(H)~Ⓟ	Guanidinium phosphate	Creatine phosphate	−10.5
			Arginine phosphate	−9.0
—C(=)—O~	RC(=CH₂)—O~Ⓟ	Enolphosphate	Phosphoenol pyruvate	−12.8
—C(=)—O~	RC(=O)—O~Ⓟ	Acyl phosphate	Acetyl phosphate	−10.1
—P(=)(HO)—O~	ROP(=O)(HO)—O~Ⓟ	Pyrophosphates	Adenosine diphosphate	−8.0 to −12.0
—C(=)~	RC(=O)~SR′	Acyl thioester	Acetyl CoA	−10.5

TABLE 5–2

LOW ENERGY COMPOUNDS

General Designation	Structure	Biochemical Example	$\Delta G°$ (kcal/mole)
Peptide bond (within protein)	$-\overset{O}{\overset{\|\|}{C}}-NH-$	...Tyrosylglycine...	−0.5
Amides	$-\overset{O}{\overset{\|\|}{C}}-NH_2$	Glutamine	−3.4
Esters, normal	$-\overset{O}{\overset{\|\|}{C}}-OR$	Ethyl acetate	−1.8
Sugar phosphate	$>C-O-Ⓟ$	Glucose-6-phosphate Glycerol-1-phosphate	−2.9 −2.3

pounds, derivatives of phosphate esters (such as adenosine triphosphate), or derivatives of complex sulfur compounds (such as acetyl coenzyme A). For contrast, Table 5–2 lists the free energies of hydrolysis for some biological molecules that have low energy bonds.

Although there are many energy-rich substances, there are, however, a few general types of chemical structures that have characteristics which contribute to a high ΔG of hydrolysis of a particular linkage and are essential for the energy richness of these compounds. In many of the energy-rich compounds, an anhydride

$$-\overset{O}{\overset{\|}{C}}-O-\overset{O}{\overset{\|}{C}}-$$

type of linkage occurs. In this regard, similar chemical structures are used by the organic chemist and in biology to effect corresponding free energy-requiring tasks. The organic chemist employs the anhydride structure in acetic anhydride,

$$CH_3\overset{O}{\overset{\|}{C}}-O-\overset{O}{\overset{\|}{C}}-CH_3$$

rather than acetic acid,

$$CH_3\overset{O}{\overset{\|}{C}}-OH$$

to make acetate esters. Anhydride-type linkages occur in metabolites

between two phosphates

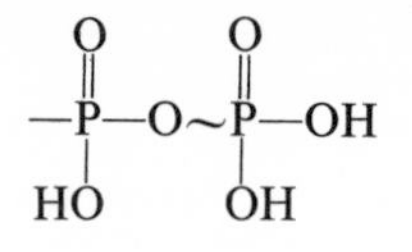

or between a phosphate and a carbonyl

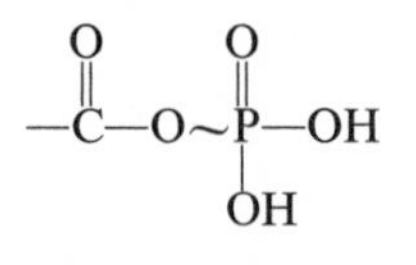

or acid enol. Other high energy compounds involve direct connections between phosphorus and nitrogen as in guanidinium phosphates,

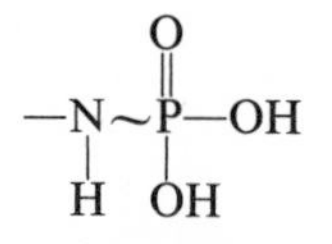

In many instances, rather than simply a phosphate group, a phosphate ester, such as AMP (Figure 5–2) or UDP (page 128), is an integral part of the high energy compound.

In still another group, phosphorus does not enter into the high energy compounds but is replaced by sulfur. One such example is the acyl mercaptide bond

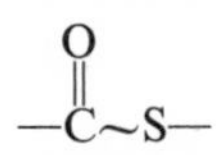

found in coenzyme A (page 144) derivatives.

Why do these compounds have high free energies of hydrolysis? Why is the phosphate residue so commonly involved? One reason for the high $-\Delta G$ of hydrolysis is that the immediate hydrolysis products of energy-rich compounds undergo secondary, spontaneous reactions which lead to thermodynamically more stable forms. This may occur either through resonance stabilization or tautomeric rearrangements of the products. A further contribution to the high free energy of hydrolysis, in the case of ATP and phosphopyruvate, for example, is the separation and randomization of the neighboring like (negative) charges in these molecules at physiological pH.

There seems to be one important reason why the phosphate residue is so well suited for its role in energy-rich compounds. Phosphate derivatives have kinetic stability in water, the biological medium, yet they also have thermodynamic lability. For example, acetic anhydride and acetyl phosphate have similar ΔG's but acetic anhydride has a half-life in water of only a few minutes, compared to a half-life of several hours for acetyl phosphate and to practically infinite stability in the case of the pyrophosphate derivatives (e.g., ATP). For this reason, the thermodynamically labile bonds are able to exist for long periods of time in biological systems, waiting for the appropriate enzyme-catalyzed reactions to make their intrinsic energy available for endergonic processes. This would not be true for similar compounds without phosphate. The central role of ATP in supplying energy for endergonic reactions and the importance of phosphorylated compounds in energy transformations cannot be overemphasized in discussion of high energy compounds.

Coupled Reactions

The way high energy compounds, which arise from exergonic reactions, drive endergonic processes involves coupled reactions. A simple hypothetical example illustrates the thermodynamic basis for coupled reactions and clarifies the role of high energy compounds in bioenergetics. An ester,

$$\mathrm{R\overset{\overset{\displaystyle O}{\|}}{C}{-}OR'}$$

can be formed from an acid,

$$\mathrm{R{-}\overset{\overset{\displaystyle O}{\|}}{C}{-}OH}$$

and an alcohol, R′OH, as in Eq. (7).

$$\mathrm{R\overset{\overset{\displaystyle O}{\|}}{C}{-}OH + R'OH \longrightarrow R\overset{\overset{\displaystyle O}{\|}}{C}{-}OR' + HOH} \qquad \Delta G_1 = +2\ \text{kcal/mole} \tag{7}$$

Thermodynamically, the reaction is energy requiring ($\Delta G > 0$) and unfavorable. A second reaction, the hydrolysis of ATP, Eq. (8),

$$\mathrm{ATP + HOH \longrightarrow ADP + Ⓟ{-}OH} \qquad \Delta G_2 = -8\ \text{kcal/mole} \tag{8}$$

is exergonic ($\Delta G < 0$) and makes energy available. By adding these two reactions, (7) and (8), the net result is:

$$\mathrm{R\overset{\overset{\displaystyle O}{\|}}{C}{-}OH + R'OH + ATP \longrightarrow R\overset{\overset{\displaystyle O}{\|}}{C}{-}OR' + ADP + Ⓟ{-}OH}$$

$$\Delta G_3 = \Delta G_1 + \Delta G_2 = -6\ \text{kcal/mole} \tag{9}$$

If it were possible to capture the energy released in reaction (8) and funnel it into reaction (7), the energetically favorable reaction (9) could be obtained. This is effectively accomplished biochemically by two different reactions, (10) and (11), having the same over-all result as (7) + (8) but which occur consecutively, and have a common intermediate that transfers energy.

$$R\overset{\overset{O}{\|}}{C}\text{—OH} + \text{ATP} \longrightarrow R\overset{\overset{O}{\|}}{C}\text{—O}\sim\text{Ⓟ} + \text{ADP} \qquad \Delta G_4 = -3 \text{ kcal/mole} \tag{10}$$

then

$$R\overset{\overset{O}{\|}}{C}\text{—O}\sim\text{Ⓟ} + \text{R'OH} \longrightarrow R\overset{\overset{O}{\|}}{C}\text{—OR'} + \text{Ⓟ—OH} \qquad \Delta G_5 = -3 \text{ kcal/mole} \tag{11}$$

or, adding (10) and (11):

$$R\overset{\overset{O}{\|}}{C}\text{—OH} + \text{ATP} + \text{R'OH} \longrightarrow R\overset{\overset{O}{\|}}{C}\text{—OR'} + \text{ADP} + \text{Ⓟ—OH}$$
$$\Delta G_6 = \Delta G_4 + \Delta G_5 = -6 \text{ kcal/mole} \tag{12}$$

Reactions (10) and (11) are partial chemical and thermodynamic reactions in the ester formation reaction (12). The over-all ΔG of reaction (12) is -6 kcal/mole and the energy-requiring synthesis of

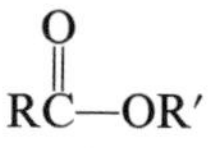

proceeds spontaneously. In reaction (10)

$$R\overset{\overset{O}{\|}}{C}\text{—OH}$$

has been raised to a higher energy level by interaction with ATP to form

$$R\overset{\overset{O}{\|}}{C}\text{—O}\sim\text{Ⓟ}$$

a high energy species.

This is now the *common intermediate* of two consecutive reactions, (10) and (11), which together have a net free energy change of -6 kcal/mole. Instead of releasing into the environment the large amount of energy obtained by splitting ATP to ADP as in (8), most of the energy in (10) is captured in the common intermediate, for subsequent release in (11). Only a small amount of energy is lost to the environment.

An analogous example is the organic chemists' recipe for preparing an ester, ethyl acetate, via acetyl chloride. Acetic acid reacts very poorly with ethyl alcohol to form ethyl acetate, Eq. (13),

$$CH_3\overset{\overset{O}{\|}}{C}\text{—OH} + CH_3CH_2OH \longrightarrow CH_3\overset{\overset{O}{\|}}{C}\text{—}OCH_2CH_3 + HOH \tag{13}$$

If, however, acetic acid is converted to acetyl chloride, Eq. (14),

$$CH_3\overset{\overset{\displaystyle O}{\|}}{C}\text{—}OH + PCl_5 \longrightarrow CH_3\overset{\overset{\displaystyle O}{\|}}{C}\text{—}Cl + POCl_3 + HCl \tag{14}$$

and the acetyl chloride is allowed to interact with ethyl alcohol, Eq. (15),

$$CH_3\overset{\overset{\displaystyle O}{\|}}{C}\text{—}Cl + CH_3CH_2OH \longrightarrow CH_3\overset{\overset{\displaystyle O}{\|}}{C}\text{—}OCH_2CH_3 + HCl \tag{15}$$

the desired ester product is obtained. The negative free energy change in reaction (15) is much greater than in reaction (13); thus (15) is thermodynamically favored. Essentially the high free energy intrinsic in PCl_5

$$PCl_5 + HOH \longrightarrow POCl_3 + 2HCl \tag{16}$$

has been transferred in reaction (14) to acetyl chloride, a compound in which the reaction potential (group potential) of

$$CH_3\text{—}\overset{\overset{\displaystyle O}{\|}}{C}\text{—}$$

is much higher than in acetic acid.

In biological systems, the exergonic reaction that is generally coupled with energy-requiring reactions involves the compound ATP (Figure 5–2). The energy inherent in ATP is used to form an activated intermediate of the type shown in Table 5–1. In these energy-rich derivatives, the groups attached to ~Ⓟ have a high potential reactivity or a high group potential, just as does the acetyl

$$CH_3\text{—}\overset{\overset{\displaystyle O}{\|}}{C}\text{—}$$

group in acetyl chloride. These groups are thus energetically prepared for involvement in endergonic processes. In the next chapter the formation of these high energy compounds will be considered in detail.

SUGGESTED READING

Klotz, I. M., *Introduction to Chemical Thermodynamics,* W. A. Benjamin, Inc., New York, 1964.

Lehninger, A. L., *Bioenergetics,* W. A. Benjamin, Inc., New York, 1965.

Lipmann, F., "Attempts Toward a Formulation of Biological Use of Energy in Terms of Chemical Potentials" in *Molecular Biology,* D. Nachmansohn (ed.), Academic Press, Inc., New York, 1960.

"I believe, therefore, that just as the place of iron in biological reactions is now made completely understandable by the work of Otto Warburg as being necessary for the catalysis of oxygen transfer, so the role of phosphate compounds in the organisms is made understandable by their importance for energy transfer."

O. Meyerhof, 1951

SIX

Adenosine Triphosphate Formation and Utilization

Photosynthetic phosphorylation in plants transforms light energy into phosphate bond energy in the form of adenosine triphosphate (ATP). Since animals are dependent on plants for potential energy, in the form of foodstuff, photosynthetic phosphorylation is the first link in the transformation of light energy into biochemical energy. Two other forms of phosphorylation or phosphate bond energy formation are characteristic of both plant and animal cells: (1) substrate level phosphorylation, and (2) oxidative phosphorylation linked to electron transport. Both these processes make use of the energy released during the breakdown of starch, fats, etc., to drive the esterification of inorganic phosphate into the ATP energy system, Eq. (1).

$$\text{Foodstuffs} \longrightarrow \text{Oxidative energy}$$

$$\text{ADP} + \text{Inorganic phosphate } (P_i) \longrightarrow \text{ATP} \quad \textbf{(1)}$$

Although both processes are important, about 90 per cent of the ATP formed in aerobic cells arises from phosphorylation linked to electron transport, Figure 6–1. There are thus three general biological processes for ATP formation:

1. Photosynthetic phosphorylation.
2. Substrate level phosphorylation.

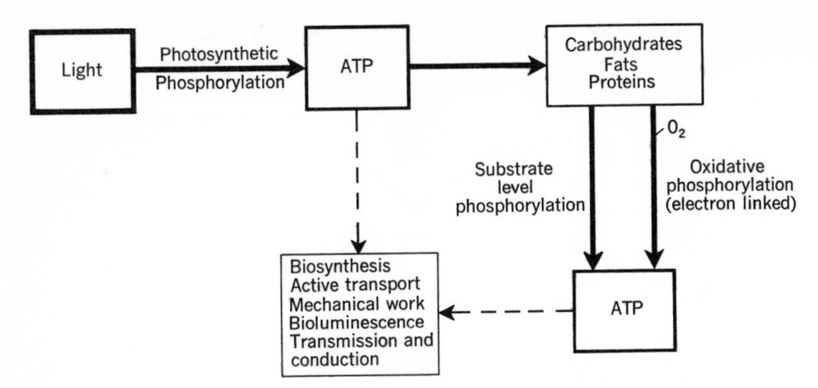

Figure 6–1. Energy flow and ATP formation.

3. Oxidative phosphorylation linked to electron transport.

Let us now consider these, the simplest first.

Substrate Level Phosphorylation

When cellular fuel, a free energy source, is utilized, small packets of the available energy become diverted into bonds of many different energy-rich compounds. These compounds, which are intermediates in the breakdown of carbohydrates, etc., are generally phosphorylated derivatives. Many can then react directly or indirectly with ADP to form ATP and the ~Ⓟ is transferred onto ADP. For example, two ADP phosphorylation reactions of the Embden-Meyerhof glycolytic pathway (page 93) are:

$$\text{1,3-Diphosphoglyceric acid} + \text{ADP} \xrightarrow[\text{kinase}]{\text{phosphoglycero-}} \text{3-Phosphoglyceric acid} + \text{ATP}$$

and

$$\text{Phosphoenol pyruvic acid} + \text{ADP} \xrightarrow[\text{kinase}]{\text{pyruvic}} \text{Pyruvic acid} + \text{ATP} \qquad \textbf{(2)}$$

These reactions result in the direct transfer of high energy phosphate onto ADP forming ATP. Substrate level phosphorylation, unlike oxidative phosphorylation linked to electron transport (next section), does not directly require oxygen for ATP formation, although oxygen may be utilized before the ATP-forming step. Furthermore, the enzymes which catalyze reactions in substrate level phosphorylation are soluble in the cytoplasm (page 180), in contrast to the mitochondrial (page 171) enzymes involved in electron-linked oxidative phosphorylation.

Oxidative Phosphorylation Linked to Electron Transport

When an engine burns fuel, it is desirable, regardless of the type of engine—mechanical or living—for the energy to be released in a controlled

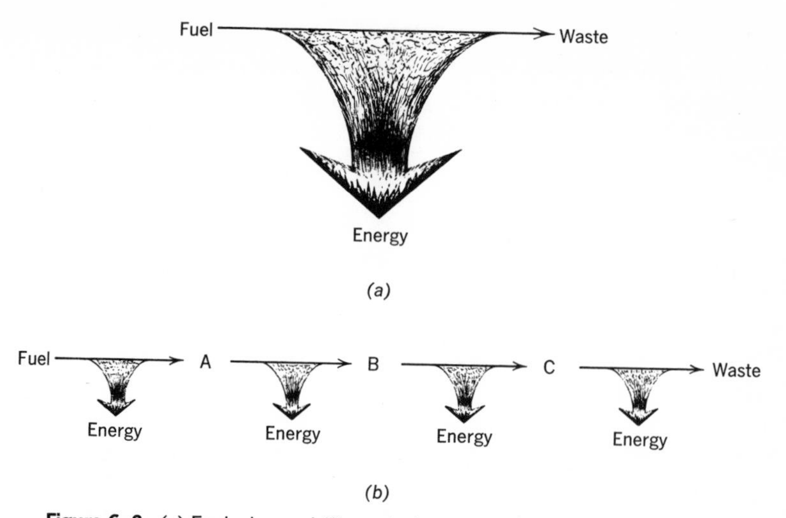

Figure 6–2. (*a*) Explosive and (*b*) gradual energy release in fuel utilization.

manner. An energy liberation in small increments is to be preferred over an explosive release which might destroy the engine or waste most of the energy (Figure 6–2*a*).

The cell operates in a manner similar to that shown in Figure 6–2*b* by tapping the metabolic energy intrinsic in foodstuffs at multiple stages and transforming it into ATP. Thus a system of gradual oxidation is used (Figure 6–3) rather than the direct oxidation of a reduced substrate (sub-

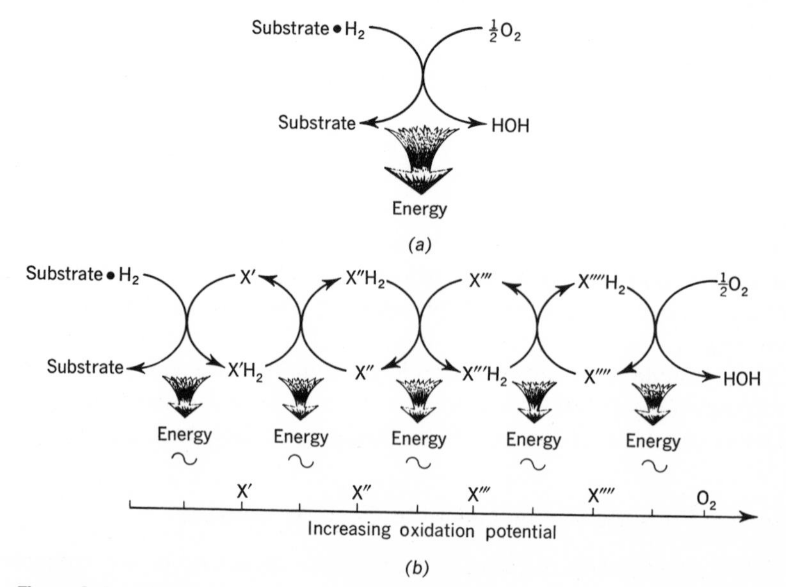

Figure 6–3. (*a*) Direct and (*b*) gradual oxidation of reduced substances by oxygen.

strate · H_2) by a substrate (e.g., oxygen) with a high oxidation potential relative to substrate · H_2. The reduced substrate is initially oxidized by a compound (X′) having an only slightly greater oxidation potential. Thus, a small amount of energy is released. X′ becomes reduced ($X'H_2$) in this process and is subsequently reoxidized by a second oxidizing agent (X″) and again a small energy release occurs. This process is repeated successively with oxidizing agents that approach more and more the oxidizing potential of the terminal oxidizing agent, oxygen. At each oxidation stage, utilizable energy becomes available and can be transformed into ATP energy.

These oxidation-reduction reactions involve the transfer of electrons. Oxidation is defined as removal of electrons from a substance with an increase in its positive valence, whereas reduction is a gain of electrons by a substance with a concomitant decrease in positive valence. Every oxidation is accompanied by a simultaneous reduction, with the electrons removed from one substance being gained by another substance. The energy required for the removal of electrons in oxidation is supplied by the accompanying reduction.

When the electron transfer picture is complex, oxidation-reduction reactions can be simply visualized as the addition of oxygen or the removal of hydrogen. For example, oxidation in biological systems can occur by the enzymatic addition of oxygen, Eq. (3), or by the removal of hydrogen, Eqs. (4).

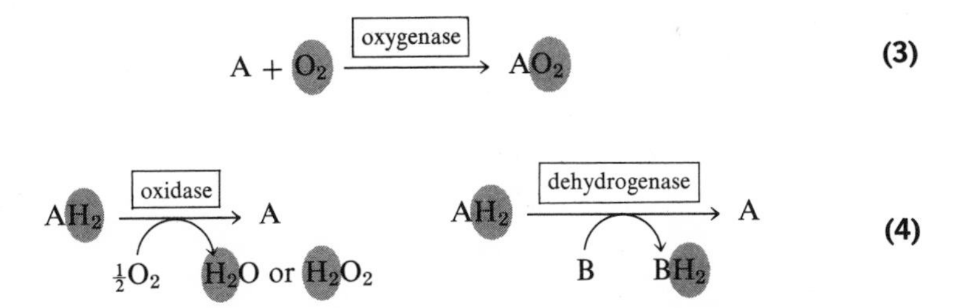

Oxidases in Eqs. (4) require oxygen as an acceptor; dehydrogenases do not. Dehydrogenation, or oxidation without oxygen, is extremely common in biological systems, and there are many specific dehydrogenases present in the cell.

The cellular system for trapping phosphate bond energy during the transport of electrons from a reduced substrate to oxygen and the energetics of the process are shown in Figure 6–4. The over-all reaction is:

$$NADH_2 + \tfrac{1}{2}O_2 + 3\text{Ⓟ}OH + 3ADP \longrightarrow NAD + 3ATP + HOH \quad (5)$$

The intermediaries between reduced substrate and oxygen are: (1) nicotinamide nucleotides, (2) flavoproteins, (3) quinones such as coenzyme Q, (4) cytochromes. From energy considerations, it should be possible

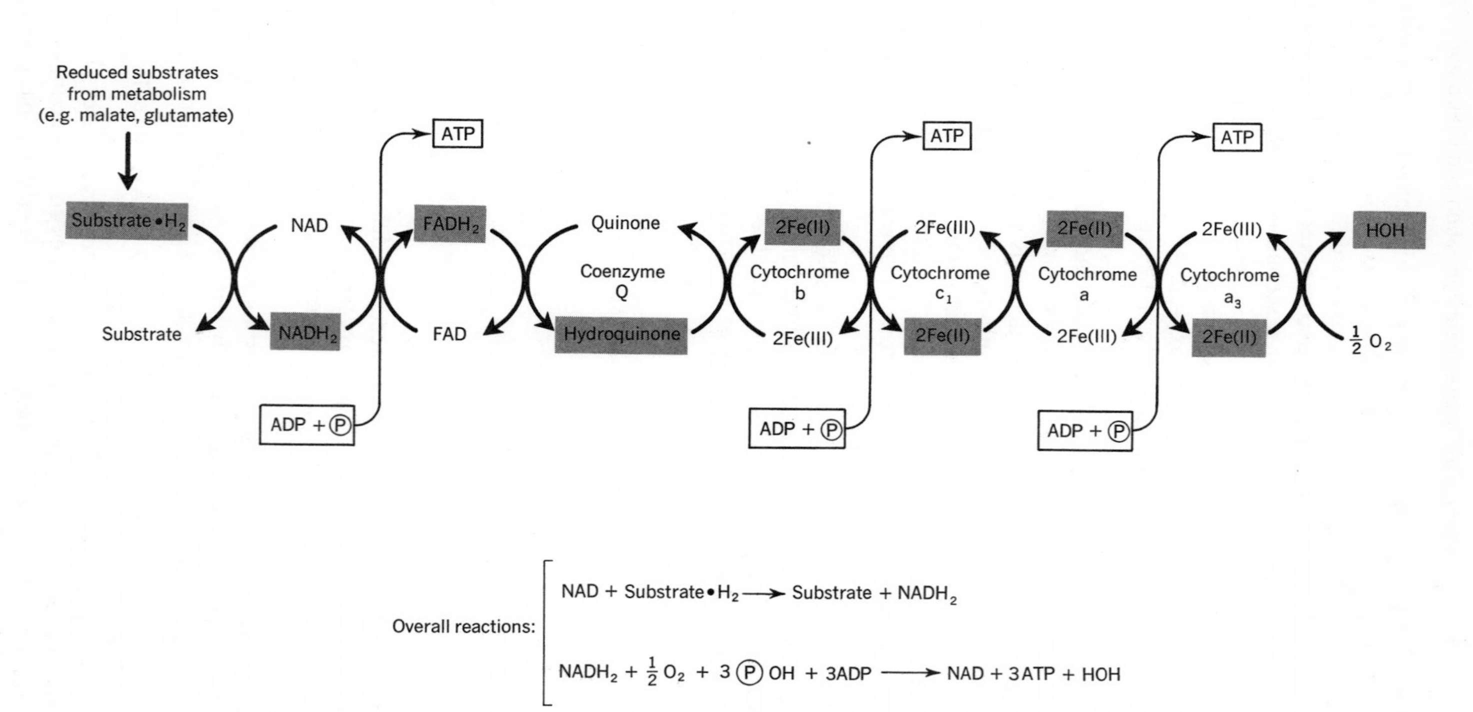

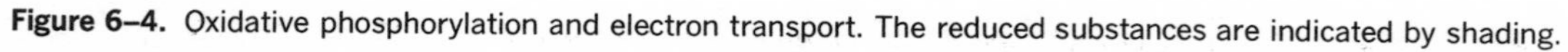

Figure 6–4. Oxidative phosphorylation and electron transport. The reduced substances are indicated by shading.

to obtain four high energy bonds during the transfer of an electron pair from $NADH_2$ to oxygen. Experimentally, however, it has been found that only three ATP molecules are formed from ADP + phosphate during the electron transport process. Thus, a $\frac{3}{4}$ or a 75 per cent efficiency of ATP production is realized during oxidative phosphorylation linked to electron transport. It should be realized that some reduced substrates (e.g., succinate) are linked to a flavoprotein rather than NAD and give rise to only two ~Ⓟ or ATP molecules. Even so the efficiency of this biochemical machine is indeed very respectable!

Recently, the International Union of Biochemistry has made recommendations about the nomenclature of nicotinamide and flavin nucleotides and cytochromes. We have decided to use the names and abbreviations they have suggested even though many of their recommended terms are less common in the literature of biochemistry (e.g., DPN is much more familiar than the recommended NAD). The composition of these compounds is summarized in Figure 6–5.

The nicotinamide nucleotides (NAD and NADP) work in collaboration with mitochondrial enzymes to effect the transport of electrons or to facilitate hydrogen transfer. Both NAD and NADP enter into electron addition (hydrogen removal or dehydrogenation) reactions in the same chemical manner. In these reactions, only the nicotinamide residue, a common constituent of the two compounds, is oxidized and reduced, Eq. (6). It can be seen that in the reduction only one atom of hydrogen is added to the pyridine ring, although two electrons are transferred to the ring; a hydrogen ion appears in the medium. This may not be obvious from the suggested nomenclature: NAD → $NADH_2$.

Common Names	Abbreviation	Composition
Nicotinamide mononucleotide	**(NMN)**	Nicotinamide—D-ribose—phosphate
Cozymase Coenzyme 1 Diphosphopyridine nucleotide **Nicotinamide-adenine dinucleotide**	 (Co 1) (DPN) **(NAD)**	Adenine——D-ribose——phosphate ┐ Nicotinamide—D-ribose—phosphate ┘
Flavin mononucleotide	**(FMN)**	Isoalloxazine—ribitol—phosphate
Flavin-adenine dinucleotide	**(FAD)**	Adenine——D-ribose——phosphate ┐ Isoalloxazine—ribitol—phosphate ┘
Phospho-cozymase Coenzyme 2 Triphosphopyridine nucleotide **Nicotinamide-adenine dinucleotide phosphate**	 (Co 2) (TPN) **(NADP)**	phosphate | Adenine——D-ribose——phosphate ┐ Nicotinamide—D-ribose—phosphate ┘

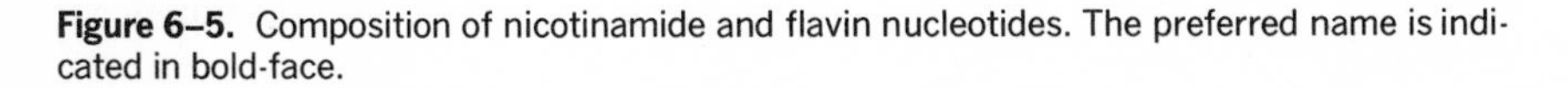

Figure 6–5. Composition of nicotinamide and flavin nucleotides. The preferred name is indicated in bold-face.

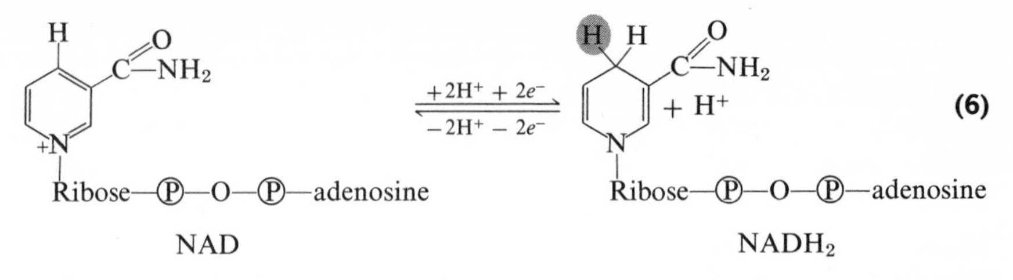

(6)

Flavoproteins, the second group in the chain of electron transport, are enzymes (dehydrogenases) composed of a protein moiety and a yellow component which gives rise to the name "flavo." The yellow constituent is either flavin mononucleotide (FMN) or flavin adenine dinucleotide (FAD). During the course of electron transport, the complex isoalloxazine component of the flavin alternatively adds and yields electrons,

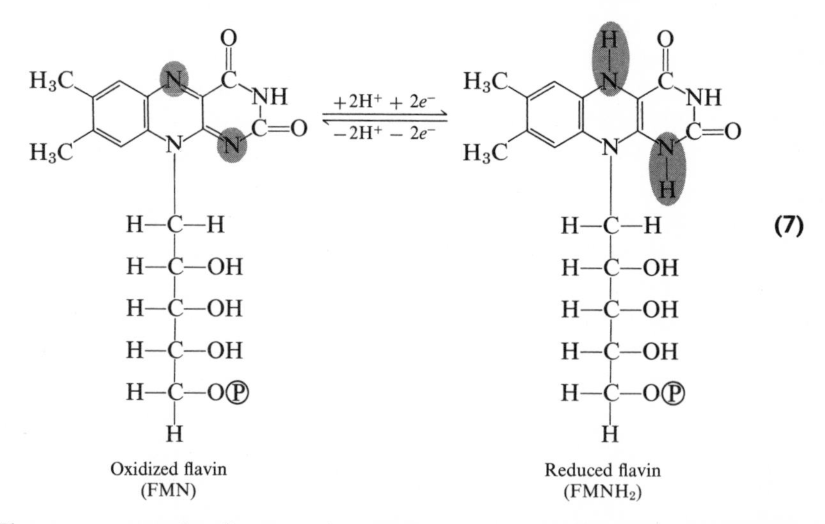

(7)

The most recently discovered components of the electron chain have been tentatively called coenzymes Q because their functional group, when oxidized, is a quinone. At the moment its chemistry is little understood but coenzyme Q_{10} is believed to change as shown in Eq. (8) during electron transport between the flavin coenzymes and the cytochromes.

The cytochromes are iron-containing proteins. The iron moiety is bound to a porphyrin group, as in hemoglobin, and iron is the element that accepts and donates electrons during oxidative phosphorylation. During the electron transport procedure the valence states of iron change from II (electron added) to III (electron removed). The different cytochromes, and there are many, are distinguished, on the basis of differences in their absorption spectra, by the letters a, b, c_1, c_2, etc. The exact number of different cytochromes involved in electron transport is unknown at present.

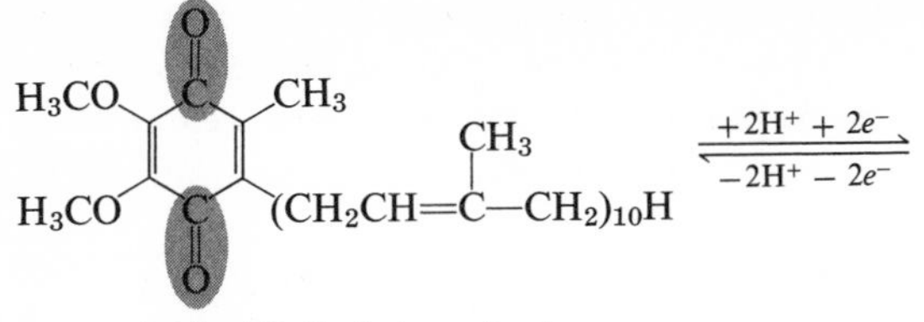

Oxidized CoQ_{10} (quinone form)

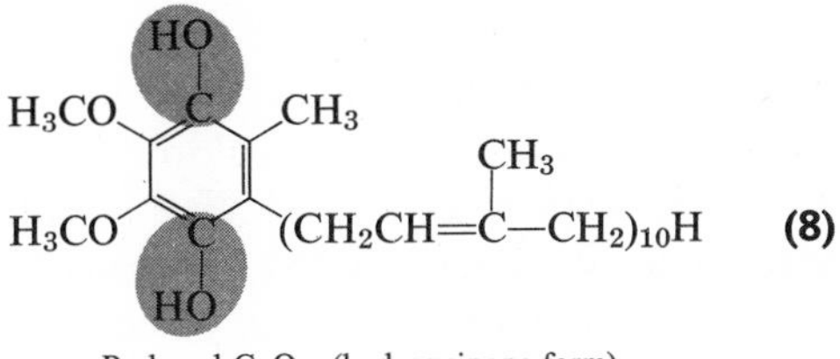

(8)

Reduced CoQ_{10} (hydroquinone form)

The functions of some cytochromes are well defined. Cytochrome c is strictly an electron carrier, and not a hydrogen carrier as are NAD and NADP or the flavoproteins. Each molecule of cytochrome c is able to add an electron and thus become reduced,

$$\underset{\text{Oxidized}}{\text{Cytochrome c-Fe(III)}} \underset{-e^-}{\overset{+e^-}{\rightleftharpoons}} \underset{\text{Reduced}}{\text{Cytochrome c-Fe(II)}} \qquad \textbf{(9)}$$

Cytochrome a_3, commonly known as cytochrome oxidase, is a true oxidase employing molecular oxygen as its hydrogen acceptor. Cytochrome a_3, which contains both Cu(II) and Fe-porphyrin as a prosthetic group, is apparently the terminal acceptor in the electron transport procedure culminating with the reduction of oxygen to water. It is a striking fact that virtually all plants and animals are so completely dependent on this one enzyme system, which, incidentally, is the enzyme system most sensitive to the well-known poison cyanide.

With some knowledge of the oxidation-reduction changes that carriers in the electron transport system undergo, it is easy to understand why we have written the equations in Figure 6–4 as cyclic processes. This has been done to emphasize that the oxidation (electron removal) of one substance involves the reduction (electron addition) of the next member of the chain. Thus, an electron is effectively carried down the transport chain.

Photosynthetic Phosphorylation

It cannot be overemphasized that life on our planet depends on the conversion of light energy into chemical energy. This energy transformation occurs during *photosynthetic phosphorylation,* a process which takes place in the chloroplasts of plants. This occurs without the aid of other cellular constituents such as leaf mitochondria.

At least two types of photosynthetic phosphorylation or photophosphorylation occur in the chloroplasts of higher plants. These are termed *cyclic* and *noncyclic* photophosphorylation and both are regarded as essential since the ATP formed in one is insufficient for the fixation of CO_2 (see Chapter Seven) in the form of carbohydrates.

Cyclic photophosphorylation (Figure 6–6) can be summarized as:

$$\text{ADP} + \text{P}_i \xrightarrow{\boxed{\text{Light}}} \text{ATP} \tag{10}$$

The initial photochemical event is the absorption of light by chlorophyll a to produce a kind of excited chlorophyll in which an electron is raised from its normal energy level to a higher level in the bond structure of this complex molecule. Such excited electrons flow from chlorophyll to an iron-containing protein, ferredoxin, from ferredoxin to cytochromes via flavins and plastoquinone back to chlorophyll a and their normal stable level. During this cyclic flow of electrons, the energy which the electrons acquired initially is funneled off, bit by bit, through oxidation-reduction reactions that produce ATP. The later phases of this process are analogous and possibly identical in some respects to their counterparts in oxidative phosphorylation. The light-induced generation of a high energy electron and also of the ultimate electron acceptor, chlorophyll, however, are peculiar to photophosphorylation.

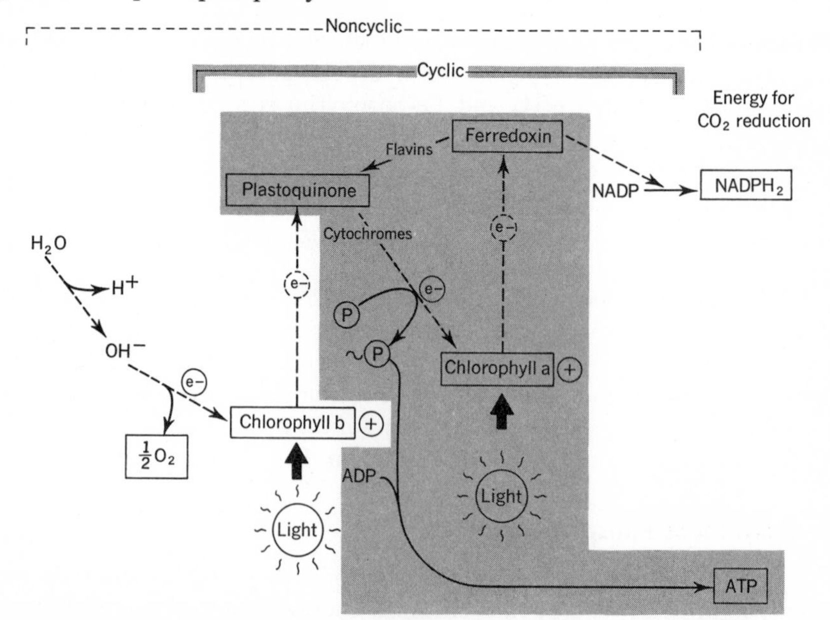

Figure 6–6. Cyclic and noncyclic photosynthetic phosphorylation. Shading indicates reactions in cyclic photophosphorylation and a broken line (---) those in non-cyclic photophosphorylation. The energy necessary for carbon fixation is produced in the form of ATP and $NADPH_2$.

Noncyclic photophosphorylation (Figure 6–6) is summarized as:

$$2NADP + 2H_2O + 2ADP + 2P_i \xrightarrow{\boxed{\text{Light}}} 2NADPH_2 + 2ATP + O_2 \quad \mathbf{(11)}$$

This process is unique in that ATP formation, unlike any other known phosphorylation, is coupled with an evolution of oxygen. Second, contrary to an analogy with oxidative phosphorylation, ATP formation results not in the ultimate oxidation but in the reduction of nicotinamide nucleotide.

Noncyclic photophosphorylation, like the cyclic process, has a primary photochemical event and a primary phosphorylation reaction at the site of a cytochrome adjacent to the excited chlorophyll molecule. The excited electron from the photochemical event is accepted by NADP and used (along with an accompanying proton) for the production of $NADPH_2$. The $NADPH_2$ can either accumulate under special conditions (in isolated chloroplasts), or be used jointly with ATP for the formation of carbohydrates during normal photosynthesis.

For the continuous operation of this system it is necessary that electrons drawn off into $NADPH_2$ be continuously replenished. This appears to be a reaction in which OH^- ions from water yield molecular oxygen and donate electrons, via a cytochrome chain, to chlorophyll where they are excited at the expense of absorbed light energy.

Biological Functions of Energy-Rich Compounds

Biochemical energy has been equated with ATP bond energy because the energy intrinsic in ATP appears to be used extensively for biochemical functions. In a now classical diagram (Figure 6–7), F. Lipmann summarized this in 1941. An abbreviated summary of the functions of ATP bond energy is included in Figure 6–1.

The role of energy-rich bonds in macromolecular biosynthesis, e.g., fats, nucleic acids, proteins, is of such great importance and scope that Chapter Eleven will be devoted to this topic.

The transformation of phosphate bond energy into mechanical work, e.g., muscle contraction and sperm motility, is little understood. The idea that hydrolysis of ATP usually is the energy-providing step of the mechanochemical process arises from the demonstration that muscle ATPase (enzyme that hydrolyzes ATP) is associated, in the main, with the contractile component of muscle—actomyosin. Although most workers agree that ATP is directly involved in the contractile process, the precise point at which ATP functions is still unknown.

Active transport processes, the preferential uptake and excretion of matter by the cell, are believed to involve energy-rich phosphate compounds. How energy is transferred from metabolism to the transport process also remains a mystery.

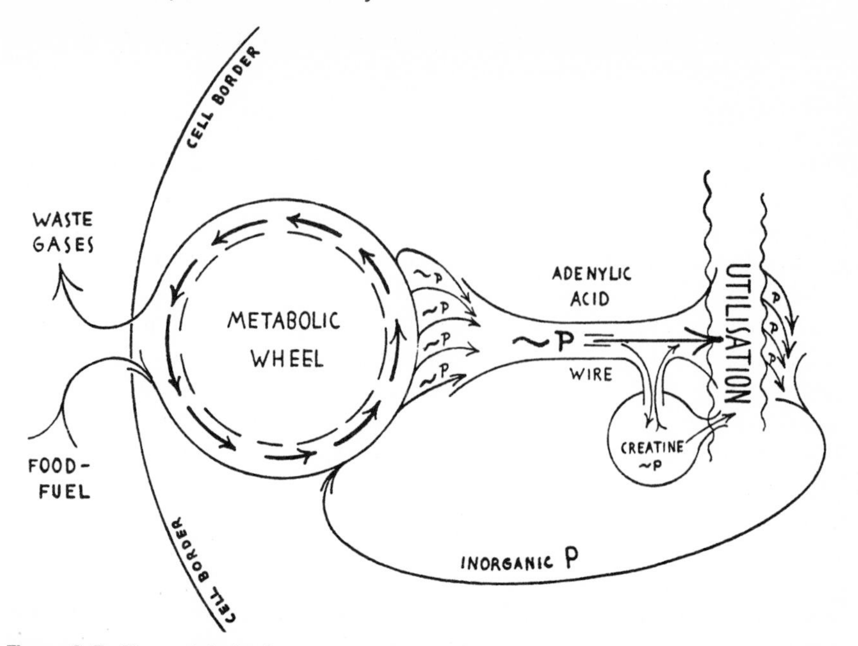

Figure 6–7. The metabolic dynamo generates ~P current. This is brushed off by adenylic acid, which likewise functions as the wiring system, distributing the current. Creatine ~P, when present, serves as P accumulator. Classical diagram by Lipmann, 1941.

Bioluminescence, in some of its forms, is a well-documented case of energy-rich bonds serving as a source of biological energy. For example, firefly luminescence has been intensively studied by McElroy and his coworkers and has been established as a process directly involving ATP. In fact, this system can be used as a highly sensitive and specific method for the analysis of microgram quantities of ATP.

SUGGESTED READING

Klotz, I. M., *Energetics in Biochemical Reactions,* Academic Press, Inc., New York, 1957.

Lehninger, A. L., *Bioenergetics,* W. A. Benjamin, Inc., New York, 1965.

Lipmann, F., "Metabolic Generation and Utilization of Phosphate Bond Energy" in *Advances in Enzymology,* vol. I, Interscience Publishers, Inc., New York, 1941.

Mahan, B. A., *Elementary Chemical Thermodynamics,* W. A. Benjamin, Inc., New York, 1963.

Racker, E., *Mechanisms in Bioenergetics,* Academic Press, Inc., New York, 1965.

Szent-Györgyi, A., *Bioenergetics,* Academic Press, Inc., New York, 1957, Chapter 1.

Szent-Györgyi, A., *Introduction to a Submolecular Biology,* Academic Press, Inc., New York, 1960.

"These facts suggest that citric acid acts as a catalyst in the oxidation of carbohydrates in the following manner

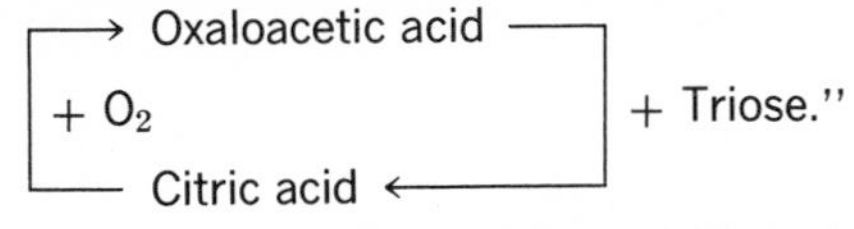

H. A. Krebs and W. A. Johnson, 1937

SEVEN

Structure and Function of Carbohydrates

Carbohydrates are biochemical staples formed in plants during the process of photosynthesis. They are thus the first intermediates in the incorporation of inorganic carbon, hydrogen, and light energy into living things.

Carbohydrates were originally represented as hydrates of carbon having the empirical formula $C_x(H_2O)_n$, thus the origin of the name of this group of compounds. Today we retain the name but are not bound by the empirical formula. For example, deoxyribose ($C_5H_{10}O_4$) and glucosamine ($C_6H_{13}O_5N$) are called carbohydrates but lactic acid ($C_3H_6O_3$) is not. Carbohydrates have the chemical structure of either polyhydroxyaldehydes or polyhydroxyketones.

In general, substances belonging to this class of compounds may be divided into three broad categories: (1) *monosaccharides,* (2) *oligosaccharides,* and (3) *polysaccharides.*

Monosaccharides have the simplest chemical structures. Oligosaccharides and polysaccharides are made of monosaccharide units.

Monosaccharides

Monosaccharides are the simplest carbohydrates and generally have the formula $C_nH_{2n}O_n$, where n can vary from 3 to values commonly no higher than 8. These compounds are grouped according to the number of carbon atoms they contain:

	Empirical Formula
Trioses	$C_3H_6O_3$
Tetroses	$C_4H_8O_4$
Pentoses	$C_5H_{10}O_5$
Hexoses	$C_6H_{12}O_6$
Heptoses	$C_7H_{14}O_7$

Glyceraldehyde (I) and dihydroxyacetone (II), the smallest molecules generally termed carbohydrates, are the only possible trioses or three carbon sugars.

CHO
HO—C—H
CH_2OH
L-Glyceraldehyde
I

CH_2OH
C=O
CH_2OH
Dihydroxyacetone
II

Erythrose is the only naturally occurring tetrose or four carbon sugar.

Pentoses, or five carbon sugars occur widely in all organisms. They are present as intermediates (phosphate derivatives) in metabolic pathways and as a part of more complex molecules, such as nucleic acids and coenzymes. 2-Deoxyribose (III) and ribose (IV) are the most common pentoses.

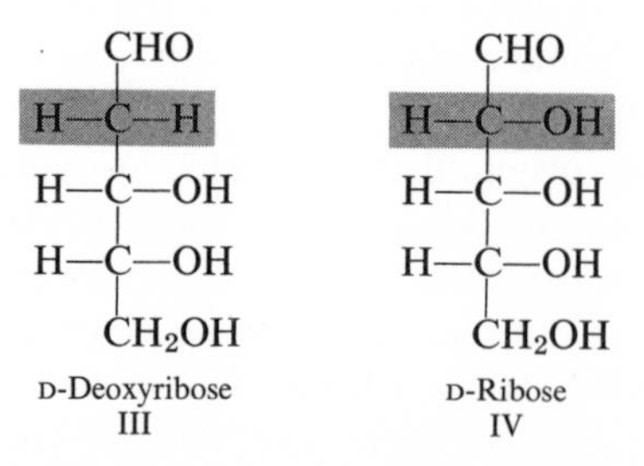

D-Deoxyribose
III

D-Ribose
IV

Hexoses, the six carbon monosaccharides, are very common in organisms and play major physiological roles. All these sugars contain the same number of atoms and the same kind of atomic groups, yet each sugar is a distinct substance. For example, the formula $C_6H_{12}O_6$ represents sixteen different simple hexoses, all possessing the structure $CH_2OH \cdot CHOH \cdot CHOH \cdot CHOH \cdot CHOH \cdot CHO$. The different sugars are due to different arrangements of the constituent group (CHOH) in space. This phenomenon represents what is called stereoisomerism (space isomerism), and these sugars are stereoisomers (see page 84). The structures of three important hexoses are illustrative. Galactose (V) and glucose (VI) have identical structures except for the space arrangement of the H and OH

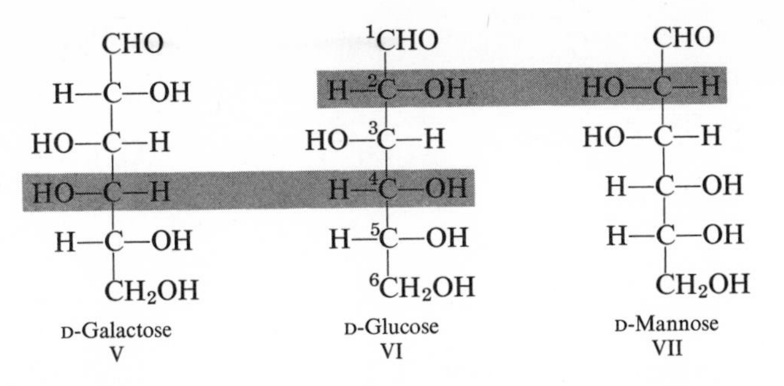

attached to carbon 4. Mannose (VII) and glucose (VI) differ with respect to carbon 2. These small changes result in three distinct sugars with different physical and chemical properties (melting point, boiling point, and optical activity).

The structural difference between fructose (VIII) and other hexoses is more readily apparent. Fructose has a keto group at carbon 2 rather than an aldehyde unit at carbon 1.

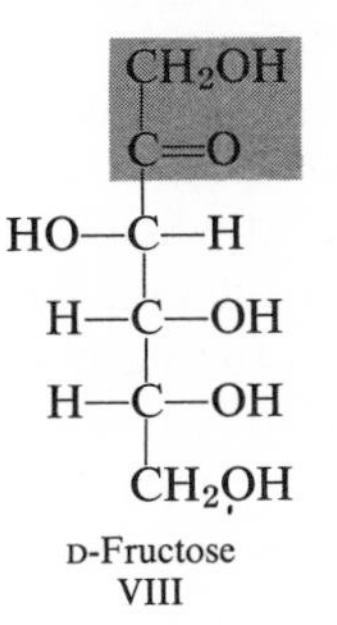

These subtle differences in the structures of carbohydrates are of such major biochemical importance that the next section has been included to focus on them.

Chemical Representation of Sugars

Several different chemical notations are used to represent a specific sugar. Each notation emphasizes certain chemical properties or structural features of the sugar. These are summarized for glucose in Figure 7–1.

Open Chain Formulation

The open chain linear structure points up several important characteristics. First, asymmetric carbon atoms are clearly shown. An asymmetric carbon atom has a different atom or group of atoms attached to each of its four valence bonds. For example, there are three asymmetric carbon atoms (carbons 2, 3, and 4) in ribose (IV) and two (carbons 3 and 4) in deoxy-

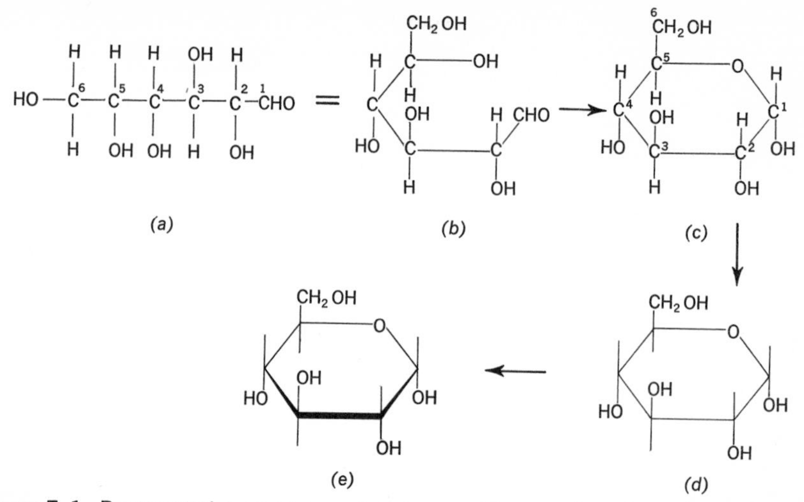

Figure 7–1. Representative structures of D glucose: (*a*) open chain linear form; (*b*) intermediate form in ring formation; (*c*) Ring form, all carbons show; (*d*) Ring form, abbreviated form; (*e*) Ring form, perspective form.

ribose (III). Second, stereoisomers, which result because of asymmetric carbon atoms, are more apparent when the linear form is drawn.

Figure 7–2 demonstrates the relation between the Fischer formula and the atomic arrangement that is the basis for isomerism. The tetrahedron formed by the valence bonds of the carbon 4 in ribose (carbon 5 in hexoses) has an atom or atomic grouping at each apex. Fischer's formula is a projection of this space arrangement in the plane of the page. The perspective representation shows this transition from the three dimensional to the two dimensional structure. Solid wedges identify bonds coming out of the plane of the page; dashed lines indicate bonds extending below the page. This convention is used in the Fischer formula, although the solid wedges generally are not used.

The ribose (I) in Figure 7–2 is the mirror image or isomer of (II). Such isomers are designated D or L on the basis of their relation to the geometrical configuration of a standard compound, glyceraldehyde. If the H and OH groups around carbon 4 in pentoses (carbon 5 in hexoses) are oriented as they are in L-glyceraldehyde (I) when the OH is written on the left, the pentose is a member of the L series; if on the right, it is a member of the D series. The asymmetric carbon most remote from the oxidized carbon (—CHO) determines the designation D or L. The majority of monosaccarides occurring in living organisms are of the D configuration.

For many years it has been possible to determine the space arrangement of configuration of atoms in sugars, relative to one another, that is, *relative configuration.* In 1954, following the development of X-ray techniques, the *absolute configuration* of L-tartaric acid was determined. It was shown at

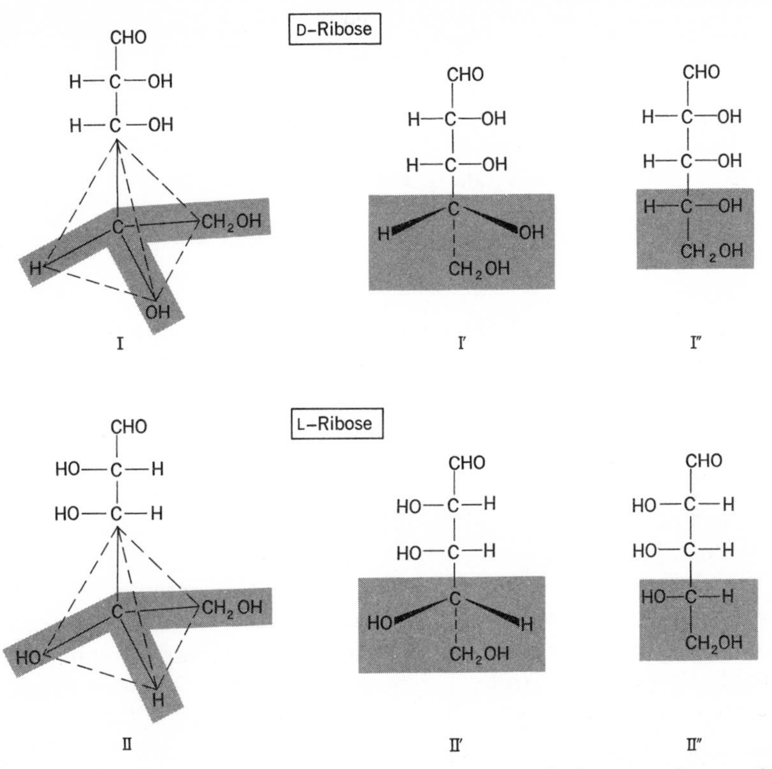

Figure 7–2. Isomerism and structural formulae for sugars. D and L forms are shown and the asymmetric grouping is indicated by shading.

that time that this compound and, consequently, all the sugars do indeed have the configurations arbitrarily assigned to them by earlier workers; thus, the space arrangements shown in Figure 7–2 are valid.

Closed Ring Formulation

An alternative way of writing the chemical formulae of sugars is to write the closed ring structure (Figure 7–1), a structure which more accurately summarizes the properties of sugars and represents 90 per cent of cellular sugars. The existence of this structure is supported by the fact that chemically the sugars do not behave like aldehydes as is suggested by their linear structural formulae but resemble hemiacetals in their reactions. The monosaccharides have an internal hemiacetal structure that is formed by an intramolecular reaction as shown in Figure 7–1. The aldehyde group at carbon 1 and the hydroxyl group at carbon 5 approach each other and react to form the cyclic hemiacetal form of sugar.

Two ring types are possible when intramolecular hemiacetal formation occurs in hexoses: a five-membered ring with one oxygen atom, or a six

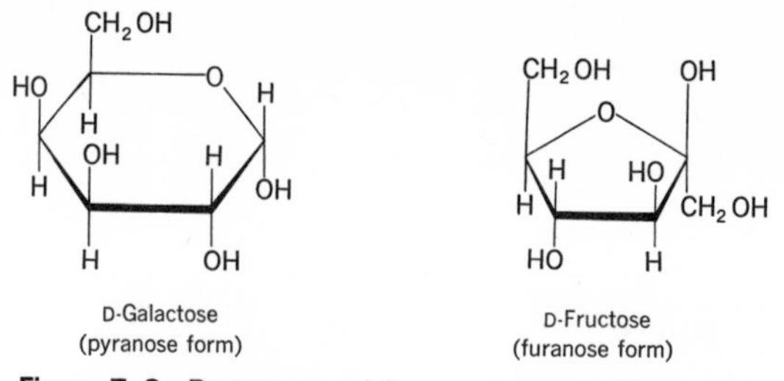

D-Galactose (pyranose form)

D-Fructose (furanose form)

Figure 7–3. Pyranose and furanose forms of hexoses.

membered ring containing one oxygen atom. Whereas five-membered rings are the most common ring form for pentoses, most hexoses form six-membered rings. In reference to the cyclic compounds *furan* (five-membered) and *pyran* (six-membered), the corresponding forms of the sugars are called *furanose* and *pyranose.* Most naturally occurring hexoses are in the pyranose form (Figure 7–3). Fructose, however, differs from other hexoses by occurring in the furanose form (Figure 7–3) characteristic of pentoses.

The closed ring structure of sugars is usually represented as shown in Figure 7–1*e*. The closed ring is no longer in the plane of the paper but projects toward the reader. This is indicated by shading those bonds indicated to be nearer the reader.

Oligosaccharides

Oligosaccharides (from the Greek *oligos,* few) are composed of monosaccharide subunits and contain, per molecule, two to ten monosaccharide residues linked to each other through an oxygen atom bridge, a *glycosidic linkage.* This linkage is between a hydroxyl group (—OH) of one sugar unit and the carbon 1, the carbonyl carbon (—C(=O)—H) of the linear formula, of another sugar. Depending on the steric configuration at the carbon 1, the glycosidic bond is called α or β.

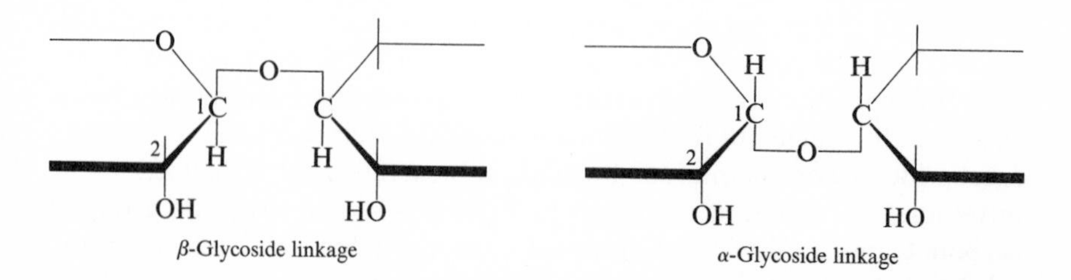

β-Glycoside linkage

α-Glycoside linkage

In these structural forms the linkage is called β when the hydrogen at carbon 1 is written downward; if the hydrogen is up, the linkage is α.

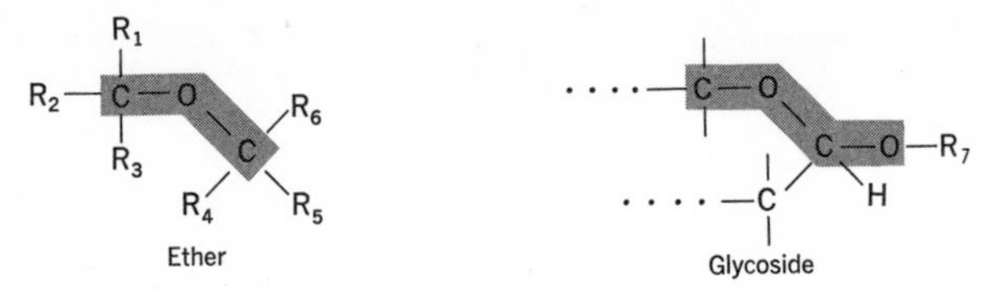

Figure 7–4. A comparison of glycoside and ether linkages. R_1-R_7 are hydrogen or carbon atoms.

The glycosidic bond system is not an *ether* (R_1—O—R_2) linkage. One of the carbon atoms in a glycoside linkage is attached to *two* oxygen atoms; in an ether this is not the case (Figure 7–4). The glycosidic bond plays a role in carbohydrate chemistry analogous to that of the peptide bond in protein chemistry, or the ester bond in the lipids.

The most common oligosaccharides are the disaccharides sucrose (IX) and lactose (X). Sucrose, which is derived commercially from sugar cane or beets, occurs in photosynthetic plants. The chemical structure of sucrose reveals a compound of glucose + fructose. The glycosidic bond involves the carbon 1 of the pyran form of glucose and the carbon 2 of fructose (furan form). Lactose (X) is composed of glucose and galactose joined through an oxygen bridge from carbon 1 of galactose to carbon 4 of glucose. This disaccharide occurs naturally in the milk of mammals to an extent of about 5 per cent.

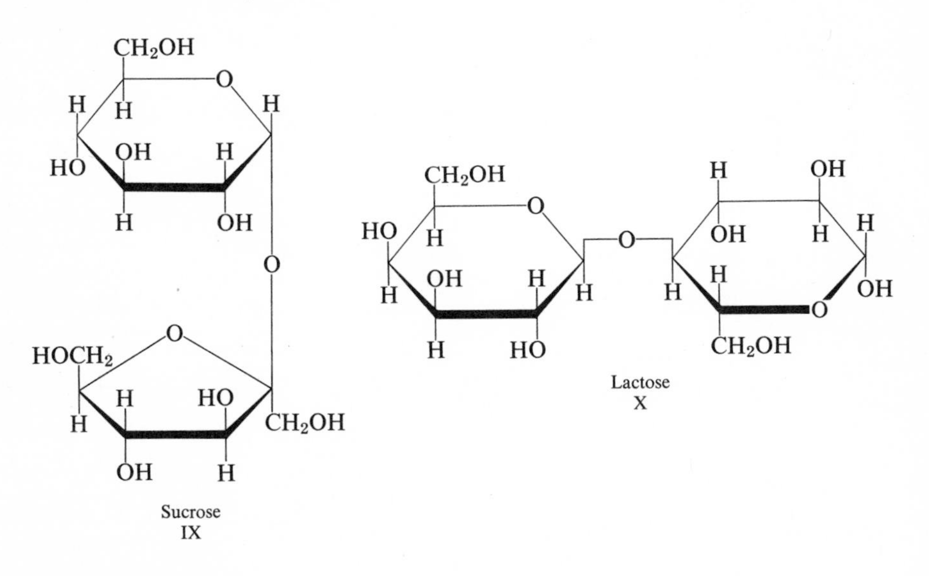

Polysaccharides

Polysaccharides are polymers of monosaccharide units joined together through glycosidic linkage. They are distinguished from oligosaccharides

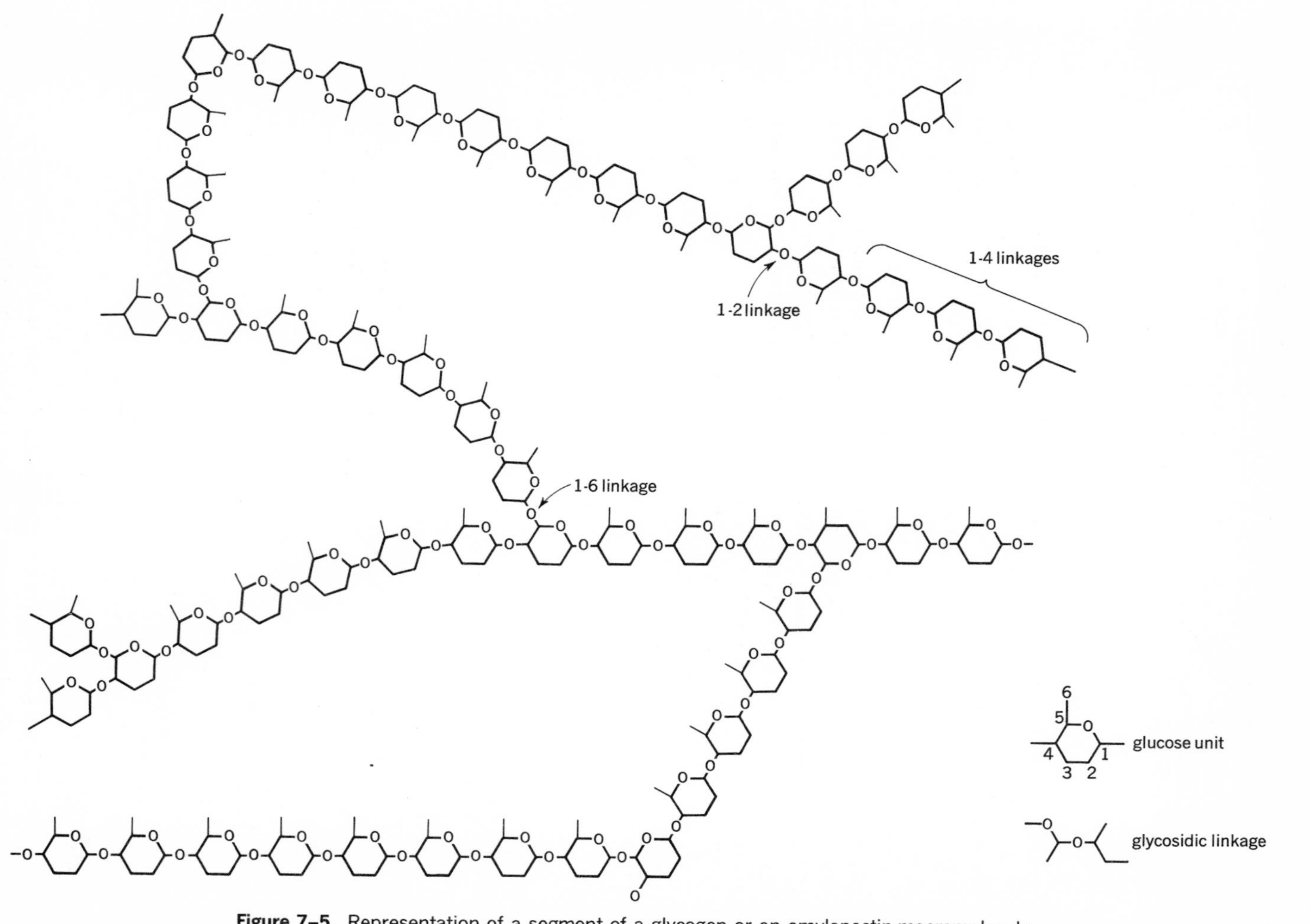

Figure 7–5. Representation of a segment of a glycogen or an amylopectin macromolecule.

by their longer chain length and greater structural complexity caused by frequent chain branching of the subunits.

The general structural feature of the polysaccharide is the repeating monosaccharide unit (Figure 7–5). D-Glucose is the most frequently encountered sugar unit, although D-fructose and D-galactose, as well as other hexoses, also occur. The individuality of polysaccharides is determined by their: (1) constituent monosaccharide composition, (2) molecular weight, (3) degree and nature of chain branching, (4) nature of the glycosidic linkage (carbon 1 of one sugar to carbon 2 of another; carbon 1 to carbon 3; carbon 1 to carbon 4, etc.), (5) the steric configuration at asymmetric carbon atoms. Thus there are a large variety of polysaccharides possible and, indeed, many have been described. The celluloses, starches, and glycogens are the best known and most important.

Cellulose, the most abundant organic compound in the world, is a polymer of glucose subunits. On partial digestion it gives rise to a disaccharide known as cellobiose (XI), which is composed of two glucose units joined by a β-glycosidic linkage. Cellulose is a structural element of most plants and many plant products. For example, cotton is at least 90 per cent pure cellulose.

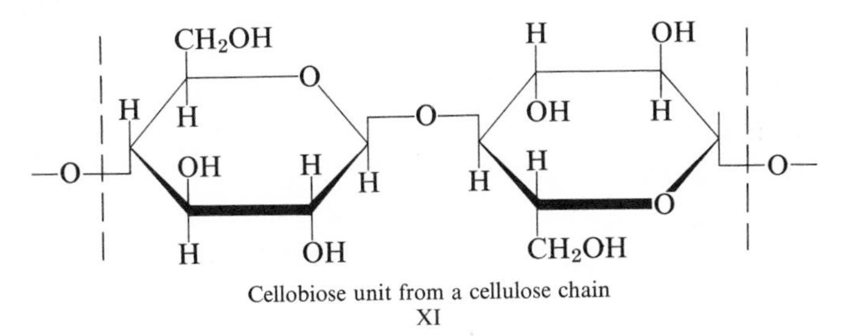

Cellobiose unit from a cellulose chain
XI

Starch (XII) is a plant polysaccharide that serves as a storage form of energy. The structure of starch is similar to that of cellulose, i.e., both are made from glucose units. The significant difference, however, is the steric nature of the glycosidic bond linking the glucose residues. In cellulose, the linkage is a so-called β-linkage, whereas in starch it is α. The repeating disaccharide unit in starch is therefore maltose, rather than cellobiose as in cellulose. Two forms of starch exist naturally. One is a long, unbranched

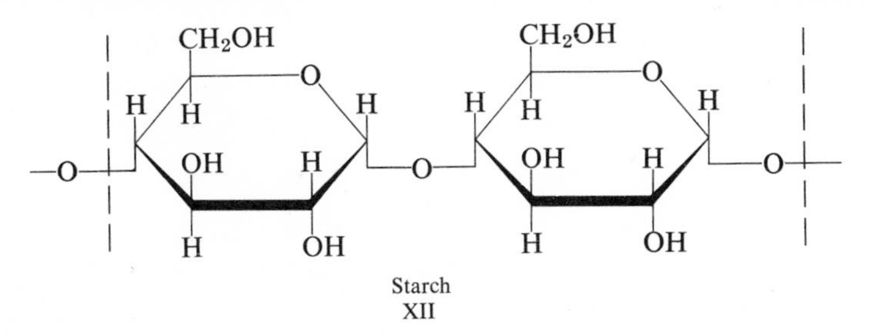

Starch
XII

chain similar to cellulose; the other is a branched chain polysaccharide with chain branches (carbon 1 of one glucose unit to carbon 6 of another) occurring every 20 to 30 glucose residues.

Glycogen, in animals, is the counterpart of starch; it serves as a storage form of hexoses. Glycogen, just as starch, is composed of α-linked glycosyl residues but is a much larger macromolecule. It has a highly branched structure and has been estimated to have molecular weights of the order of 270,000 to 100,000,000 (Figure 7–5). The amount of glycogen present in animals varies widely among different tissues (muscle, liver, etc.) and with diet and physiological state. In general, liver contains the largest amount of glycogen per unit tissue weight.

Functions of Carbohydrates

Carbohydrates are the basis for important structural elements in both plants and animals. In addition, they supply about one-half the total energy requirements of the living organism.

The chief constituent of the framework of plants is cellulose. The cellulose content of flax, ramie, and cotton amounts to 90 per cent to 99 per cent, whereas the content in woods varies from 41 per cent to 53 per cent. Other polysaccharides, such as the xylans—composed of the pentose xylose—and the pectic acids have important roles in the structural make-up of plants.

An important structural polysaccharide of animals is *chitin,* the horny material in the shells of lobsters, crabs, and insects. Some other polysaccharides associated with the structure of animal tissues are hyaluronic acid and chondroitin sulfates. These substances are members of a group of carbohydrates, *mucopolysaccharides,* which have amino sugars as an important constituent. These compounds are important structural elements present in cartilage, adult bone, heart valves, and the cornea.

Energy and Metabolite Production by Carbohydrates

Carbohydrates have a central role in biological energetics, in the production of ATP. In both plants and animals, the progressive breakdown of polysaccharides and monosaccharides to simpler compounds is a major source of energy-rich compounds. Essentially the energy stored in the carbohydrate molecule during photosynthesis is released during catabolism and the stable molecules CO_2 and H_2O are generated.

$$C_6H_{12}O_6 + 6O_2 \longrightarrow 6H_2O + 6CO_2 + \text{Energy} \qquad (1)$$

The organism accomplishes this net reaction by a series of reactions that liberate small amounts of utilizable energy which is funneled into the phosphate bond energy of ATP.

Before they can be utilized in the organism, polysaccharides, such as starch and glycogen, as well as the disaccharides, must be converted to simple monosaccharides, e.g., glucose. This conversion or breakdown (digestion) is catalyzed by various hydrolytic enzymes called polysaccharidases and phosphorylases. Polysaccharidases catalyze the hydrolytic breakage of glycosidic bonds; phosphorylases, the phosphorolytic or phosphoric acid cleavage (Figure 7–6). Polysaccharidase action results in the production of a free sugar; phosphorylases, a sugar phosphate. The resultant six carbon derivative compounds are suitable for further metabolic degradation coupled with energy release and capture as ATP.

The general biochemical breakdown pattern of monosaccharides to simpler constituents is similar in the tissues of most animals and plants. There are three major interrelated pathways of carbohydrate metabolism:

1. The Embden-Meyerhof glycolytic pathway.
2. The Krebs citric acid cycle.
3. The phosphogluconate oxidative pathway or pentose phosphate pathway.

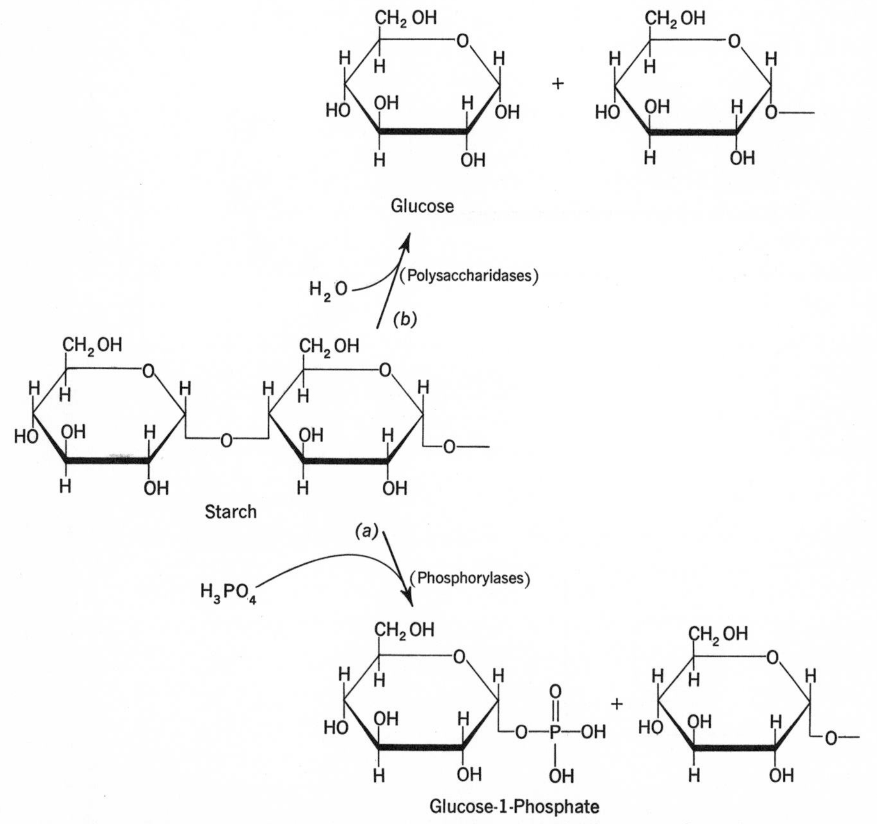

Figure 7–6. (*a*) Phosphorolytic and (*b*) hydrolytic cleavage of starch.

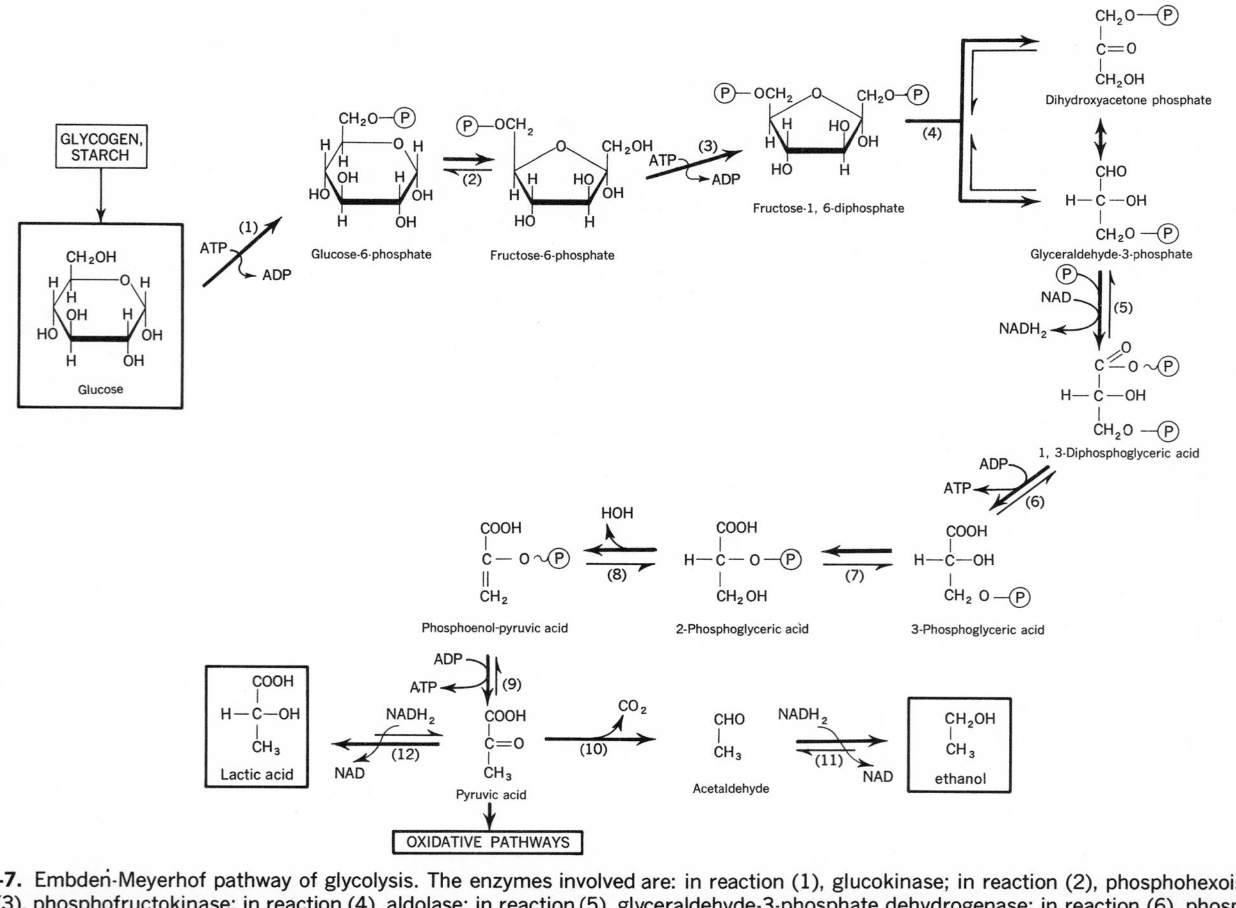

Figure 7–7. Embden-Meyerhof pathway of glycolysis. The enzymes involved are: in reaction (1), glucokinase; in reaction (2), phosphohexoisomerase; in reaction (3), phosphofructokinase; in reaction (4), aldolase; in reaction (5), glyceraldehyde-3-phosphate dehydrogenase; in reaction (6), phosphoglycerokinase; in reaction (7), phosphoglyceromutase; in reaction (8), enolase; in reaction (9), pyruvic kinase; in reaction (10), pyruvic carboxylase; in reaction (11), alcohol dehydrogenase; and in reaction (12), lactic dehydrogenase.

To understand the functional role of carbohydrates in living organisms, it is necessary to consider the biochemical nature of these metabolic pathways. A summary of these metabolic reactions will reveal that many important metabolites, in addition to energy, are produced from carbohydrates.

Embden-Meyerhof Pathway

This pathway of glycolysis, elucidated in the period 1920–1940 primarily by G. Embden and O. Meyerhof, is a sequence of reactions which can operate without oxygen (anaerobically).

A summary of the reactions and intermediates involved in anaerobic glycolysis is presented in Figure 7–7. The simple sugars glucose and fructose enter into the glycolytic pathway only after each has been phosphorylated. For each sugar a specific enzyme is required to catalyze the phosphorylation, and ATP acts as phosphate donor. Subsequently, a series of linked reactions result in the successive degradation of glucose phosphate to the three carbon compound pyruvic acid.

No oxygen is consumed in the over-all process of conversion of glucose to either lactic acid or ethyl alcohol. Two of the individual steps, however, are oxidation-reduction reactions: the oxidation of glyceraldehyde-3-phosphate to 1,3-diphosphoglyceric acid (reaction (5) of Figure 7–7) and the reduction of pyruvic acid to ethanol (reactions (10) and (11) of Figure 7–7) or lactic acid (reaction (12) of Figure 7–7). The $NADH_2$ produced in reaction (5) of Figure 7–7 can be utilized in reaction (11) or (12) of Figure 7–7. The coincident operation of these two reactions therefore results in no net oxidation or reduction.

The net yield of phosphate bond energy (moles of ATP) derived from glycolysis of 1 mole of glucose can be easily computed (Figure 7–7). One mole of ATP is consumed in the primary phosphorylation step (reaction (1) of Figure 7–7), Eq. 2:

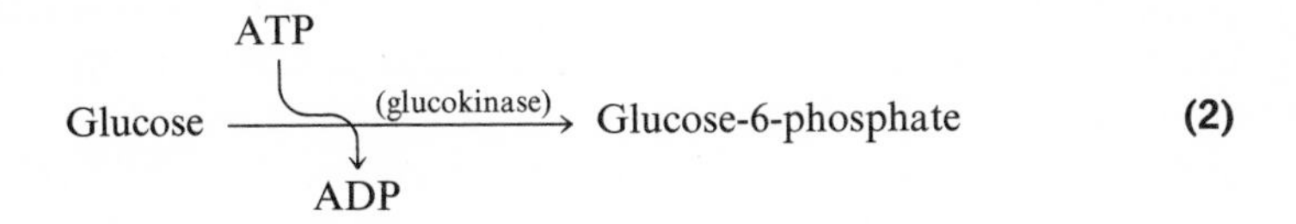

and a second is consumed in reaction (3) of Figure 7–7:

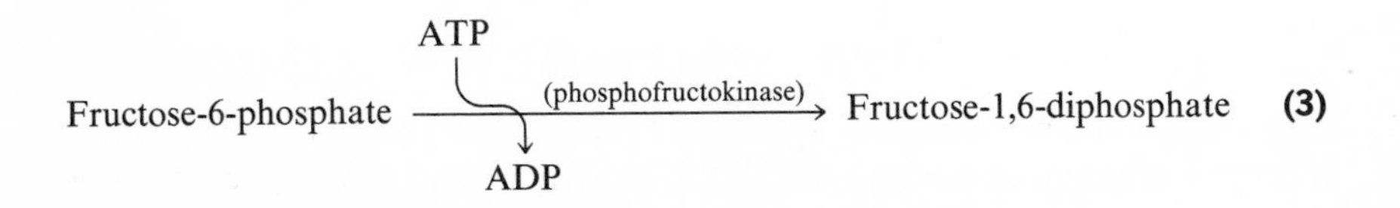

Reaction (6) of Figure 7–7, as shown in Eq. (4),

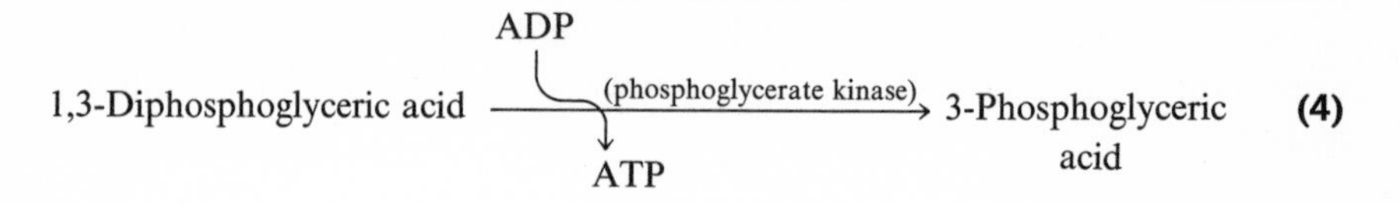

yields 1 mole of ATP, or 2 moles per glucose molecule. A similar yield of ATP results in reaction (9) of Figure 7–7, as shown in Eq. (5):

$$\text{2-Phosphoenol pyruvic acid} \xrightarrow[\text{ADP} \rightarrow \text{ATP}]{\text{(pyruvic kinase)}} \text{Pyruvic acid} \qquad \textbf{(5)}$$

Thus, per mole of glucose broken down, 2 moles of ATP are initially consumed and 4 moles are ultimately generated, with a net gain of 2 moles of ATP. If one starts with glycogen instead of glucose, the net gain in ATP is 3 moles per mole of glucose rather than 2 moles.

The Embden-Meyerhof pathway is also the entrance for glucose into aerobic metabolic pathways, such as the Krebs citric acid cycle. In cells containing the additional aerobic pathways, the $NADH_2$ that forms in reaction (5) of Figure 7–7 enters the oxidative phosphorylation scheme (page 73) and results in ATP generation. Thus, in aerobic cells the Embden-Meyerhof pathway results in a total of eight ATP's per mole of glucose metabolized.

The Krebs Citric Acid Cycle

The citric acid cycle (tricarboxylic acid cycle, Krebs cycle), which was postulated as an abbreviation of its present form in 1937 by H. Krebs and W. A. Johnson, is an oxygen-requiring continuation of the Embden-Meyerhof pathway. It functions to convert lactic and pyruvic acids, the end products of anaerobic glycolysis in animals, to CO_2 and water. Furthermore, the Krebs cycle is a common channel not only for the oxidation of the products of glycolysis but also for the ultimate oxidation of fatty acids and the carbon skeletons of many amino acids. Thus, the Krebs cycle is a final common pathway in the metabolism of members of many biochemical classes.

Figure 7–8 presents diagrammatically the reactions of the Krebs cycle. The over-all reaction for the conversion of pyruvic acid to carbon dioxide

$$C_3H_4O_3 + \tfrac{5}{2}O_2 + 15ADP + 15P_i \longrightarrow 3CO_2 + 2H_2O + 15ATP \qquad \textbf{(6)}$$

and water is shown in Eq. (6). It should be noted that pyruvic acid occupies a central position in several metabolic sequences and may have one of a

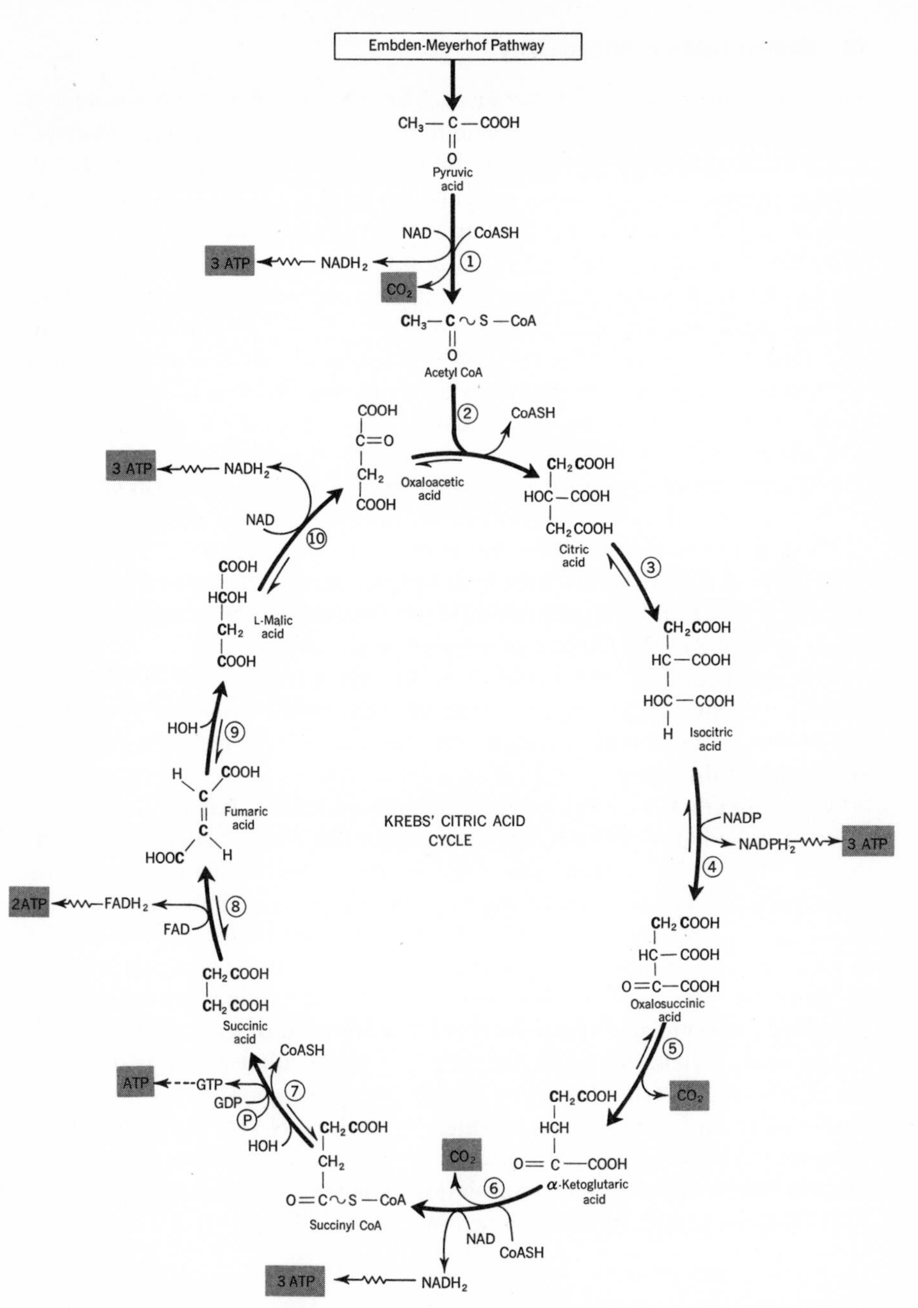

Figure 7–8. Krebs' citric acid cycle. The over-all reaction is:

$$C_3H_4O_3 + \tfrac{5}{2}O_2 + 15ADP + 15P_i \longrightarrow 3CO_2 + 2H_2O + 15ATP$$

The reactions are stereospecific and only at succinic acid does a randomization occur of the carbon atoms (bold face) originally in acetyl CoA. The enzymes involved are: (1) pyruvic oxidase, (2) condensing enzyme, (3) aconitase, (4) and (5) isocitric enzyme, (6) α-ketoglutarate dehydrogenase, (7) succinyl thiokinase, (8) succinic dehydrogenase, (9) fumarase, (10) malic dehydrogenase.

number of different metabolic fates. The fate which will be considered here is the conversion of pyruvic acid to CO_2 and water via the Krebs cycle.

Pyruvate enters the Krebs cycle by losing CO_2 and being converted to a two carbon acetyl residue attached to coenzyme A. The acetyl unit then enters the cycle by condensing with oxaloacetic acid, a four carbon dicarboxylic acid, to yield the six carbon tricarboxylic acid, citric acid. By the successive loss and recapture of water this compound is rearranged into isocitric acid. Isocitric acid is subsequently oxidized to oxalosuccinic acid, and this in turn loses CO_2 to form α-ketoglutaric acid. Succinic acid is formed from this last compound by an oxidation and loss of CO_2. Oxaloacetic acid is regenerated by an oxidation, a hydration, and a second oxidation.

For each revolution of the cycle, 1 mole of acetate in the form of acetyl CoA is consumed and two moles of CO_2 are evolved. The oxaloacetic acid utilized in the initial condensation is regenerated, permitting the process to operate in a continuous fashion as long as acetyl continues to enter the cycle and water and CO_2 are removed. At five stages usable energy can be made available in the form of phosphate bond energy.

The significance of the Krebs cycle for the manifestation of the functional properties of carbohydrates can be appreciated if one considers both the important biochemical metabolites and the energy that arises through operation of this cycle.

Many metabolites, both of defined and undefined function, originate from intermediates of the Krebs cycle. For example, the citric acid which occurs in elevated concentrations in tissues of higher plants is a Krebs cycle product. Other acids formed by this cycle have functional roles in molds and plant tissues. The initial step in the synthesis of many amino acids originates in this cycle. For example, α-ketoglutaric acid can give rise to glutamic acid, and its derivatives, ornithine, proline, glutamine and histidine. Aspartic acid can arise from fumaric acid or oxaloacetate.

The energy yield of the Krebs cycle can be calculated as was done for the Embden-Meyerhof pathway (pages 94). The operation of the citric acid cycle includes three steps in which $NADH_2$ or $NADPH_2$ arises. These reduced pyridine nucleotides, of course, are able to produce ATP by the process of oxidative phosphorylation (page 73). The $NADH_2$- or $NADPH_2$-supplying steps, as shown in Figure 7–8 are:

$$\text{Isocitrate} \xrightarrow[\text{NADP} \rightarrow \text{NADPH}_2 \rightsquigarrow 3\text{ATP}]{\text{(isocitric dehydrogenase)}} \alpha\text{-Ketoglutaric acid} + CO_2 \quad \textbf{(7)}$$

$$\alpha\text{-Ketoglutaric acid} \xrightarrow[\text{NAD} \rightarrow \text{NADH}_2 \rightsquigarrow 3\text{ATP}]{(\alpha\text{-ketoglutaric dehydrogenase})} \text{Succinyl CoA} + CO_2 \quad \textbf{(8)}$$

and

$$\text{L-Malic acid} \xrightarrow[\text{NADH}_2 \rightsquigarrow 3\text{ATP}]{\text{NAD} \quad (\text{malic dehydrogenase})} \text{Oxaloacetic acid} \tag{9}$$

Subsequent oxidation of $NADH_2$ or $NADPH_2$ (via $NADH_2$) through the cytochrome system gives rise to 3 moles of ATP per molecule of $NADH_2$ or $NADPH_2$. A nucleotide diphosphate (GDP)-linked conversion of succinyl CoA to succinic acid results in 1 mole of ATP.

$$\text{Succinyl CoA} + \text{Phosphate} + \text{GDP} \xrightleftharpoons{\text{succinyl thiokinase}} \text{Succinic acid} + \text{CoA} + \text{GTP} \tag{10}$$

$$\text{GTP} + \text{ADP} \rightleftharpoons \text{GDP} + \boxed{\text{ATP}} \tag{11}$$

Two additional moles of ATP are derived from the oxidation of succinate or succinic acid to fumarate.

$$\text{Succinic acid} \xrightarrow[\text{FADH}_2 \rightsquigarrow 2\text{ATP}]{\text{FAD} \quad (\text{succinic dehydrogenase})} \text{Fumaric acid} \tag{12}$$

This reaction involves the flavin nucleotide FAD. As was indicated earlier (page 74) the reduced form of FAD, that is, $FADH_2$, can be oxidized via the cytochrome system to yield two ATP molecules. In summary, Table 7–1 lists the energy yielding reactions of the Krebs cycle and the moles of ATP formed. Thus, the oxidation of acetyl CoA to CO_2 and H_2O via the Krebs cycle generates 12 moles of ATP per mole of acetyl consumed. Since 12 moles each of inorganic phosphate (P_i) and ADP are utilized and the acetyl begins as acetyl CoA, the over-all oxidation may be written:

$$\text{CH}_3\overset{\overset{\text{O}}{\|}}{\text{C}}\sim\text{SCoA} + 2\text{O}_2 + 12\text{ADP} + 12\text{P}_i \longrightarrow 2\text{CO}_2 + \text{CoASH} + 12\text{ATP} \tag{13}$$

TABLE 7–1

ENERGY YIELD OF THE KREBS CYCLE

Reaction	ATP, Yield/mole of acetate
Isocitric acid $\longrightarrow$ α-Ketoglutaric acid + CO_2	3
α-Ketoglutaric acid $\longrightarrow$ Succinyl CoA + CO_2	3
Succinyl CoA $\longrightarrow$ Succinic acid + CoA	1
Succinic acid $\longrightarrow$ Fumaric acid	2
Malic acid $\longrightarrow$ Oxaloacetic acid	3
Total	12

The Phosphogluconate Oxidative Pathway

This pathway of carbohydrate metabolism has also been called *hexose monophosphate shunt* and *pentose phosphate pathway.* The former designation reflects the early idea, which was that this pathway or shunt performed essentially the same function as the Embden-Meyerhof pathway; this is not the case. The designation pentose phosphate pathway represents the present ideas about one of the major functions of this pathway, namely, its acting as a source of pentoses. The designation *phosphogluconate oxidative pathway* refers to the first intermediate in this metabolic sequence, 6-phosphogluconate, and the fact that oxidation is a first reaction step.

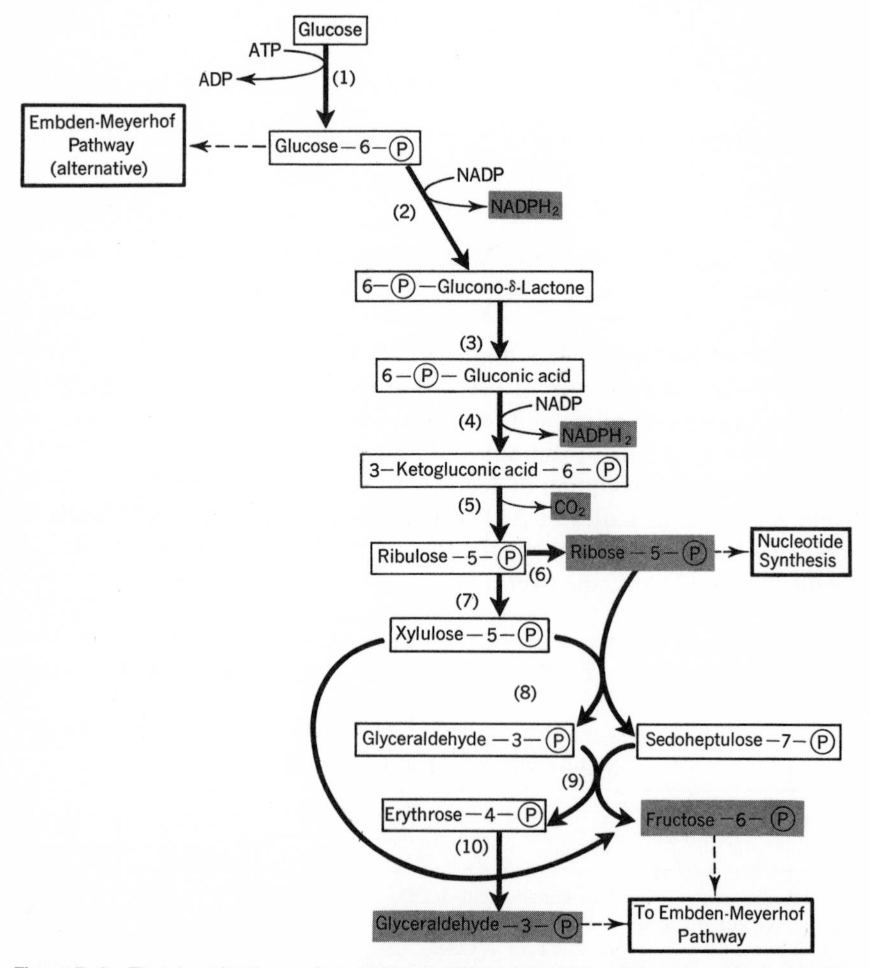

Figure 7–9. The phosphogluconate oxidative pathway. All reactions shown are reversible. For simplicity unidirectional arrows have been used to indicate the reaction flow. The end products, indicated by shading, are fructose phosphate, glyceraldehyde phosphate, $NADPH_2$, CO_2, and ribose phosphate. Possibilities for subsequent pathways are indicated by --->.

The reactions and intermediates in this cycle are shown in Figure 7–9. The initial reaction is the oxidative conversion of glucose-6-phosphate to 6-phosphogluconate. This reaction is linked with the coenzyme NADP, and $NADPH_2$ is a reaction product. The further oxidation of 6-phosphogluconate is catalyzed by a NADP-linked enzyme; $NADPH_2$ and ribulose-5-phosphate are formed. Enzymes which effect a series of novel transformations of pentoses, from one to another, are responsible for the reactions which result in xylulose-5-phosphate or ribose-5-phosphate. Ultimately fructose-6-phosphate, which is readily convertible to glucose-6-phosphate, is formed, thus completing the cycle.

This pathway is markedly different from the Embden-Meyerhof pathway. Oxidation occurs very early, and CO_2, which is not produced at all in the Embden-Meyerhof pathway, is a characteristic product of the phosphogluconate route.

Relationships of Pathways

It should be noted that the Embden-Meyerhof pathway and Krebs cycle are the major sources of ATP energy. In addition, they are responsible for glycogen breakdown and provide intermediates for lipid and amino acid synthesis.

The phosphogluconate pathway provides pentoses, essential components of nucleic acids and nucleotides. More important however, is that this pathway provides $NADPH_2$, which is essential in many reductive biosynthetic processes, such as in fatty acid and steroid synthesis.

The relation of the pathways of carbohydrate metabolism to one another and to other metabolic schemes is shown in Figure 8–4. The Embden-Meyerhof pathway leads to the production of energy as ATP and culminates in either lactic acid, or ethanol, CO_2 and water. The pentose pathway, in contrast, yields ribose phosphate and $NADPH_2$. It should be noted that the Embden-Meyerhof-Krebs pathway is related primarily to NAD, whereas the pentose pathway involves a NADP-requiring sequence of reactions. The relative significance of the two pathways for glucose metabolism has not been conclusively established.

Photosynthesis—Carbon Fixation

The process of photosynthesis in plants, the conversion of CO_2 and water into carbohydrate,

$$6CO_2 + 6H_2O \xrightarrow{\text{Light energy}} C_6H_{12}O_6 + 6O_2 \qquad (14)$$

occurs via a pathway which includes many intermediates of the phosphogluconate and Embden-Meyerhof pathways. The path of CO_2 fixation

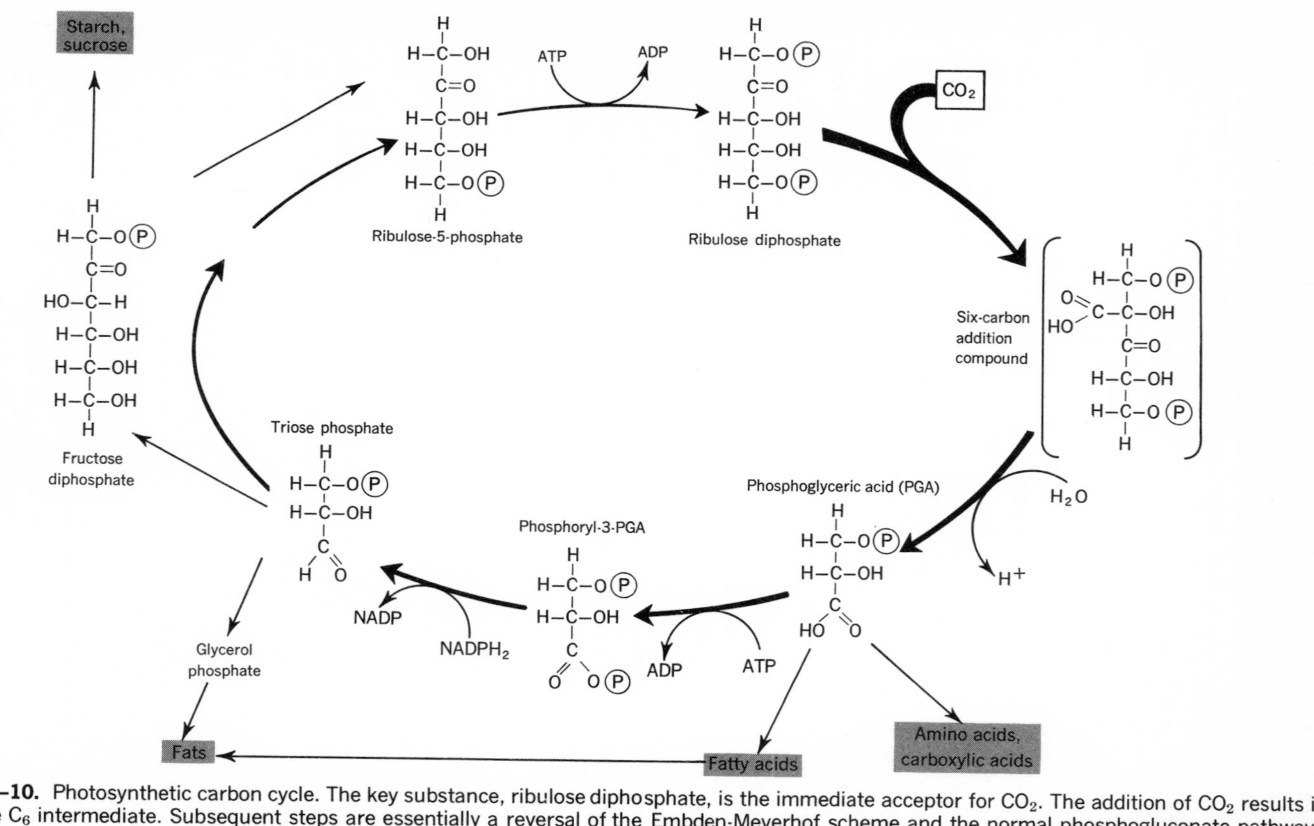

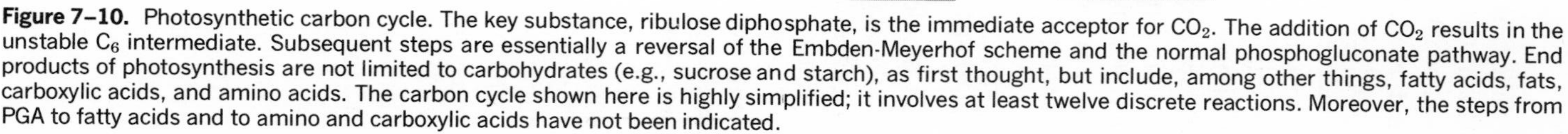

Figure 7–10. Photosynthetic carbon cycle. The key substance, ribulose diphosphate, is the immediate acceptor for CO_2. The addition of CO_2 results in the unstable C_6 intermediate. Subsequent steps are essentially a reversal of the Embden-Meyerhof scheme and the normal phosphogluconate pathway. End products of photosynthesis are not limited to carbohydrates (e.g., sucrose and starch), as first thought, but include, among other things, fatty acids, fats, carboxylic acids, and amino acids. The carbon cycle shown here is highly simplified; it involves at least twelve discrete reactions. Moreover, the steps from PGA to fatty acids and to amino and carboxylic acids have not been indicated.

(conversion into carbohydrate) may be discussed in relation to the direct oxidative pathway of glucose. Figure 7–10 summarizes the steps of this pathway, which is responsible for the initial transformation of carbon into life materials. The over-all reaction is:

$$3CO_2 + 9ATP + 5H_2O + \underset{\text{or }(NADPH_2)}{6NADH_2} \longrightarrow \text{Triose phosphate} + 9ADP + \underset{\text{or }(NADP)}{6NAD} + 8P_i \quad \textbf{(15)}$$

The key substrate, ribulose-1,5-diphosphate, is the immediate acceptor for carbon dioxide. Carbon dioxide adds to carbon 2 of this acceptor in the presence of a carboxylating enzyme to form two moles of 3-phosphoglyceric acid in a reaction which involves an unstable C_6 intermediate. Phosphoglyceric acid is then reduced by a specific NADP—triose phosphate dehydrogenase to triose phosphate. Triose phosphates can then be condensed by aldolase to fructose phosphate and then to glucose. These can then be converted to starch or cellulose or degraded for energy release. For the continuous operation of the photosynthetic cycle, a constant supply of ribulose-1,5-diphosphate is essential. This is provided by the operation of a modified phosphogluconate pathway.

The energy for carbon fixation is derived ultimately from light energy, which is transformed into phosphate bond energy during photophosphorylation (page 77). The reactions shown in Figure 7–10 are so-called *dark reactions* of photosynthesis; light is not needed for their occurrence if ATP or $NADPH_2$ is present.

SUGGESTED READING

Axelrod, B., "Glycolysis" in *Metabolic Pathways,* D. M. Greenberg (ed.), vol. I, Academic Press, Inc., New York, 1961, pp. 97–129.

Calvin, M., and J. A. Bassham, *The Photosynthesis of Carbon Compounds,* W. A. Benjamin, Inc., New York, 1962.

Krebs, H. A., "The Tricarboxylic Acid Cycle" in *The Harvey Lectures,* 1949–1950, Academic Press, Inc., New York, 1950.

Krebs, H. A., and W. A. Johnson, "The Role of Citric Acid in Intermediate Metabolism in Animal Tissues," *Enzymologia, 4,* 148–156 (1937).

Pigman, W., *The Carbohydrates, Chemistry, Biochemistry, Physiology,* Academic Press, Inc., New York, 1957.

Racker, E., "Micro- and Macrocycles in Carbohydrate Metabolism" in *The Harvey Lectures, 1955–1956,* Academic Press, Inc., New York, 1957.

"... one is compelled to conclude that the normal animal's body fats, despite their qualitative and quantitative constancy, are in a state of rapid flux."

R. Schoenheimer, 1941

EIGHT

Lipids

Lipid is a class name applied to fat-like substances which are widely distributed throughout animals and plants. The substances to which the term lipid is applied have never been firmly settled. Even the spelling may vary from lipid to lipide or lipin, without change in definition. Although the term lipid has been used to include substances which are insoluble in water but soluble in fat solvents (ether, benzene, chloroform), in this chapter, generally, lipid will be restricted to naturally occurring substances that yield, on hydrolysis, long chain aliphatic acids called fatty acids. Thus, sterols, carotenoids, anthocyanins, and related compounds which are classed together as unsaponifiable lipids will not be discussed in detail.

A general classification of lipids is:

1. *Simple lipids:* (*a*) fats, (*b*) waxes.
2. *Compound lipids:* (*a*) phospholipids, (*b*) glycolipids, (*c*) lipoproteins.

A chemical characteristic of members of the two major groups is the presence of a *fatty acid* in ester or amide linkage. Simple lipids are esters of fatty acids with various alcohols. Compound lipids are esters containing groups in addition to an alcohol and the fatty acid. These additional groups may be simple inorganic constituents such as phosphorus in some phospholipids or complex macromolecular moieties such as the protein in lipoproteins. Because of the central role of fatty acids in lipid structure, a discussion of fatty acids is appropriate at this time.

TABLE 8-1

SATURATED FATTY ACIDS: CHEMICAL CHARACTERISTICS

Common Name	Systematic Name	Formula	Common Source*
Butyric	Butanoic	C_3H_7COOH	Butter fat
Caproic	Hexanoic	$C_5H_{11}COOH$	Milk fats
Caprylic	Octanoic	$C_7H_{15}COOH$	Coconut oil
Lauric	Dodecanoic	$C_{11}H_{23}COOH$	Laurel kernel oil
Myristic	Tetradecanoic	$C_{13}H_{27}COOH$	Nutmeg butter
Palmitic	Hexadecanoic	$C_{15}H_{31}COOH$	Palm oil
Stearic	Octadecanoic	$C_{17}H_{35}COOH$	Mutton tallow, cocoa butter
Geddic	Tetratriacontanoic	$C_{33}H_{67}COOH$	Ghedda wax

* All occur as constituents of fats of plants or animals.

Fatty Acids

Fatty acids are integral parts of lipids, and may be divided into: (1) saturated acids; (2) unsaturated acids; (3) branched chain acids; (4) cyclic acids.

Several characteristics common to the four groups are:

1. The fatty acids are, in the main, monocarboxylic acids with hydrocarbon groups attached to the carboxyl carbon atom.

2. Virtually all the acids of the naturally occurring fats have an even number of carbon atoms.

Saturated Fatty Acids

The general formula for saturated fatty acids is

$$R—COOH$$

I

where R is $CH_3(CH_2)_n$.* The number of methylene, $—CH_2—$, units may vary from zero in acetic acid (CH_3COOH) to 86 in mycolic acids. The common names and formulae of some of the saturated fatty acids are given in Table 8-1. The most abundant saturated fatty acid in animal fats is palmitic (C_{16}), with stearic (C_{18}) second. Shorter chain fatty acids (C_{14} to C_{12}) do occur in small quantity as do longer chain members.

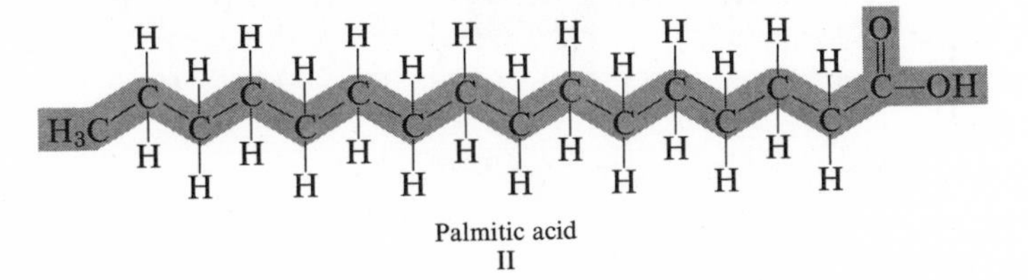

Palmitic acid

II

* R is a general designation used by organic chemists and has meaning only in the context in which it is presented. Thus, the meaning here is different from that in Chapter Three.

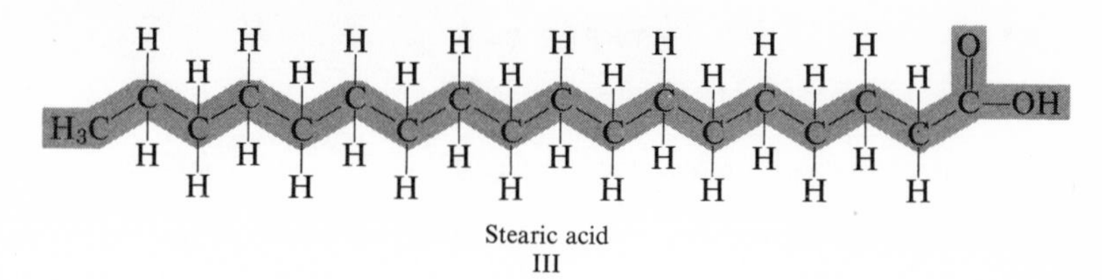

Stearic acid
III

Unsaturated Fatty Acids

Unsaturation, or the presence of one or more double bonds, is a chemical characteristic of an important group of fatty acids. In general, monounsaturated acids have the formula

$$R{-}CH{=}CH(CH_2)_7{-}COOH$$

IV

where a double bond first occurs after a nine carbon chain beginning with the carboxyl group, that is, a double bond first occurs between carbons 9 and 10. If the R-group also contains double bonds, the fatty acid is said to be polyunsaturated.

The presence of a double bond gives rise to the possibility of a type of geometrical isomerism known as *cis-trans* isomerism. This results because the four valence bonds arising from the ethylene unit ($>C{=}C<$) lie in one plane and there is no freedom of rotation about the axis of the double bond. The isomeric forms of octadecenoic acid are:

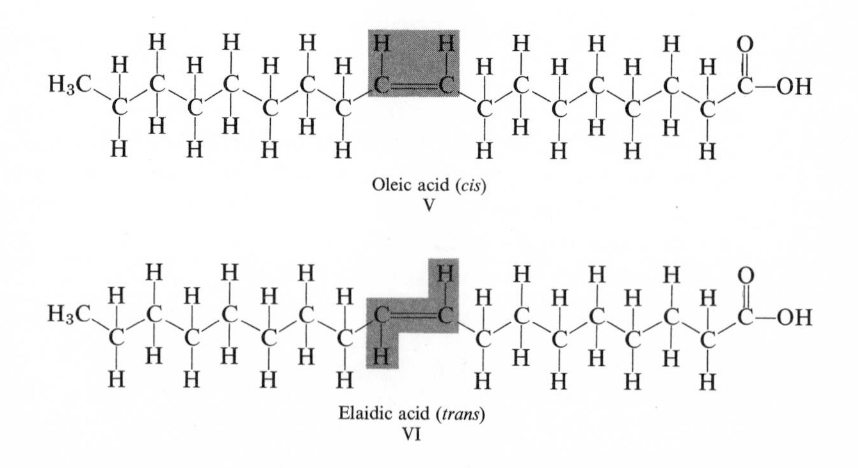

Oleic acid (*cis*)
V

Elaidic acid (*trans*)
VI

In this and other cases in the fatty acid series, it is the *cis* configuration which is found in nature. The two most abundant unsaturated fatty acids of animal lipids are oleic acid (C_{18}) and palmitoleic acid (C_{16}).

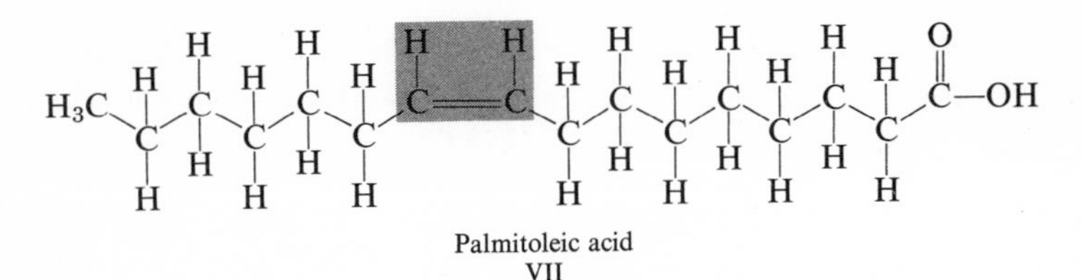

Palmitoleic acid
VII

The names and structures of certain of the more common unsaturated fatty acids are given in Table 8–2.

TABLE 8–2

UNSATURATED FATTY ACIDS: CHEMICAL CHARACTERISTICS

COMMON NAME	SYSTEMATIC NAME	FORMULA	COMMON SOURCE
Caproleic	9-Decenoic	$C_{10}H_{18}O_2$	Whale oil, butter fat
Lauroleic	5-Dodecenoic	$C_{12}H_{22}O_2$	Herring oil
Palmitoleic	9-Hexadecenoic	$C_{16}H_{30}O_2$	Milk fat
Oleic	9-Octadecenoic	$C_{18}H_{34}O_2$	Olive oil, pork fat
Erucic	13-Docosenoic	$C_{22}H_{42}O_2$	Mustard seed oil
Linoleic	9,12-Octadecadienoic	$C_{18}H_{32}O_2$	Soybean oil, linseed oil
Linolenic	9,12,15-Octadecatrienoic	$C_{18}H_{30}O_2$	Linseed and hempseed oil
Arachidonic	5,8,11,14-Eicosatetraenoic	$C_{20}H_{32}O_2$	Glandular organs

Branched Chain Fatty Acids

Although the naturally occurring fatty acids are generally straight chain compounds, the presence of branched chain fatty acids is more widespread than was earlier believed. The branched chain fatty acids isolated from animal fat consist of the odd (number of carbon atoms) series of acids

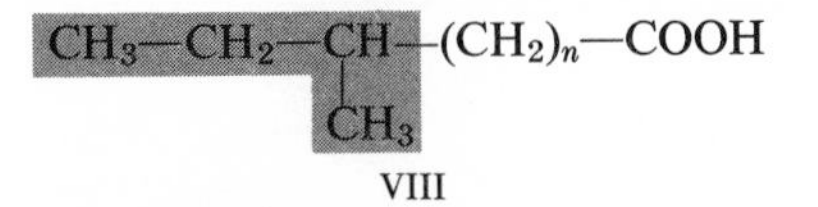

VIII

from C_{13} to C_{17} inclusive, and the odd and even series of acids

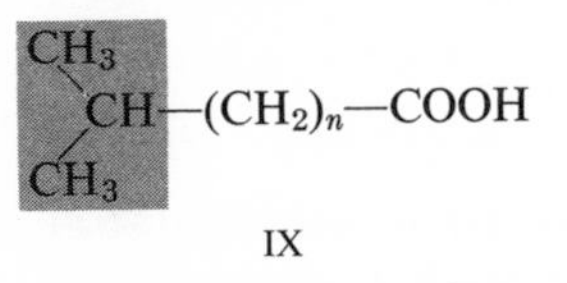

IX

from C_{13} to C_{18} inclusive. Acids with more than one side chain have also been reported.

Cyclic Acids

Fatty acids containing cyclic systems are rare. The lipids of lactobacilli, however, contain a fatty acid with a cyclopropane

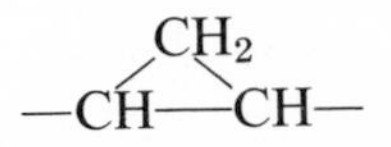

ring system as a constituent. In addition, a group of fatty acids which are of importance in leprosy therapy contain a terminal cyclopentyl ring. The best known of these cyclic fatty acids is chaulmoogric, $C_{18}H_{32}O_2$:

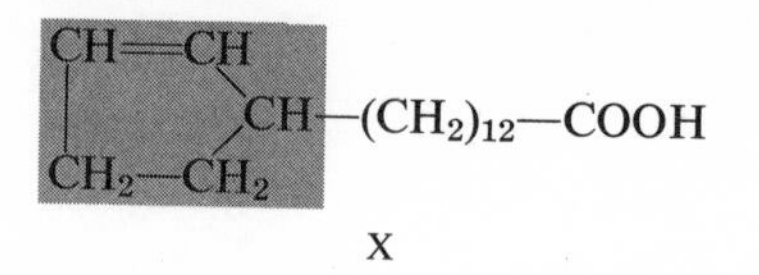

X

which has long been recognized to have bactericidal action upon the leprosy bacillus, *Bacillus leprae.*

Simple Lipids

Simple lipids include fats, or triglycerides, and waxes. Fats are esters of glycerol and fatty acids; waxes are esters of higher alcohols and fatty acids. Fats comprise the most abundant group of lipids in nature. In the normal mammal 10 per cent or more of the body weight may be in the form of triglyceride. Fat is widely distributed throughout the animal body and is localized in depots of highly specialized connective tissue. In plants, fats are found in abundance only in seeds.

The general formula for fats of the triglyceride type is:

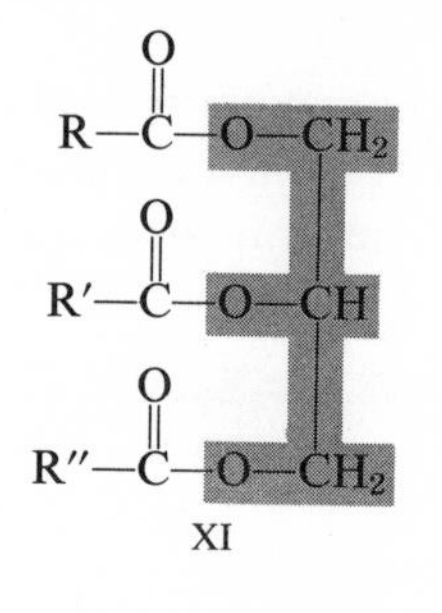

XI

in which

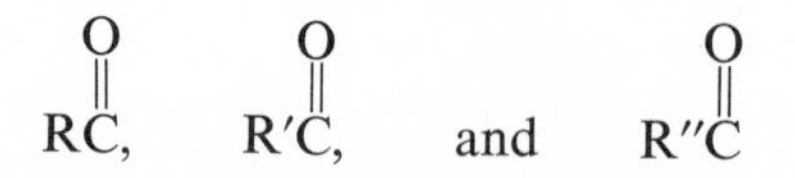

represent three fatty acid residues, derived from either the same or different fatty acids, linked to an alcohol, glycerol,

$$\underset{\text{OH}}{\text{CH}_2}\text{—}\underset{\text{OH}}{\text{CH}}\text{—}\underset{\text{OH}}{\text{CH}_2}$$

through an ester linkage

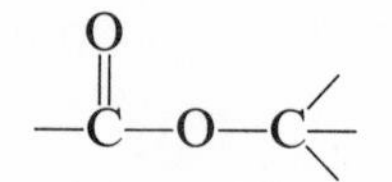

The naming of neutral fats is based on the names of the constituent fatty acids. If R, R′, and R″ were stearic acid residues, the fat would be called tristearin; if oleic acid was substituted for one stearic acid unit, oleodistearin. A random distribution in the linkage of fatty acids to glycerol has been found in studies on fat samples from many sources. That is, in oleodistearin, the oleic acid is attached equally frequently to any of the glycerol carbon atoms.

An important chemical reaction of fats is their hydrolysis, which yields three molecules of fatty acid and one of glycerol, Eq. (1). As will be seen later, this reaction, which can be accelerated by enzymes called lipases, is a first step in the biological utilization of fats.

Waxes are chemically differentiated from fats because of the presence of a long chain alcohol instead of glycerol. For example, beeswax (XII) consists primarily of the ester of palmitic acid with the straight chain alcohol myricyl alcohol ($CH_3—(CH_2)_{29}—OH$).

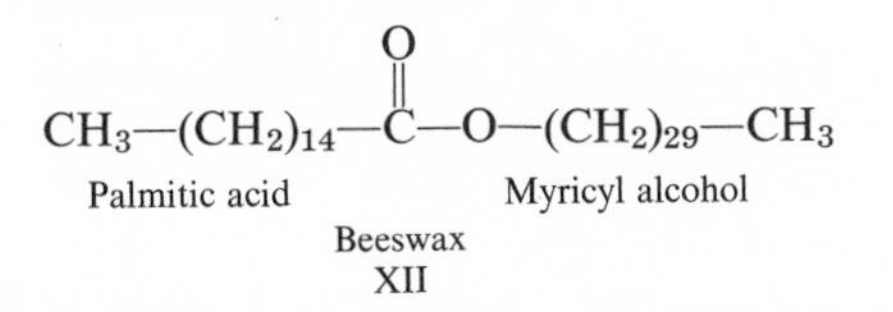

Beeswax
XII

Cuticle waxes, found in flower petals, fruit skin, and vegetable leaves, contain long chain fatty acids (C_{24} to C_{35}) combined with equally long chain primary and secondary alcohols.

Compound Lipids

Compound or conjugate lipids contain other elements in addition to the carbon, hydrogen, and oxygen found in simple lipids. These additional elements may be sulfur, nitrogen, or phosphorus.

The common phospholipids include several derivatives of phosphatidic acid:

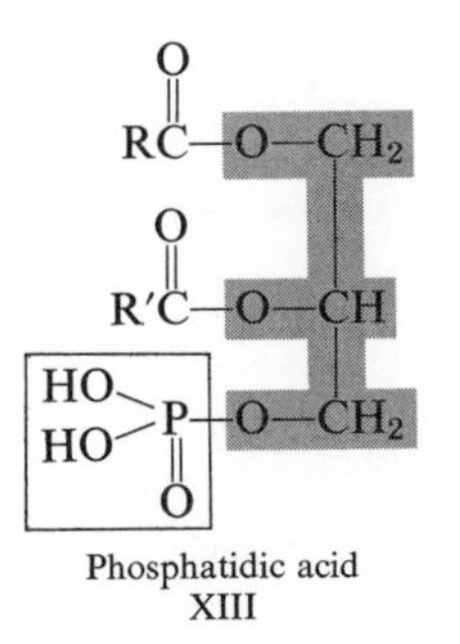

Phosphatidic acid
XIII

In these lipids the phosphoryl group of phosphatidic acid is bound in ester linkage to choline (XIV), β-ethanolamine (XV), serine (XVI).

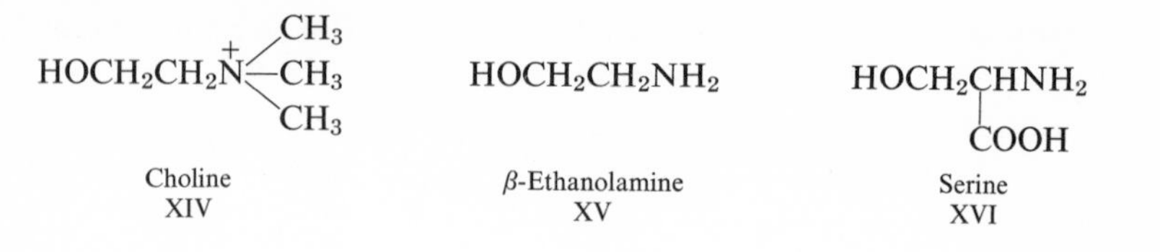

Choline XIV   β-Ethanolamine XV   Serine XVI

Phosphatidyl choline (formerly called lecithin) has the following formula:

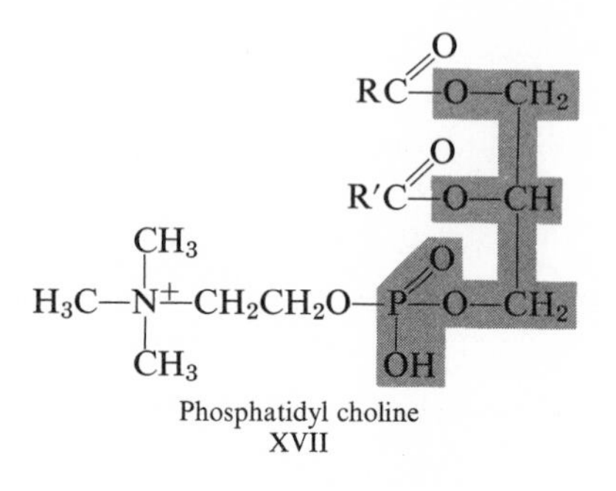

Phosphatidyl choline
XVII

Phosphatidyl ethanolamine (XVIII) and phosphatidyl serine (XIX), which were formerly collectively termed cephalins, have the following structures:

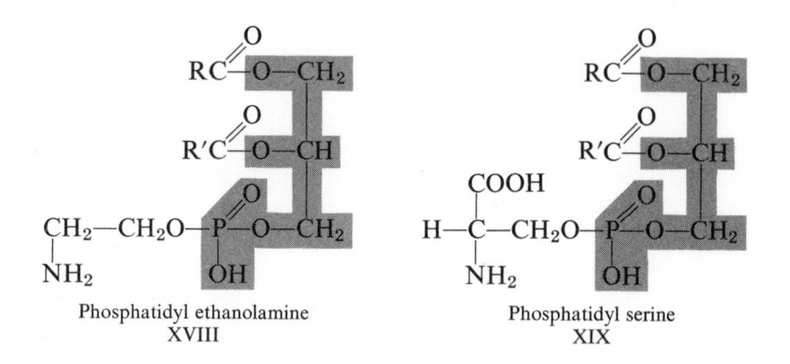

Phosphatidyl ethanolamine XVIII   Phosphatidyl serine XIX

Sphingolipids, or sphingomyelins, are derivatives of the basic compound sphingosine:

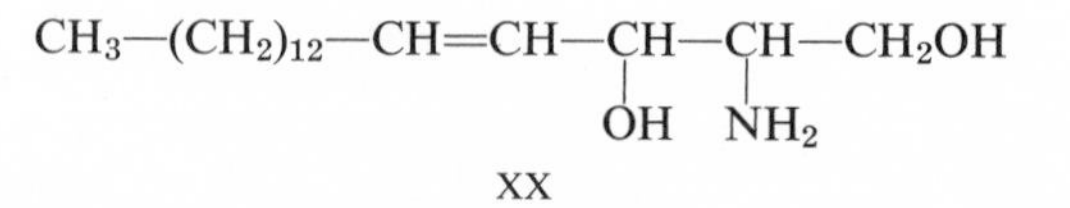

XX

In sphingolipids (XXI) the amino group is attached to a fatty acid and the terminal alcoholic group to phosphocholine.

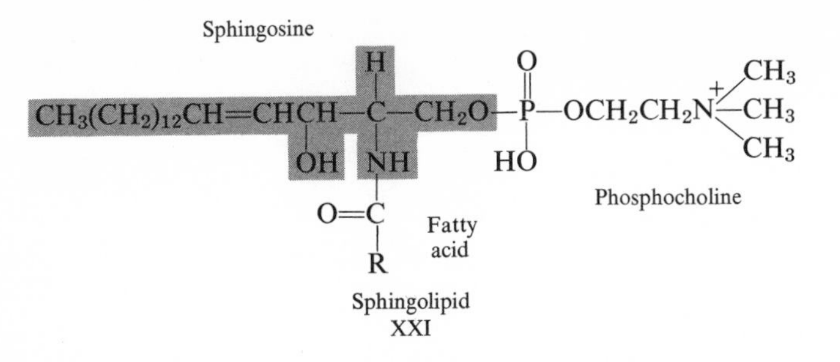

Sphingolipid
XXI

Glycolipids (XXII) form a class of conjugate lipids in which a sugar moiety is an integral part of the molecule. Glycolipids, or cerebrosides as they are often termed, contain no phosphorus but yield on hydrolysis a sugar, most frequently a hexose, a nitrogen-containing moiety, and fatty acid. They are related to sphingolipids in that the nitrogen-containing unit is sphingosine. In glycolipids the terminal alcoholic group of sphingosine is joined to hexose; the fatty acid unit is attached to the amino group of sphingosine.

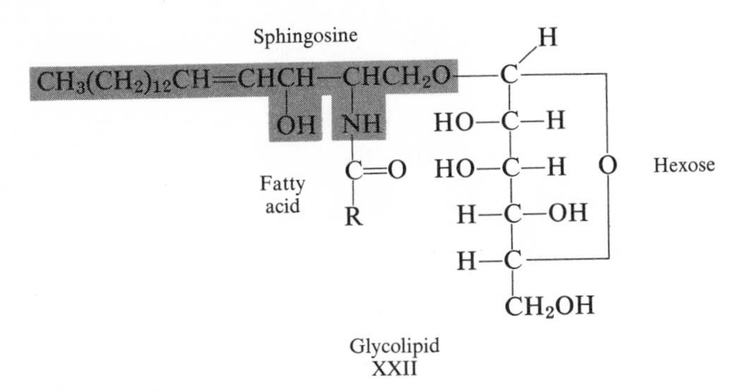

Glycolipid
XXII

Lipoproteins, as the name implies, are conjugates of lipid and protein. Fatty acids such as stearic, palmitic, and oleic acids are the major acid components. It is probable that lipoproteins are loose complexes of proteins and lipid held together by secondary forces such as van der Waals interaction and not by covalent bonds.

The macromolecular characteristics of some lipids are shown in Figure 8–1. A typical triglyceride, Figure 8–1*a*, is shown with arachidonic acid (four double bonds), stearic acid (saturated), and linoleic acid (two double bonds) joined to glycerol. Phosphatidyl serine, Figure 8–1*b*, represents a typical phospholipid, and is shown with one residue of linoleic acid and one of palmitic acid, joined through a glycerol residue to phosphoserine. Finally, there is a typical sphingomyelin, Figure 8–1*c*, with a linoleic acid residue joined through an amide linkage to the —NH— of sphingosine, and phosphocholine joined through an ester linkage to the terminal hydroxyl of sphingosine.

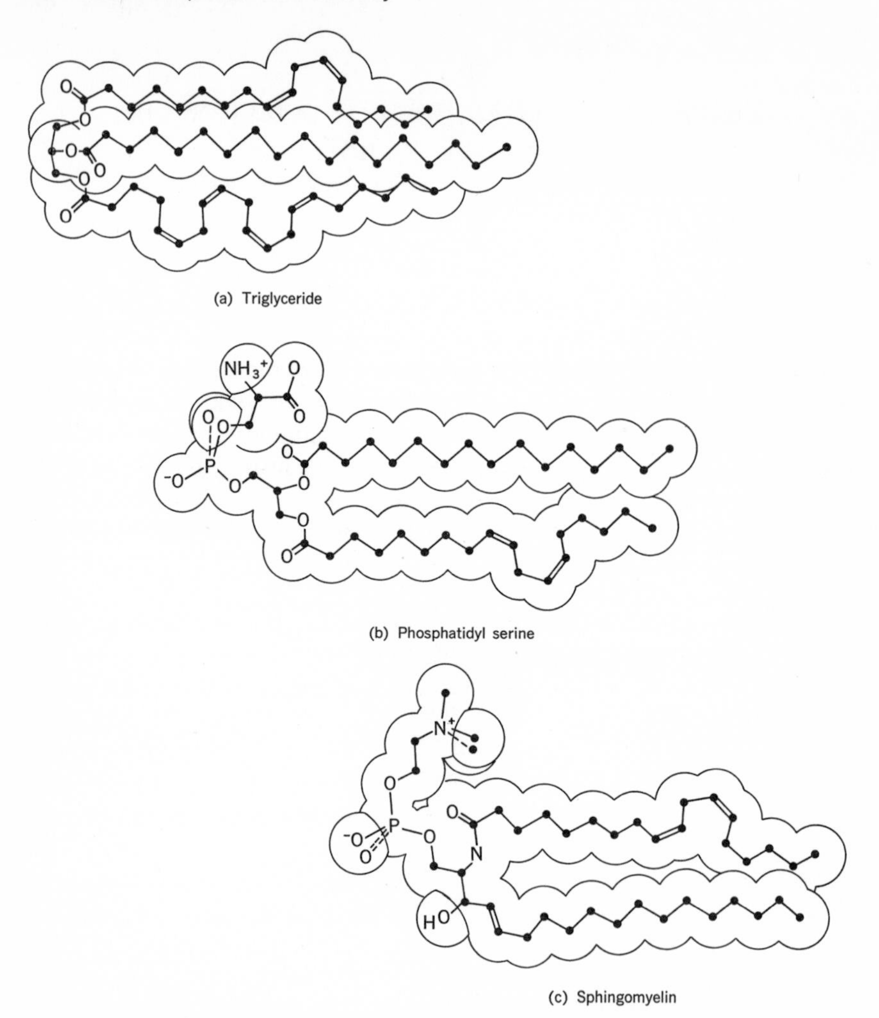

(a) Triglyceride

(b) Phosphatidyl serine

(c) Sphingomyelin

Figure 8–1. Some selected lipid structures. (From Oncley, 1961.)

Steroids

Steroids are called lipids even though they are derived from a phenanthrene structure

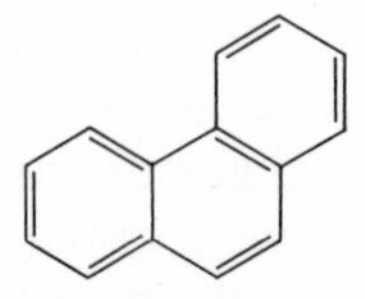

and hence are very different from lipids made up of fatty acids. Steroids function as structural components of cell membranes and as hormones, and in this way they play an important role in physiological regulation. Further, as bile acids they are involved in digestion. Table 8–3 summarizes the chemical structures of some common steroids and their biological roles (see page 112).

Functions of Lipids

Lipids have two main functions in the living organism. They act as the prime fuel reserve for metabolism, and they form an important part of the structure of living tissues.

The main function of fats, or triglycerides, is that of serving as the principal and most effective source of stored caloric energy, in both animals and plants (seeds). The chemical composition and structure of fats results in their having a higher heat content than carbohydrates, proteins, or other lipids, such as phospholipids. For this reason they are especially suited for their role as the organism's chief energy storage form.* The way this stored energy is mobilized is the topic of *fat metabolism* and will be considered in a later section of this chapter.

Lipids are often found concentrated in biological membranes and at interfaces. Their biological importance here may be associated with their chemical structures, which enable them to bridge the gap from water-soluble to insoluble phases without necessitating a shape discontinuity.

There are additional functions of lipids, although it is possible that some of the functions are fortuitous evolutionary adaptions and related to energy storage. For example, fat is often deposited, largely subcutaneously, in warm-blooded animals and serves as insulation against an unfavorable environment. Also, fatty tissues laid down around vital organs frequently serve the organism as a protection against mechanical injuries.

Waxes occasionally function as energy reserves in both plants and animals. More often, however, their function appears to be as a protective covering on the surface of an organism. The surface of leaves, stems, and fruit are rendered resistant to water, insects, and bacteria by a wax coating. Cuticle waxes also provide protection for wool fibers and the skin of practically all fur-bearing animals.

Very little is known about the metabolic role of members of the phospholipid group. As a class of compounds, the phospholipids have been found in every cellular organism which has been examined for them and they are probably a constituent of every living cell. The distribution, however, of a given phospholipid varies not only from species to species, but also from one tissue to another in the same organism. The significance of such a distribution for metabolic functioning is not clear. Many phospholipids, e.g., the sphingomyelins, are concentrated in nervous tissue. Brain,

* This should not be confused with the role of phosphates (page 64), which are the organism's chief form for metabolic free energy storage.

TABLE 8-3

CHEMICAL STRUCTURE AND BIOLOGICAL ROLE OF SOME COMMON STEROIDS

General Group	Representative Compound	Structure	Occurrence and Function
Sterols	Cholesterol	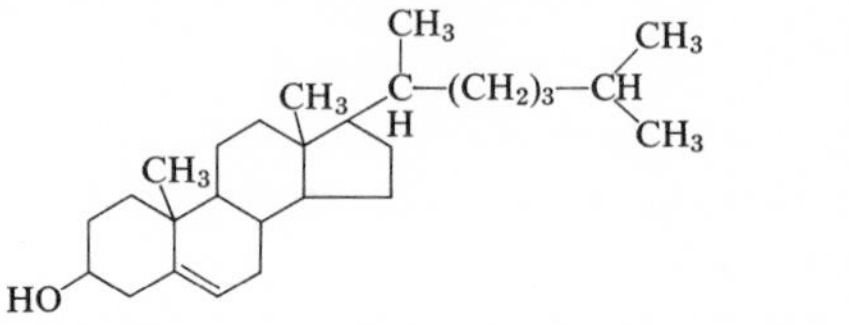 CH_3 CH_3 CH_3—C(H)—$(CH_2)_3$—CH(—CH_3) CH_3 HO	Structural component of cell membranes, precursor of other steroids
	Ergosterol	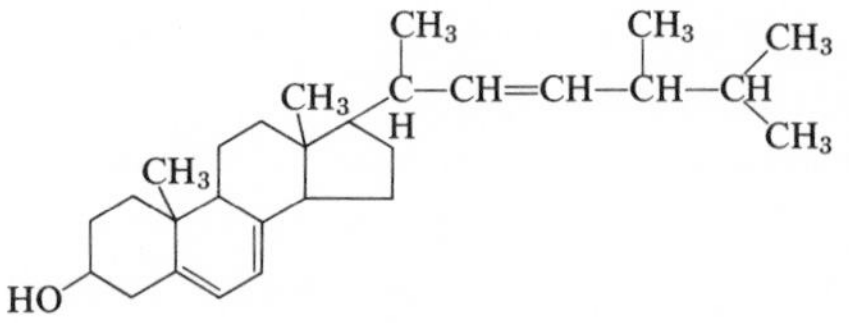 CH_3 CH_3 CH_3 CH_3—C(H)—CH=CH—CH—CH(—CH_3) CH_3 HO	Provitamin D, precursor of vitamin D
Bile acids	Cholic acid	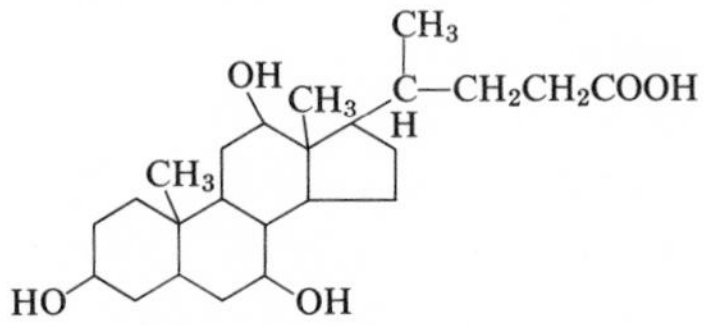 CH_3 OH CH_3—C(H)—CH_2CH_2COOH CH_3 HO OH	Lipase activator, fat adsorption and digestion
Hormones	Aldosterone	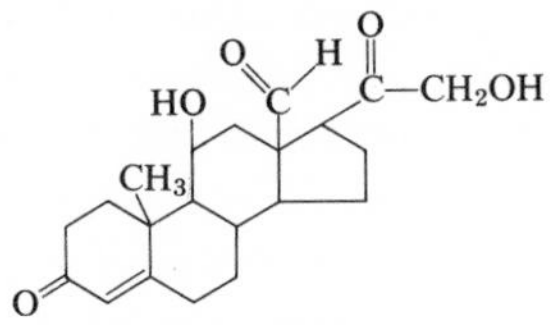 O H C O C—CH_2OH HO CH_3 O	Regulates salt and water balance, adrenocortical hormone
	Testosterone	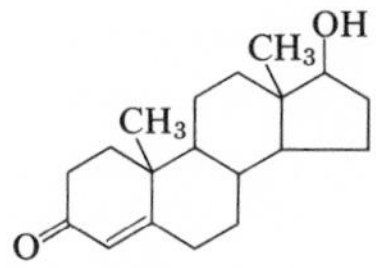 CH_3 OH CH_3 O	Testicular hormone, masculine hormone
	Progesterone	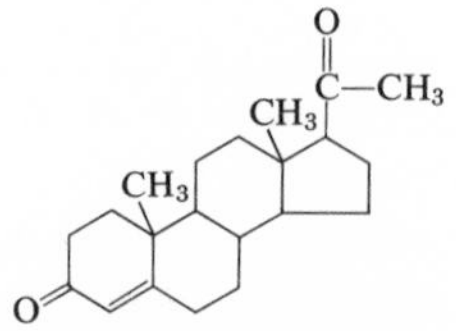 O C—CH_3 CH_3 CH_3 O	Corpus luteum hormone, precursor of corticoids, suppresses estrus and ovulation
	Estradiol	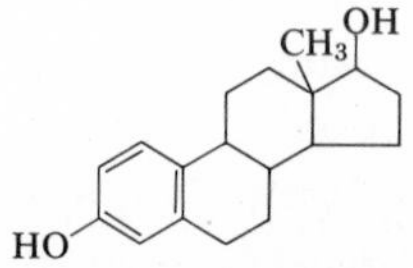 CH_3 OH HO	Follicular hormone, induces estrus

of all the tissues which have been studied, has the greatest phospholipid content. From 25 per cent to 30 per cent of the dry weight of brain consists of phospholipids, as compared to half this proportion in liver. Glycolipids occur most abundantly in the myelin sheaths of nerves. Lipoproteins have been tentatively assigned roles in lipid transport and in determining intracellular structure. Much of the lipid material in the plasma of higher animals is bound to protein in the form of lipoproteins. It is probable that these are important transport forms of lipid; the exact role is, however, uncertain. In addition, intracellular organelles, such as mitochondria of liver cells and grana of chloroplasts, contain lipoproteins, which are believed to be important in their structural maintenance and functional integrity.

Fat Metabolism

The function of fats, or triglycerides, as reservoirs of food material has been mentioned. The way these substances are mobilized from their storage sites and utilized for the benefit of the organism can be understood only through a discussion of fat metabolism.

The general features of fat metabolism in a higher organism are outlined in Figure 8–2. In this metabolic scheme triglycerides are in a state of dynamic equilibrium, in a state of constant transport and utilization from one site to another. This is shown by double-headed arrows (↔), which indicate the movement of fat between its principal sites of location and utilization in higher organisms. Depending on the requirements of the animal, the emphasis of the arrows may shift. That is, when fats are ingested a large proportion is transported across the intestinal membrane into the blood via the lymphatic system. The blood transports some fat to the liver or other tissues where it is utilized to provide energy (~) for

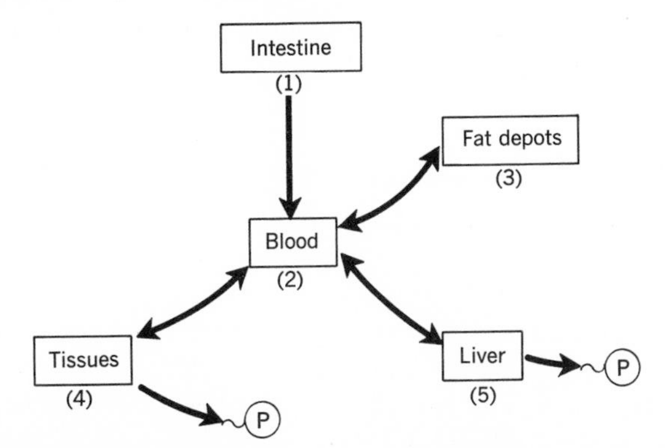

Figure 8–2. Fat metabolism in higher animals: (1) Fat absorption, (2) fat transport system, (3) fat storage, (4) fat utilization and energy production, (5) fatty acid oxidation (principal site) and fat synthesis.

cellular functions. Excess fat is transported by the blood to depots for storage. This form of stored energy can be withdrawn from its deposit site when it is needed by the organism. Since it is possible for the animal to biosynthesize fats (page 164) from products of carbohydrate metabolism, fats are produced in the liver during times when there is an excess of sugars available. The fat produced ends up in a depot site.

As indicated in Figure 8–2, a product of fat metabolism is energy (~Ⓟ). From the point of view of the organism, this energy production is one of the most important functions of fats. This is illustrated by the fact that complete combustion of 1 gram of fat yields approximately 9 kcal compared with 5.6 kcal/gram of protein, and 4.2 kcal/gram of carbohydrate. In order to obtain this energy, the cell has a series of well-integrated reactions for the stepwise degradation of fats with the liberation of utilizable energy (page 117). In the chapter on bioenergetics, the stepwise degradation of metabolites, with energy liberation, was discussed at some length. The reader is referred to these pages for review at this point.

Fat breakdown or catabolism begins with the hydrolysis of triglycerides to glycerol and fatty acid residues, Eq. (1). This reaction is catalyzed

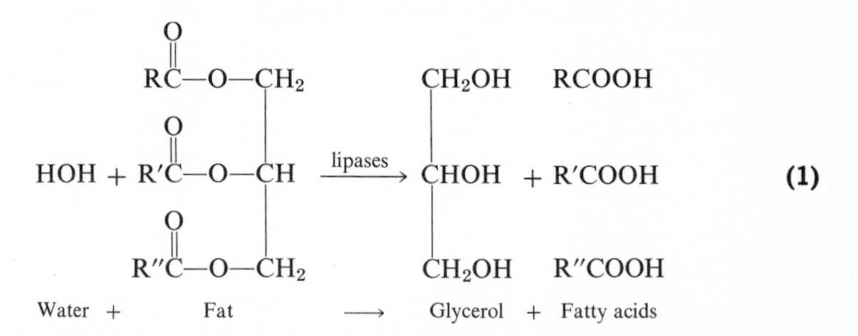

by enzymes called lipases, or esterases. The glycerol produced is converted into carbohydrate via glycerol phosphate, which is formed from glycerol by a specific enzyme plus ATP, or through the same intermediate, into energy (~Ⓟ), CO_2, and H_2O (page 92).

Fatty Acid Oxidation

Fatty acids, in higher animals, are degraded by a series of stepwise reactions. These reactions, some of which are oxidative, result in the breakdown of the acids to the two carbon fragment, acetyl CoA (page 96). Figure 8–3, a schematic representation of the breakdown process, shows that the breakdown requires the collaboration of five different enzymes and, initially, ATP + CoA. The two carbon unit acetyl CoA is removed from a fatty acid by means of (reaction (1) of Figure 8–3) a flavin-dependent oxidation reaction; (reaction (2) of Figure 8–3) an addition of water; (reaction (3) of Figure 8–3) NAD-dependent oxidation; and (reaction (4) of

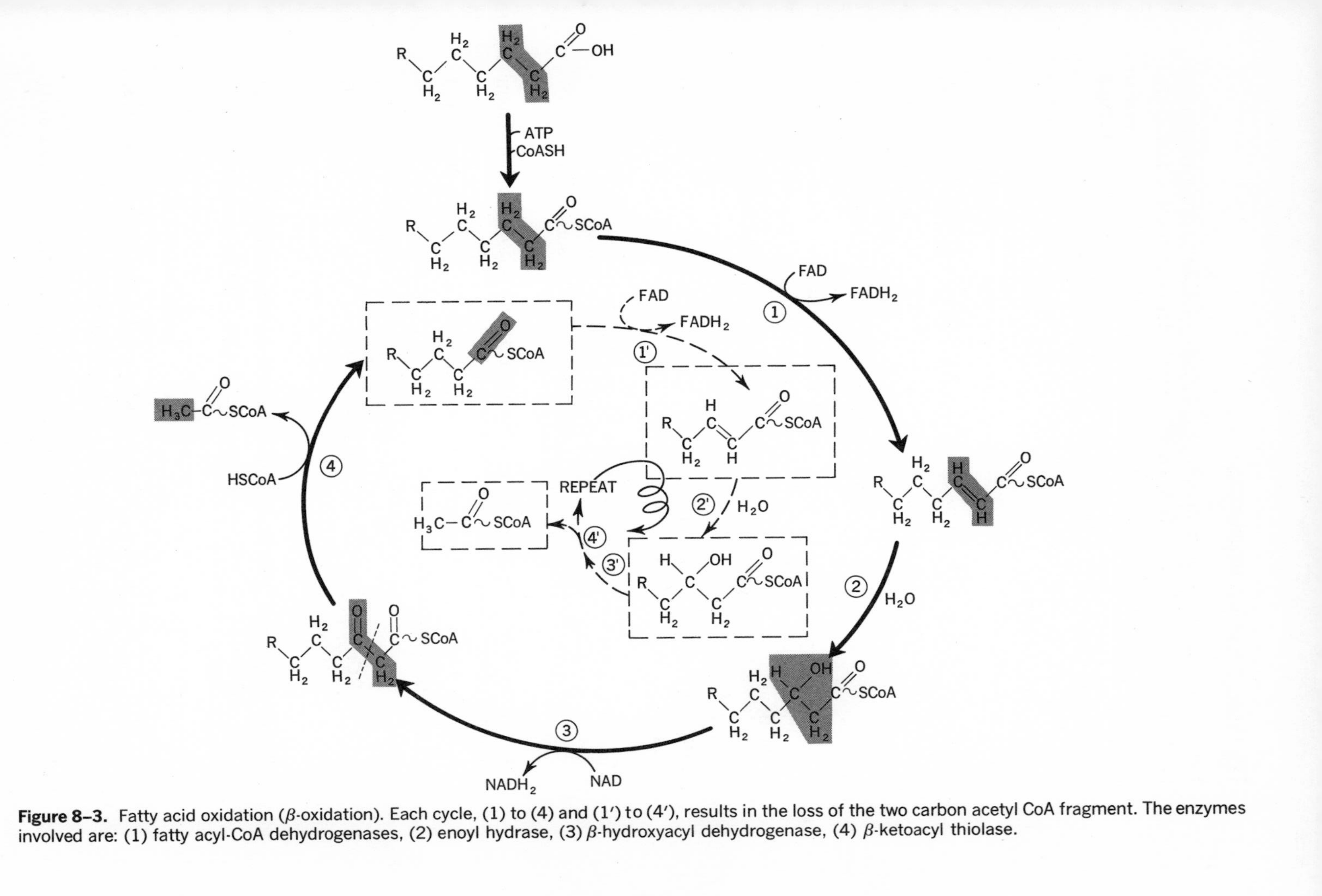

Figure 8–3. Fatty acid oxidation (β-oxidation). Each cycle, (1) to (4) and (1′) to (4′), results in the loss of the two carbon acetyl CoA fragment. The enzymes involved are: (1) fatty acyl-CoA dehydrogenases, (2) enoyl hydrase, (3) β-hydroxyacyl dehydrogenase, (4) β-ketoacyl thiolase.

Figure 8–3) a cleavage reaction. Repetition of this process ultimately results in the complete breakdown of the fatty acid. At many stages of the breakdown process potential energy (~Ⓟ) is made available for cellular functions. The enzymes and the reactions they catalyze in the conversion of a straight chain fatty acid to a two carbon unit are listed below.

1. *Thiokinases* catalyze the formation of fatty acyl CoA, a coenzyme A derivative of fatty acid:

$$\underset{\text{Fatty acid}}{RCH_2CH_2\overset{O}{\overset{\|}{C}}{-}OH} + ATP + \underset{\text{Coenzyme A}}{CoASH} \xrightarrow{Mg^{II}} \underset{\text{Fatty acyl CoA}}{RCH_2CH_2\overset{O}{\overset{\|}{C}}{\sim}SCoA} + AMP + \underset{\text{Pyrophosphate}}{Ⓟ{\sim}O{-}Ⓟ} \quad (2)$$

2. *Acyl dehydrogenase* coupled with a flavin coenzyme results in oxidation (at the α and β carbons) of fatty acyl CoA and concomitant reduction of the flavin.

$$\underset{\text{Fatty acyl CoA}}{R\overset{\beta}{C}H_2\overset{\alpha}{C}H_2\overset{O}{\overset{\|}{C}}{\sim}SCoA} + \underset{\text{Oxidized flavin}}{Flavoprotein} \longrightarrow \underset{\alpha,\beta\text{-Unsaturated fatty acyl CoA}}{R\overset{\beta}{C}H{=}\overset{\alpha}{C}H\overset{O}{\overset{\|}{C}}{\sim}SCoA} + \underset{\text{Reduced flavin}}{Flavoprotein \cdot H_2} \quad (3)$$

The reduced flavoprotein can be reoxidized by the mitochondrial system through cytochrome c. The result is phosphate bond energy.

3. *Enoyl hydrase* catalyzes the addition of water to the α,β-unsaturated fatty acid intermediate.

$$\underset{\alpha,\beta\text{-Unsaturated fatty acyl CoA}}{RCH{=}CH\overset{O}{\overset{\|}{C}}{\sim}SCoA} + HOH \longrightarrow \underset{\beta\text{-Hydroxy fatty acyl CoA}}{R\overset{OH}{\overset{|}{C}}H{-}CH_2{-}\overset{O}{\overset{\|}{C}}{\sim}SCoA} \quad (4)$$

4. *β-Hydroxyacyl dehydrogenase* is a nicotinamide nucleotide linked enzyme which catalyzes the oxidation of the β-hydroxyl group to a β-ketone unit.

$$\underset{\beta\text{-Hydroxy fatty acyl CoA}}{R\overset{OH}{\overset{|}{C}}H{-}CH_2\overset{O}{\overset{\|}{C}}{\sim}SCoA} + NAD \rightleftharpoons \underset{\beta\text{-Keto fatty acyl CoA}}{R\overset{O}{\overset{\|}{C}}{-}CH_2\overset{O}{\overset{\|}{C}}{\sim}SCoA} + NADH_2 \quad (5)$$

Reoxidation of $NADH_2$ via the oxidative phosphorylation system results in ~Ⓟ, ATP.

5. *β-Ketoacyl thiolase* catalyzes a coenzyme A-dependent cleavage of the β-keto fatty acyl molecule. This results in a fatty acyl CoA unit plus acetyl CoA.

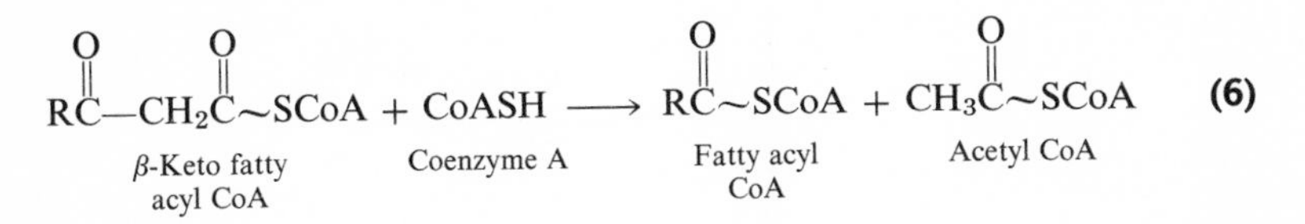

The fatty acyl CoA produced in this reaction can be further degraded by Eqs. (3) through (6) until the entire fatty acid unit is converted to acetyl CoA. The acetyl CoA that is formed reacts with oxaloacetic acid to form citric acid and is oxidized to CO_2 and HOH in the Krebs cycle (page 94), Figure 7–8.

Energetics of Fatty Acid Oxidation

The energy yield in fatty acid oxidation can be easily calculated. The oxidation of acetyl CoA through the Krebs cycle yields 12 ~Ⓟ, as described on page 97. In the process of β-oxidation, as shown in Eqs. (3) and (5), flavoprotein and NAD are reduced. The transport of electrons from these coenzymes during oxidative phosphorylation (page 74) results in additional ~Ⓟ; three for the NAD system and at least two for the flavoprotein system. Thus for each molecule of C_{16} fatty acid (palmitic acid) oxidized, eight C_2 units, acetyl CoA's, are formed. These yield upon complete oxidation in the Krebs cycle $8 \times 12 = 96$ ~Ⓟ bonds. In addition, seven of these C_2 units contribute to the high energy pool, through the NAD and flavoprotein systems, as they are formed in β-oxidation, Eqs. (3) and (5). This produces at least $7 \times 5 = 35$ ~Ⓟ bonds. The total is thus $35 + 96 = 131$ ~Ⓟ bonds per mole of C_{16} acid oxidized. From this must be subtracted the two ~Ⓟ bonds used in the initial activation of the fatty acid, Eq. (2). Therefore, 129 ~Ⓟ bonds result when 1 mole of palmitic acid is oxidized. Since 1 mole of palmitic acid equals 256 grams, there are 129 ~Ⓟ/256 = almost 0.5 ~Ⓟ bonds per gram of palmitic acid utilized. This should be compared with glucose, which yields 38 ~Ⓟ per mole on complete oxidation via the Embden-Meyerhof-Krebs pathway. This is equivalent to 38 ~Ⓟ/138 = almost 0.3 ~Ⓟ per gram glucose.

Glyoxylate Cycle

Figure 8–4 shows the relationship of fat metabolism to that of carbohydrate and protein. Although it is a common observation that carbohydrates are readily converted to fats in animal tissues, there is no evidence

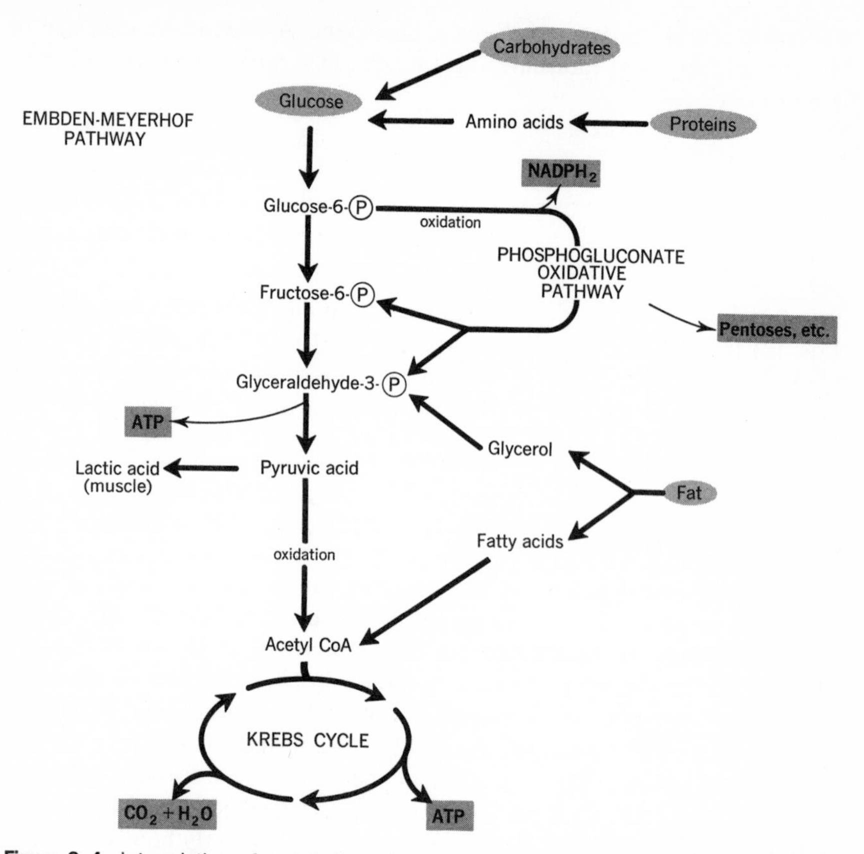

Figure 8–4. Interrelation of metabolic pathways for fat, carbohydrate, and protein catabolism. The intermediates linking the pathways are shown. In addition, the principle product of each scheme is shown in bold face. In the absence of oxygen only anaerobic metabolism resulting in lactic acid can occur.

to suggest that the reverse, namely, the conversion of fats to carbohydrates, occurs. In some plant tissues, bacteria, and fungi, fat deposits can, however, be rapidly converted to sucrose and other complex sugars and into protein.

It is now apparent that the non-animal tissues which convert fat to carbohydrate and protein utilize a series of enzymatic reactions not carried out in other tissues. In these tissues there are two points of entry into the Krebs cycle (Figure 8–5). One reaction is catalyzed by the common Krebs cycle enzyme.

$$\text{Acetyl CoA} + \text{Oxaloacetate} \longrightarrow \text{Citrate} + \text{CoASH}$$

The second reaction involves glyoxylate and results in malate, a Krebs cycle intermediate.

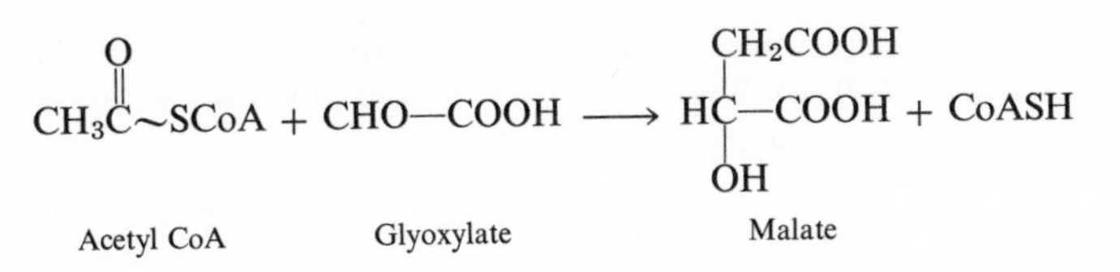

The glyoxylate needed for this reaction is supplied from the breakdown of isocitrate by the enzyme isocitrase. Thus, over all, 2 moles of acetate are converted to 1 mole of succinate. The succinate can of course enter the Krebs cycle and thereby become a source of carbohydrate and protein carbon atoms. Thus the difference between the Krebs cycle and this by-pass, or glyoxylate cycle, is that acetate carbons are oxidized by the Krebs cycle, whereas they are converted to oxaloacetate and hence to carbohydrate and protein by the glyoxylate cycle (Figure 8–5). In the Krebs cycle, malate is generated from isocitrate via oxalosuccinic acid, through fumarate, during which two carbons (CO_2) are lost; these are equivalent to the input from acetyl CoA. In the glyoxylate cycle, these CO_2-producing reactions are bypassed and the two carbon (acetate) input is conserved.

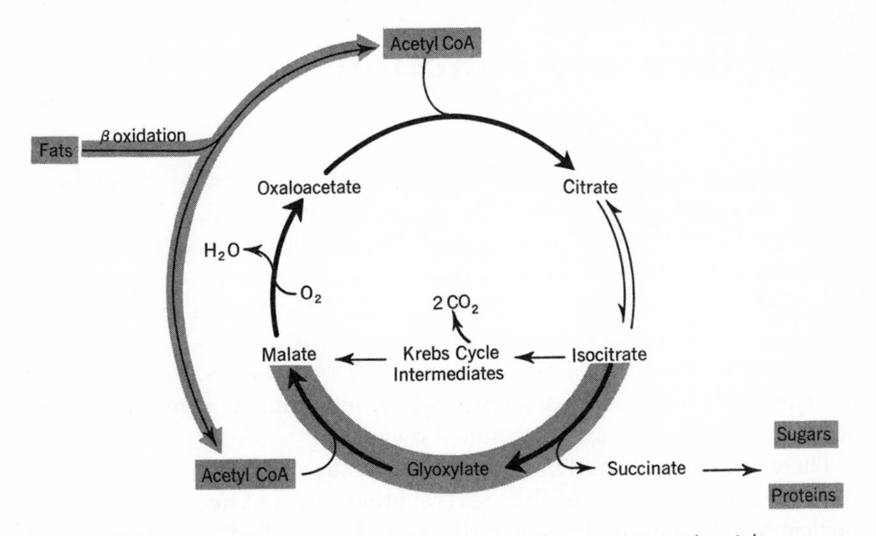

Figure 8–5. Glyoxylate cycle, conversion of fatty acids to sugars and proteins.

SUGGESTED READING

Bloch, K. (ed.), *Lipid Metabolism,* John Wiley & Sons, Inc., New York, 1960.

Green, D., "The Synthesis of Fat," *Scientific American,* February 1960.

Lovern, J. A., *The Chemistry of Lipides of Biochemical Significance,* Methuen & Co., Ltd., London, 1955.

"We wish to suggest a structure for the salt of deoxyribose nucleic acid (D.N.A.). This structure has novel features which are of considerable biological interest."

J. D. Watson and F. H. C. Crick, 1953

NINE

Nucleic Acids: Structure and Function

Genetic information has long been known to be carried by the chromosomes. For years, the region on the chromosome which determines a particular character has been called a gene. The idea, however, of the gene as a molecule with a definite chemical structure and defined biochemical function is relatively new. It is now known that, biochemically, genes are a particular form of a macromolecule known as deoxyribonucleic acid (DNA). It is also known that the structure of enzymes, as well as the mechanisms controlling the rates at which individual enzymes or groups of enzymes are made, are determined by genes.

The expression of the DNA gene, that is, the determination of protein structure and synthesis, involves several other forms of nucleic acid. These nucleic acids contain the sugar ribose and are called ribonucleic acids (RNA). They are specifically designated as template or messenger RNA (*m*RNA), ribosomal (*r*RNA), and transfer RNA (*t*RNA). These RNA's are involved in the transmission of genetic information and the process of protein production.

What is the chemical nature of these nucleic acid macromolecules? What are their functions, and how are these performed?

Nucleic acids are polymeric chains with a backbone of repeating sugar units connected by phosphate bridges (Figures 9–1, 9–2, and 9–3). Attached to each sugar unit is an organic base termed a purine or pyrimidine.

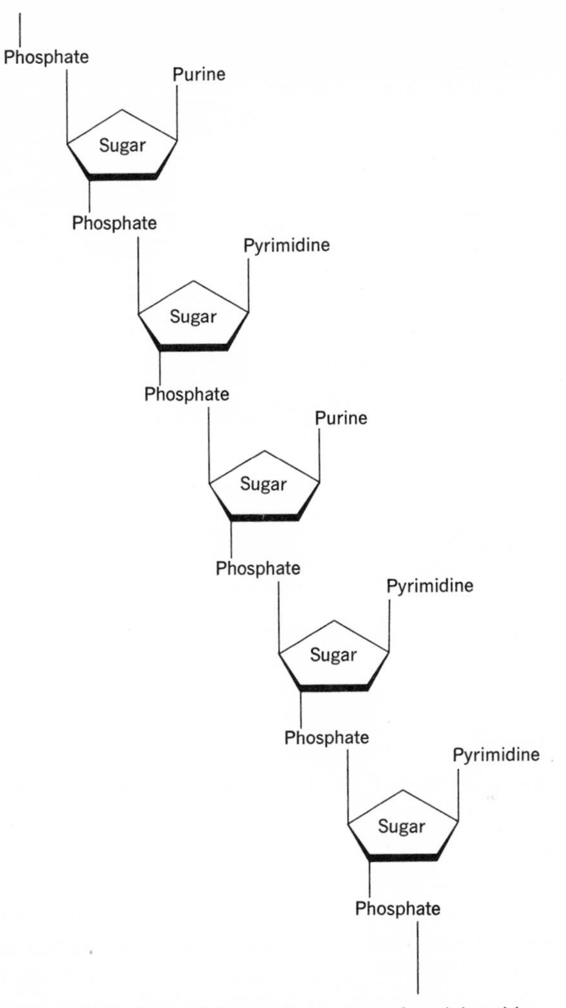

Figure 9–1. General chemical structure of nucleic acids.

The individuality of RNA's and DNA's found in nature depends on: (1) the number of repeating nucleotide subunits, (2) the nature of the purine or pyrimidine attached to each repeating sugar unit. There are five different major bases contained in nucleic acids, in addition to innumerable minor bases which form a small per cent of the total of purines and pyrimidines. The major bases are adenine, guanine, thymine, cytosine, and uracil.

The structure and function of nucleic acids can most easily be understood by considering the components which go into building the nucleic acids. An outline of successive levels of structural complexity, terminating in nucleic acids, is presented in Figure 9–4. Purines and pyrimidines added

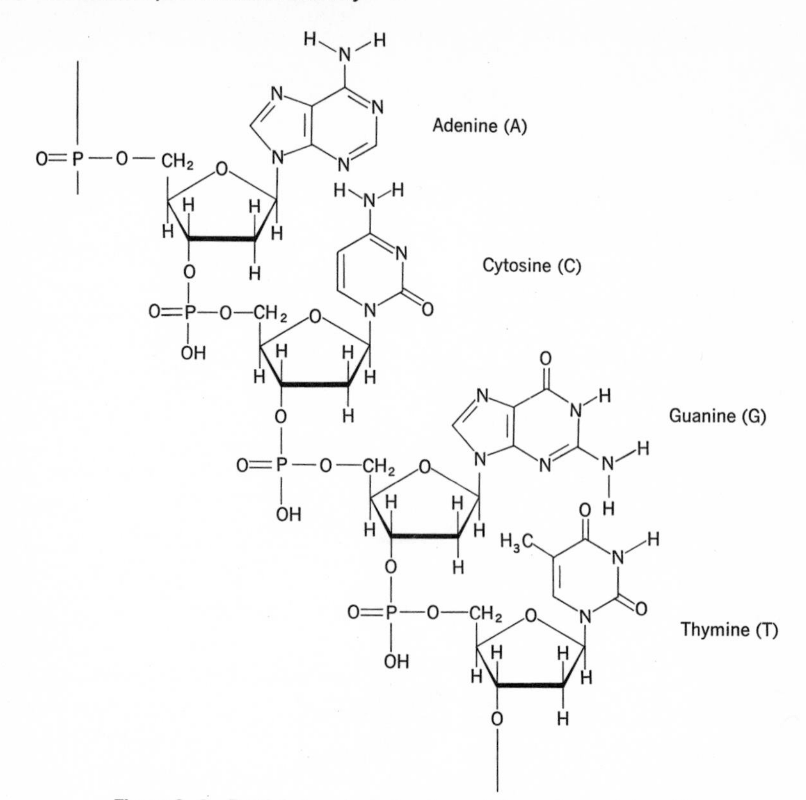

Figure 9–2. Partial chemical structure of deoxyribonucleic acid.

to a sugar moiety form *nucleosides.* The addition of a phosphate group to a nucleoside results in a *nucleotide.* The construction of nucleic acids is based on nucleotide subunits. Many biologically active forms of nucleic acids are found conjugated with protein and are called *nucleoproteins.*

Pyrimidine Bases

The pyrimidines found in nucleic acids are all derived from the parent compound, pyrimidine (I).* The derivatives are formed by the substitution

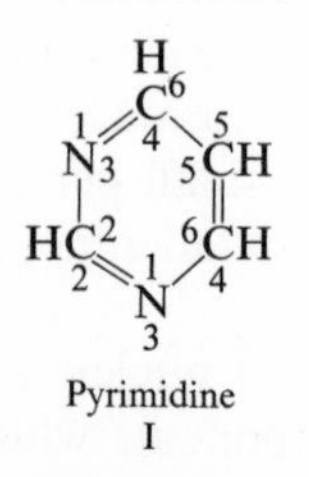

Pyrimidine
I

* The position numbers shown inside the ring are numbered in the sequence used in the new International system. The older Fischer system used the numbers shown in the sequence outside the ring. The International system is used in this book.

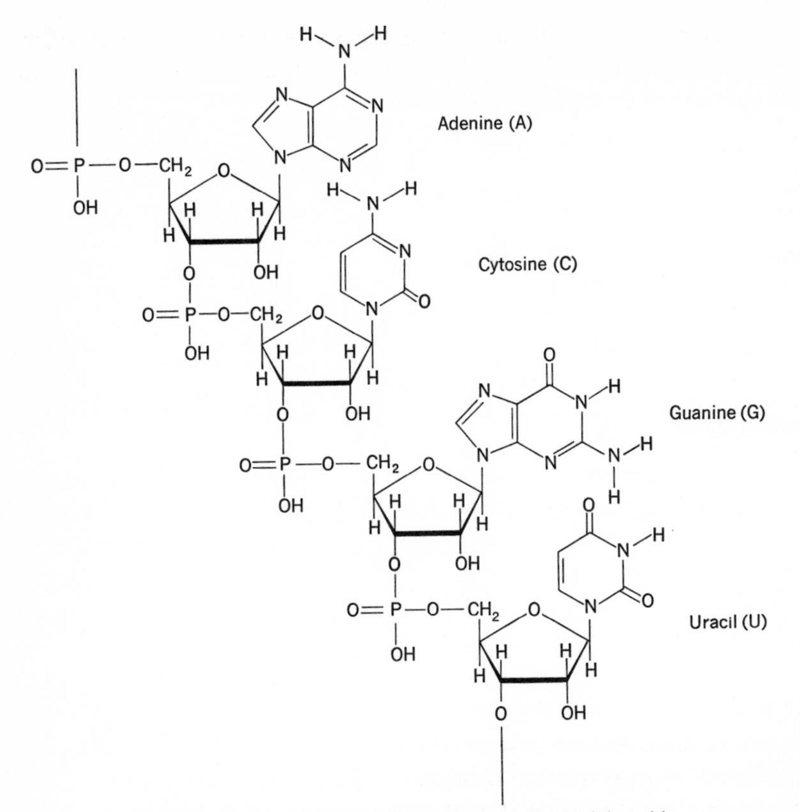

Figure 9–3. Partial chemical structure of ribonucleic acid.

of amino, hydroxyl, and methyl groups for hydrogen atoms at positions 2, 4, or 5. Uracil (II) is found predominantly in RNA; thymine (III) and 5-methyl cytosine (IV) in DNA. Cytosine (V) is found in both types of

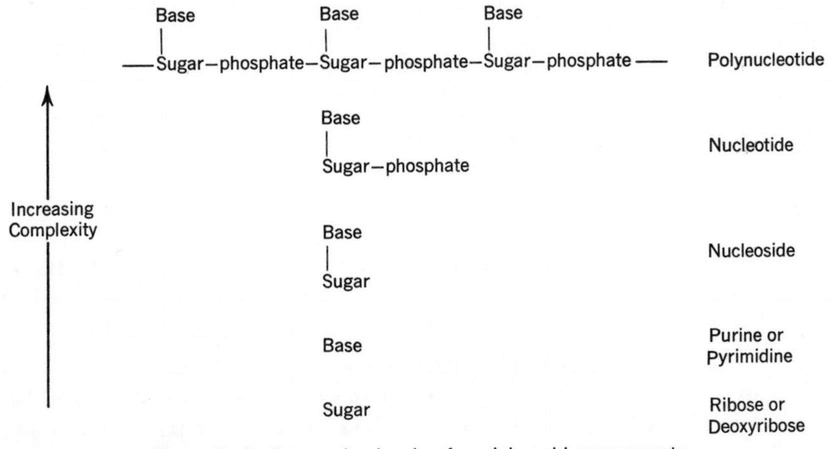

Figure 9–4. Successive levels of nucleic acid components.

nucleic acid. Other naturally occurring pyrimidine derivatives of major biological importance include vitamin B_1 (thiamine) and orotic acid, an intermediate in pyrimidine biosynthesis.

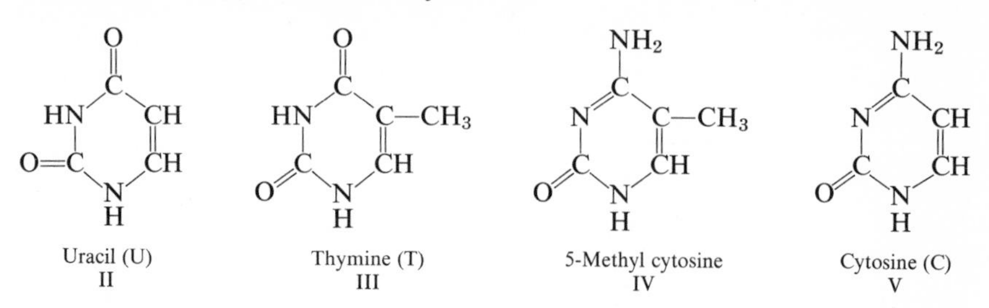

Uracil (U) II — Thymine (T) III — 5-Methyl cytosine IV — Cytosine (C) V

Purine Bases

The attachment of a five-membered imidazole ring to the six-membered pyrimidine ring results in purine (VI), the parent of the purine bases. RNA

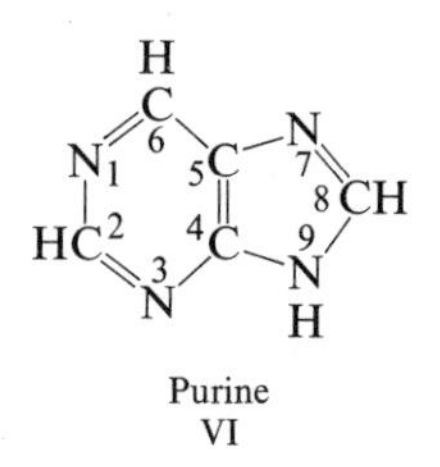

Purine
VI

and DNA contain the same purine derivatives, adenine (VII) and guanine (VIII). Other naturally occurring purines of importance include, hypoxanthine, xanthine (IX), and uric acid. These are involved in metabolism of purines.

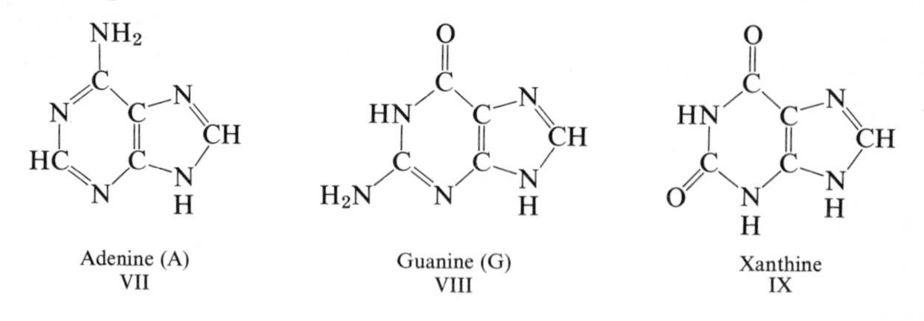

Adenine (A) VII — Guanine (G) VIII — Xanthine IX

Sugar Group

The sugar moiety found along the nucleic acid backbone can be the cyclic form of either ribose (in RNA) or deoxyribose (in DNA), which differ only by the presence or absence of a hydroxyl group on carbon 2 (so-called 2′) (page 82). Both sugars occur in the furanose form, i.e., in the form of a ring involving four of the five carbon atoms and one oxygen. In nucleic acids, the sugar units are linked through the phosphate group which is attached to carbon 3 (or 3′) of one pentose and carbon 5′ of a second molecule. Purine or pyrimidine bases are attached to carbon 1′.

Nucleosides

Nucleosides are formed by attaching a purine or pyrimidine base to the carbon 1′ position of ribose or deoxyribose. Thus, the nucleoside adenosine (X) is formed by attaching adenine to ribose. Guanosine (XI), cytidine (XII), and uridine are formed from ribose and respectively, guanine, cytosine, and uracil. Thymidine (XIII) is the deoxyribonucleoside formed from thymine and deoxyribose. In the pyrimidine nucleosides, sugar and base are joined by a β-glycosidic linkage from carbon 1′ of the pentose to nitrogen 1 of the base as shown for cytidine and thymidine. The purine nucleosides adenosine and guanosine are nitrogen 9 ribosides.

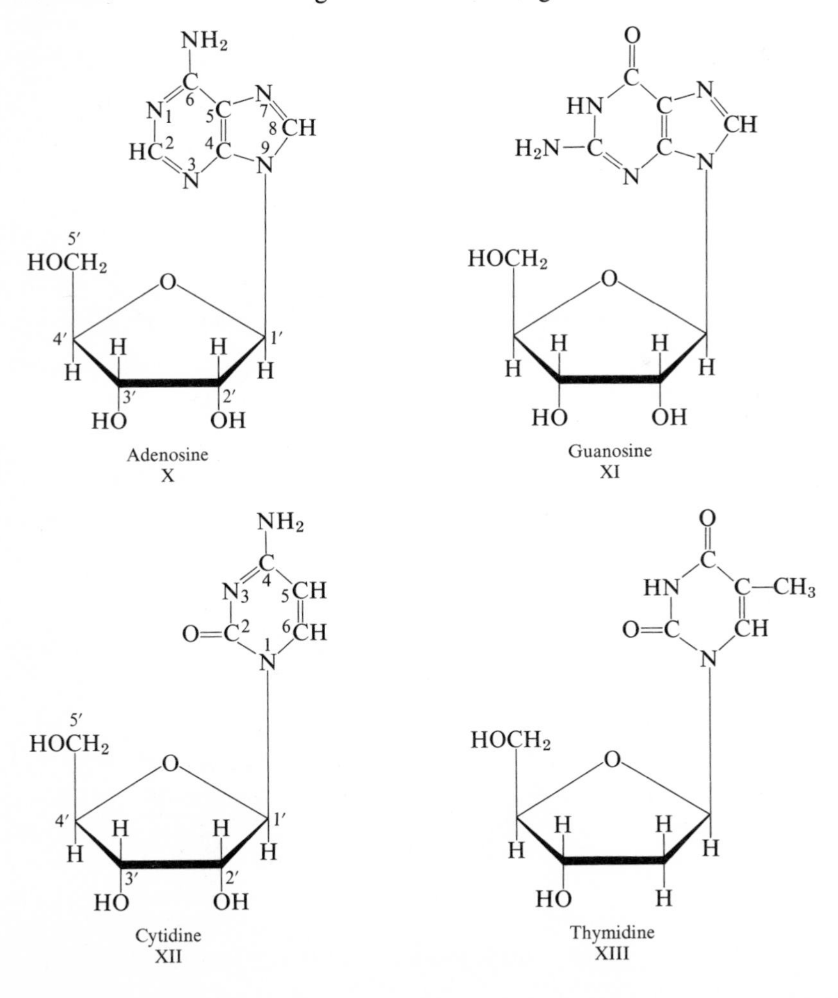

Adenosine
X

Guanosine
XI

Cytidine
XII

Thymidine
XIII

Nucleotides

The general structure of a nucleotide is:

Base—Sugar—Phosphate

Nucleotides are thus phosphate esters of a nucleoside. The nucleotides cytidylic (CMP) (XIV), adenylic (AMP), guanylic (GMP), thymidylic (TMP), and uridylic (UMP) acids are phosphate derivatives of cytidine, adenosine, guanosine, etc. An alternate nomenclature names the nucleotides as a nucleoside phosphate, e.g., cytidine monophosphate. Since the ribose nucleosides have three available hydroxyl groups at carbons, 2′, 3′, and 5′, three possible nucleoside monophosphates or nucleotides can be

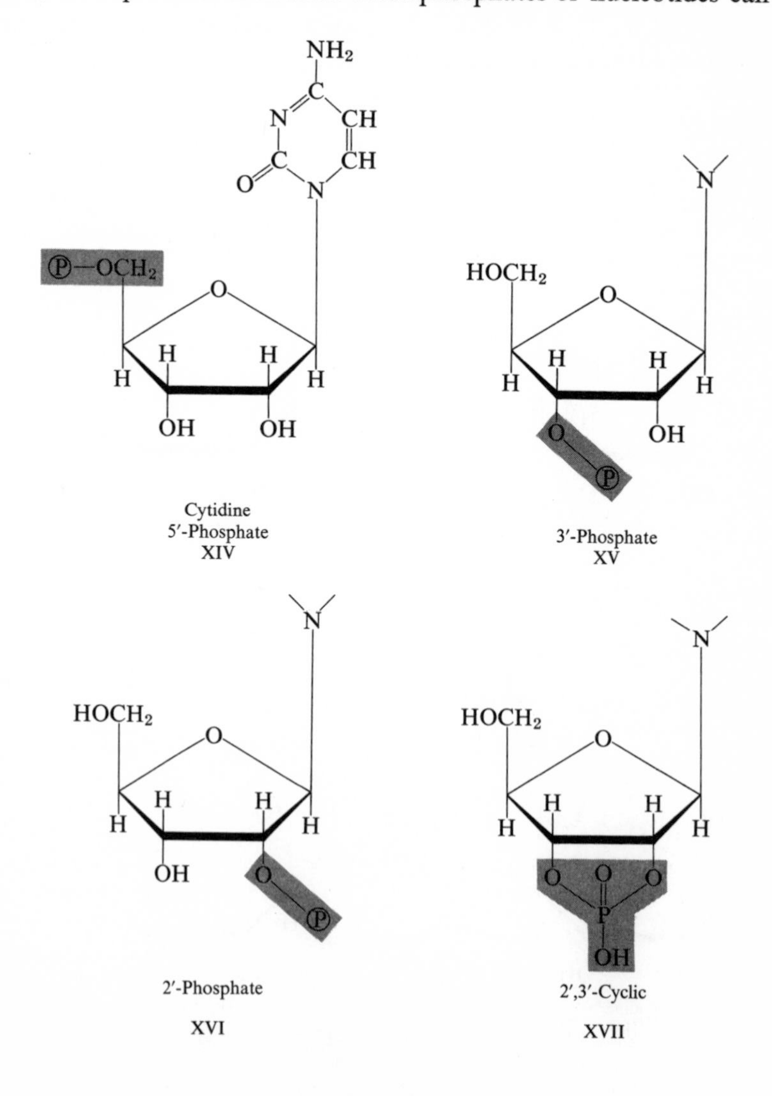

Cytidine
5′-Phosphate
XIV

3′-Phosphate
XV

2′-Phosphate

XVI

2′,3′-Cyclic

XVII

formed, namely, the 5′ (XIV), 3′ (XV), and 2′ (XVI) derivatives. An additional form (XVII), in which the phosphate group is attached to both the carbon 2′ and carbon 3′ positions (2′,3′-cyclic phosphate) is also known. For nucleotides of all bases, these four possible forms are known. In addition to these nucleoside monophosphates, there are nucleotides in which the phosphoryl group is attached to a phosphate or a pyrophosphate; the result is diphosphates and triphosphates. Thus, guanosine-5′-phosphate (XVIII) (GMP) yields guanosine diphosphate (XIX) (GDP) and guanosine triphosphate (XX) (GTP). Similarly, the nucleoside-5′-phosphates of other bases yield such di- and triphosphates as ADP, CDP, UDP, ATP, CTP, and UTP. A listing of biologically important nucleoside di- and triphosphates is given in Table 9–1.

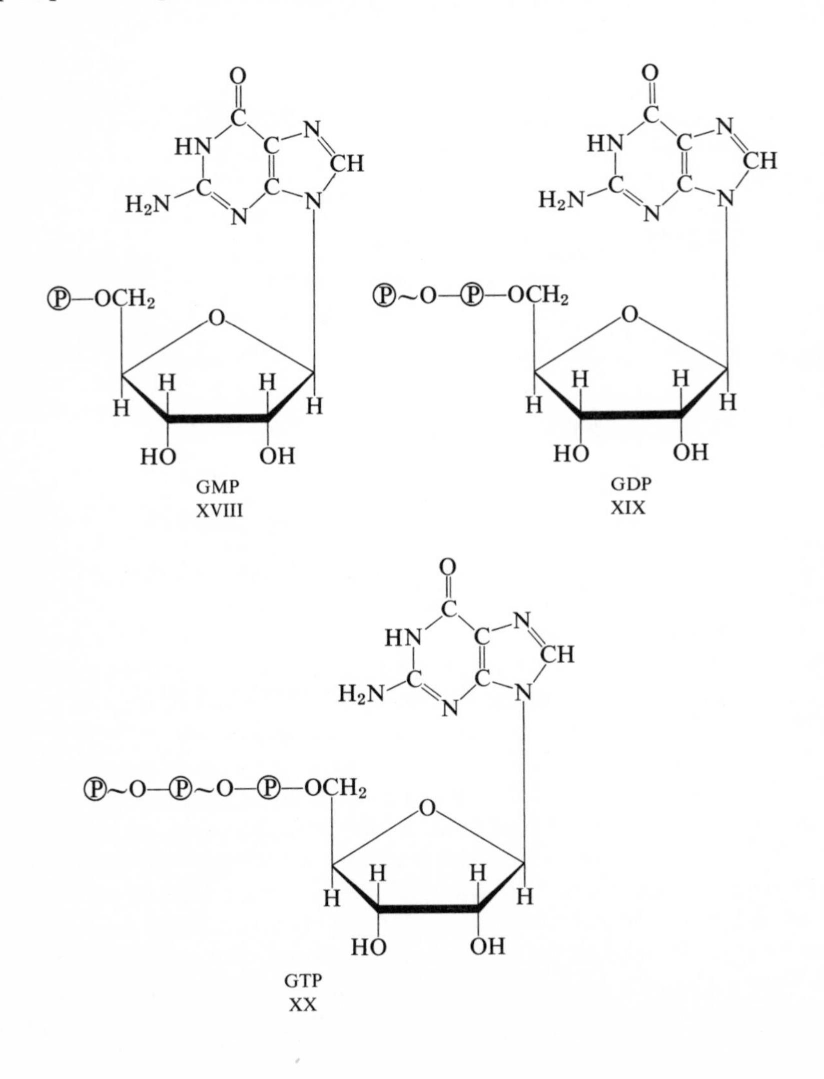

TABLE 9–1

ABBREVIATIONS FOR NUCLEOTIDES*

Adenosine monophosphate (adenylic acid)	AMP
Adenosine diphosphate	ADP
Adenosine triphosphate	ATP
Guanosine monophosphate (guanylic acid)	GMP
Guanosine diphosphate	GDP
Guanosine triphosphate	GTP
Cytidine monophosphate (cytidylic acid)	CMP
Cytidine diphosphate	CDP
Cytidine triphosphate	CTP
Uridine monophosphate (uridylic acid)	UMP
Uridine diphosphate	UDP
Uridine triphosphate	UTP
Thymidine monophosphate (thymidylic acid)	TMP
Thymidine diphosphate	TDP
Thymidine triphosphate	TTP

* The above notation assumes that the phosphate grouping in the monophosphates is attached to the sugar in the 5′ position. The three possible monophosphates may be distinguished thus: 5′-AMP, 3′-AMP, 2′-AMP.

The deoxyribonucleotides corresponding to AMP, GMP, and CMP may be indicated by the abbreviations *d*AMP, *d*GMP and *d*CMP.

Nucleic Acids

These are polynucleotides and have the general structure:

```
         Base                 Base                 Base
          |                    |                    |
· · ·5′-Sugar—Phosphate—Sugar—Phosphate—Sugar-3′· · ·
```

Figures 9–1, 9–2, and 9–3 give a more precise chemical picture of the way nucleotides are linked together to form polynucleotides.

In DNA, the sugar is deoxyribose, whereas in RNA it is ribose. Both of the nucleic acids have four major types of bases; two purines and two pyrimidines. Three of these are found in both DNA and RNA. DNA and RNA contain the purines adenine (A) and guanine (G), as well as the pyrimidine cytosine (C). RNA has, in addition, the pyrimidine uracil (U), whereas DNA has the closely related pyrimidine, 5-methyluracil (thymine (T)). The number of base units in nucleic acids may be as high as 10^7 to 10^8 in chromosomal DNA strands and as low as 80 in transfer RNA. Although irregularity exists in the total number of purine and pyrimidine bases in DNA from different sources, for most DNA the number of A units has been found equal to T units, and of G units to C units. That is, the ratio A/T or G/C equals 1. Such a simple relationship does not exist for bases in RNA except for some viral RNA's. The importance of this numerical

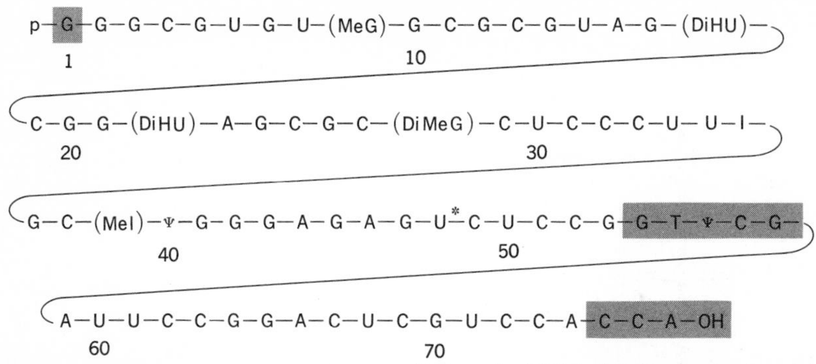

Figure 9–5. The structure of an alanine—specific transfer RNA isolated from yeast as determined by R. W. Holley and coworkers. Features common to all *t*RNA's are indicated by shading. Abbreviations: p and · are used interchangeably to represent a phosphate residue; A·, adenosine 3′-phosphate; C·, cytidine 3′-phosphate; COH, cytidine (with the free 3′-hydroxyl group emphasized); DiHU·, 5,6-dihydrouridine 3′-phosphate; DiMeG·, N^2-dimethylguanosine 3′-phosphate; I·, inosine 3′-phosphate; MeG·, 1-methylguanosine 3′-phosphate; MeI·, 1-methylinosine 3′-phosphate; ψ·, pseudouridine 3′-phosphate; T·, ribothymidine 3′-phosphate; U·, uridine 3′-phosphate; U*·, a mixture of U·, and DiHU·.

relationship of base units in relation to the over-all structure of nucleic acids will become apparent in later sections.

The specific sequential arrangement of purine and pyrimidine bases in nucleic acids has proven exceedingly difficult to determine. Only in the case of one nucleic acid, the alanine specific *t*RNA of yeast (Figure 9–5), is the base sequence known.

DNA Structure

Although the chemical formula of DNA reveals that it is a chain (Figure 9–2), this does not in itself tell us the shape of the molecule. The chain has many single bonds around which it may rotate and it thus might assume any one of countless shapes. The specific way coiling occurs and the shape of DNA was first suggested in 1953 by J. D. Watson and F. H. C. Crick. The molecular model they suggested was based in large part on the X-ray diffraction studies of M. Wilkins and his associates, who have subsequently furnished proof for the correctness of the model.

The Watson-Crick model for DNA (Figure 9–6) consists of two polynucleotide chains that run in opposite directions and are helically wrapped around each other, with the sugar-phosphate chain on the outside and the purine and pyrimidine bases on the inside. The purine and pyrimidine bases from the two chains are joined to form specific pairs. In any pair there must always be one big base (purine) and one little one (pyrimidine), Figure 9–7. A pair of pyrimidines is too short to bridge the gap between the two chains, and a pair of purines is too big to fit into the space. Thus, adenine fits well with thymine, and guanine with cytosine. The base-to-base linkages are hydrogen bonds. These act as horizontal supports across

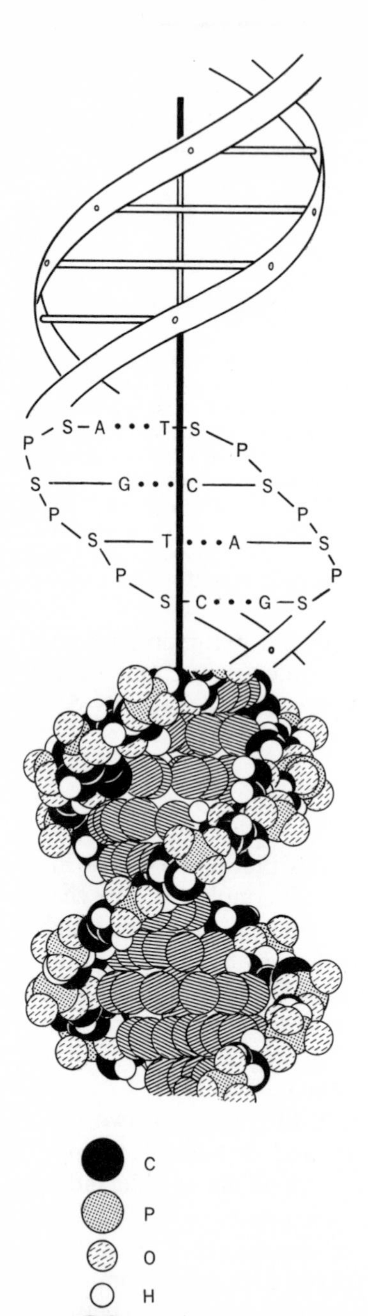

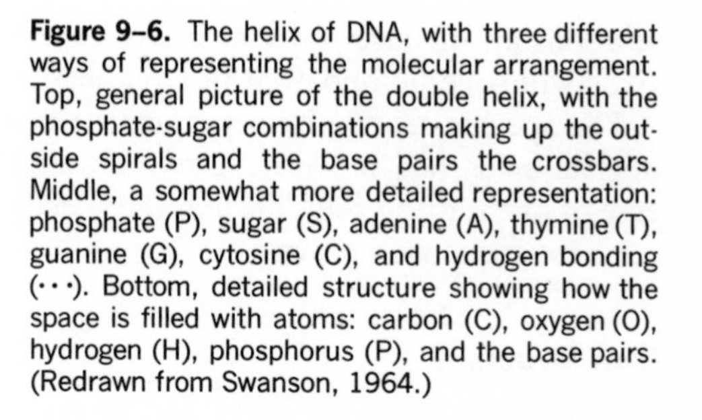

Figure 9–6. The helix of DNA, with three different ways of representing the molecular arrangement. Top, general picture of the double helix, with the phosphate-sugar combinations making up the outside spirals and the base pairs the crossbars. Middle, a somewhat more detailed representation: phosphate (P), sugar (S), adenine (A), thymine (T), guanine (G), cytosine (C), and hydrogen bonding (· · ·). Bottom, detailed structure showing how the space is filled with atoms: carbon (C), oxygen (O), hydrogen (H), phosphorus (P), and the base pairs. (Redrawn from Swanson, 1964.)

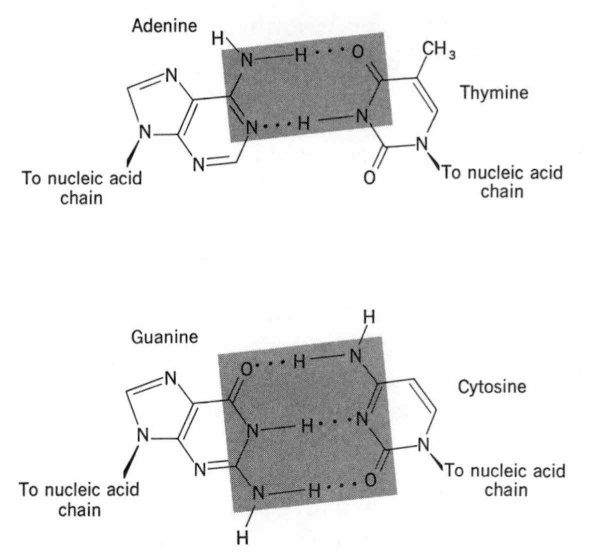

Figure 9–7. The pairing of thymine and adenine (top) and cytosine and guanine (bottom) by means of hydrogen bonding as in DNA.

the axis of the double helix and hold the two chains together. These chains are thus complementary and antiparallel so that the arrangement of bases on one strand fixes the arrangement of the other. If the bases along one strand are arranged in the order A—G—C—T—C—A, the opposite bases on the complementary strand will be T—C—G—A—G—T.

Base pairing, the base-to-base linkage, is illustrated in Figure 9–7. The ability of these bases to be bridged by hydrogen bonds, as shown, depends on the existence of the particular isomeric form indicated, e.g.,

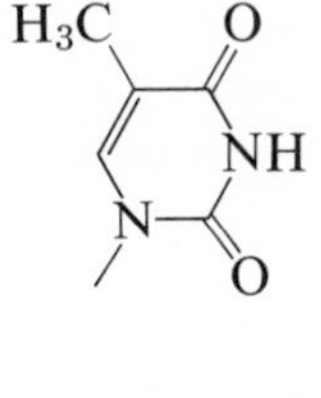

rather than

H3C OH
N
N
O

This hydrogen bonding that employs one particular form of each base is now believed to be of fundamental importance in nucleic acid interactions.

Several pieces of evidence, in addition to the X-ray data, pointed to the model Watson and Crick proposed. A stoichiometric equality between the sum of purine and pyrimidine bases in DNA had earlier been demonstrated. That is, an equivalence had been shown in the adenine and thymine content of DNA, and also an equivalence of guanine and cytosine. Further, titration studies suggested that the polynucleotide chains comprising DNA were joined together through hydrogen bonding between the base residues.

X-ray investigations have provided additional quantitative information about the DNA helix. The bases lie in a plane approximately at right angles to the helical axis. There are ten bases in each turn of the helix, separated by an axial distance of 3.4 Å, and each turn has a height of 34 Å, giving the helix an exact tenfold screw axis.

Recently it has become apparent that in certain viruses DNA consists not of two interwoven strands, but of only one strand. This single-stranded DNA is able to function as hereditary material just as does double-stranded DNA. For example, the DNA of bacteriophage ϕX174 (lab code number) has been shown to contain adenine, thymine, guanine, and cytosine in a ratio of 1.0 to 1.3 to 0.98 to 0.75, respectively. This is not the equivalence expected ($A/T = 1$, $G/C = 1$) for double-stranded DNA. A second remarkable feature of the ϕX174 DNA is that the single strand appears to be closed on itself in the form of a ring.

The total length and molecular weight of most forms of DNA is still uncertain. One of the smallest known chromosomes is the single-stranded DNA of ϕX174. This consists of approximately 5500 nucleotides in a linear array. The DNA on the entire chromosome of T2 bacteriophage has also been generally characterized. This DNA has a molecular weight of about 1.2 to 1.6×10^8 and is composed of a double helix comprising about 200,000 nucleotide pairs. Recently, autoradiographs of DNA from the bacterium *Escherichia coli* have been obtained. These show the DNA to be unbroken threads about 400 microns (μ) long, corresponding to a molecular weight of the order of 10^9, and suggest that the entire *E. coli* chromosome might be in one circular piece (see Figure 11–1).

RNA Structure

Four functionally distinct RNA's are known: (1) transfer RNA (also called soluble RNA), (2) template or messenger RNA, (3) high molecular weight or ribosomal RNA, (4) virus RNA. Thus, any discussion of the structure of ribonucleic acid must take into account the RNA type. All forms of RNA have in common the sugar ribose, and the absence of thymine (although *t*RNA does contain ribothymine) as a constituent base.

Transfer RNA (*t*RNA) has also been called soluble and acceptor RNA. "Soluble RNA" refers to its physicochemical property of extreme solubility in contrast to viral and ribosomal RNA. Acceptor and transfer RNA refer to the amino acid-carrying role this species of RNA plays in protein biosynthesis. Unfractionated preparations of transfer RNA consist of a mixture of different molecular species with distinct base sequences, each capable of combining with only one of the 20 commonly occurring amino acids. A *t*RNA molecule contains between 70–80 nucleotides and has a molecular weight of approximately 25,000. In addition to the bases commonly found in other ribonucleic acids, many methylated purines and pyrimidine residues and abnormal bases such as 5-ribosyl uracil nucleotide (abbreviated ψ) occur in *t*RNA. All transfer RNA's seem to have in common a terminal group —cytidylyl—cytidylyl—adenosine (C—C—A) and a common internal sequence G—T—ψ—C—G. The terminal adenosine has a ribose unit with free 2′- and 3′-hydroxyl groups to one of which an activated amino acid becomes attached (Figure 11–1). The recent determination of the nucleotide sequence in alanine *t*RNA by R. W. Holley and his coworkers (Figure 9–5) parallels the determination of the amino acid sequence in insulin by F. Sanger. Holley has provided the first molecular structure for a nucleic acid, just as Sanger did for a protein.

Template or messenger RNA (*m*RNA) has a primary structure complementary to a portion of one DNA strand. That is, a particular region of the DNA molecule is copied during the synthesis of this RNA. For example, a DNA segment A—T—C—G—T is transcribed into U—A—G—C—A in *m*RNA structure. As will be seen in Chapter Eleven, this copy process involves base pairing properties, i.e., the RNA produced has complementary bases to the DNA copied (i.e., U for A, G for C, etc.). The size of

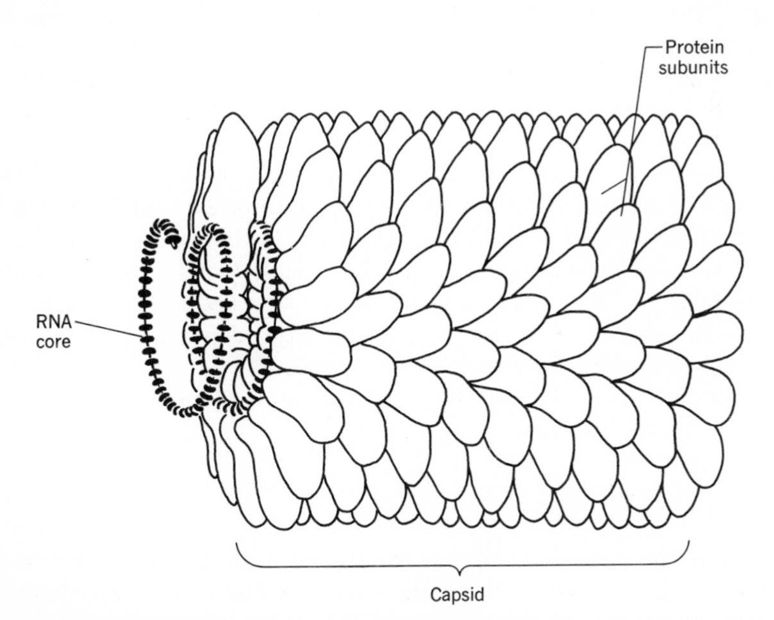

Figure 9–8. A drawing of the structure of tobacco mosaic virus. The helical chain represents RNA and the loaves protein molecules (Klug and Caspar, 1960).

*m*RNA is expected to vary considerably and will depend on the number and size of proteins it codes for.

High molecular weight RNA refers to the RNA not accounted for as transfer or messenger RNA, and is primarily ribosomal in origin. This RNA is the classical ribonucleic acid which served as a basis for early studies on RNA. In composition, high molecular weight RNA has no distinct features. It is single stranded and contains four major and several minor bases in a proportion that varies considerably and depends on the biological source of the RNA. Two sizes of *r*RNA are found in all ribosomes (page 175) where they are an integral component and can not be removed without destruction of the ribosome structure. The smaller *r*RNA molecule, which is found in the smaller ribosome subunit, has a molecular weight of about one-half million, whereas the larger *r*RNA, a component of the larger ribosomal subunit, has a molecular weight of about one million.

The structure of RNA in solution depends on temperature and ionic strength. At high temperatures or at low salt concentration, RNA tends to form random coils. At room temperature and moderate ionic strength the RNA contains helical regions in which the bases are hydrogen bonded at least over part of the length of each chain.

Virus RNA includes the ribonucleic acid found in plant, animal, and bacterial viruses. Examples of these RNA-containing viruses are mosaic virus of tobacco (TMV), reo virus of mouse cells, and various bacteriophages. All of the viral RNA's are high molecular weight molecules. For example, tobacco mosaic virus RNA is a single strand of RNA wound into a helix. The helix has a radius of 40 Å and contains 49 nucleotides in each turn, repeating at intervals of 5.1 Å. The chain contains approximately 6400 nucleotides and when fully stretched would have a length of nearly 5 microns. The nucleic acid is intermeshed with a protective coating or sheath of protein. Together, the protein and nucleic acid form a highly organized rod-shaped virus particle (Figure 9–8). Reo virus, which is widespread among vertebrates, has recently been shown to contain double-stranded RNA. Just as in DNA, the double-stranded RNA helix has ten nucleotide residues per turn. There is current evidence that other viruses also contain double-stranded RNA.

A brief outline of the functional interrelations of the various kinds of nucleic acids is illustrated in Figure 9–9.

Biological Role of DNA

DNA is an informational molecule. The information it contains is *genetic:* the directions for the production of specific proteins and information for the propagation of the species in a relatively unvarying manner. DNA has two general functions: first, it must provide directions for self-

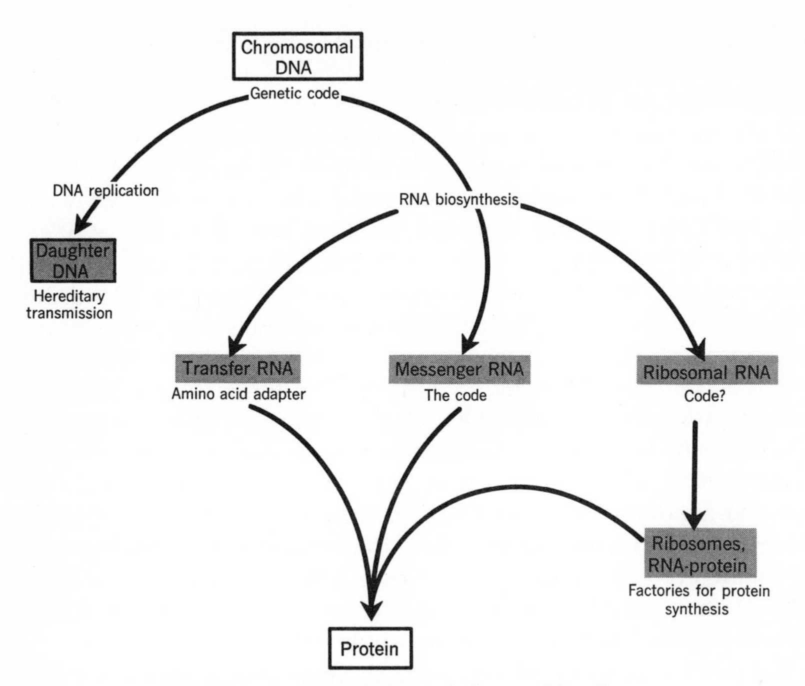

Figure 9–9. Nucleic acid interrelations and functions.

duplication during cell division so that its inherent information can be transmitted to daughter cells; and second, it must express its encoded information for metabolic function and control during the lifetime of the cell. These functions are mediated, respectively, via DNA-determined DNA replication or biosynthesis and DNA-determined *m*RNA biosynthesis. The biosynthetic relationships will be more fully developed in Chapter Eleven.

The central role of DNA in the propagation of the species and the determination of heritable characters has been deduced from innumerable converging experimental observations. Cytochemical studies have long indicated a localization of DNA in chromosomes. The DNA content of diploid (paired chromosomes present) somatic cells is constant from tissue in a single species but haploid or single chromosome (e.g., sperm) cells contain exactly half as much DNA. Mutagenic substances such as ultraviolet light appear to be more reactive with nucleic acids than with other biologically important macromolecules.

The first thread of experimental evidence for the control of characters and metabolism by DNA came from observations made by F. Griffith in 1928. Griffith injected into mice pneumococci without capsules (rough type), which are not virulent, together with killed pneumococci of a virulent strain which had capsules (smooth type). To his surprise, the tissues of the mice were soon teaming with live, virulent smooth pneumococci.

Since the dead smooth cells could not have come to life, it was evident that they contained a material which had endowed the rough pneumococci with the capacity to synthesize the capsule characteristic of smooth cells.

The chemical nature of the active principle which caused this transformation remained obscure until 1944 when O. T. Avery, C. M. MacLeod, and M. McCarty showed that the transforming factor was DNA and in fact that DNA extracted from encapsulated smooth strains of pneumococci could, on addition *in vitro,* transform rough cells into the smooth type. The smooth cells which developed could be propagated indefinitely in the smooth form, and produced DNA which could cause transformation to the smooth type. The pneumococcal DNA had therefore initiated its own replication as well as induced the specific inheritable property of capsule synthesis. The genetic stability of the transformable trait was highly suggestive of true gene transfer. The further demonstration that DNA alone, and not a protein or carbohydrate contaminant, could transform a cell into a variant has come from studies on transformation of pneumococci strains to drug resistance. These studies have shown that bacteria can be simultaneously transformed for more than one characteristic by using DNA with genetically linked markers. Experimental steps in the transformation of a bacterial culture are shown in Figure 9–10.

The manner in which DNA in the chromosomes reproduces itself was first suggested by Watson and Crick and is becoming biochemically under-

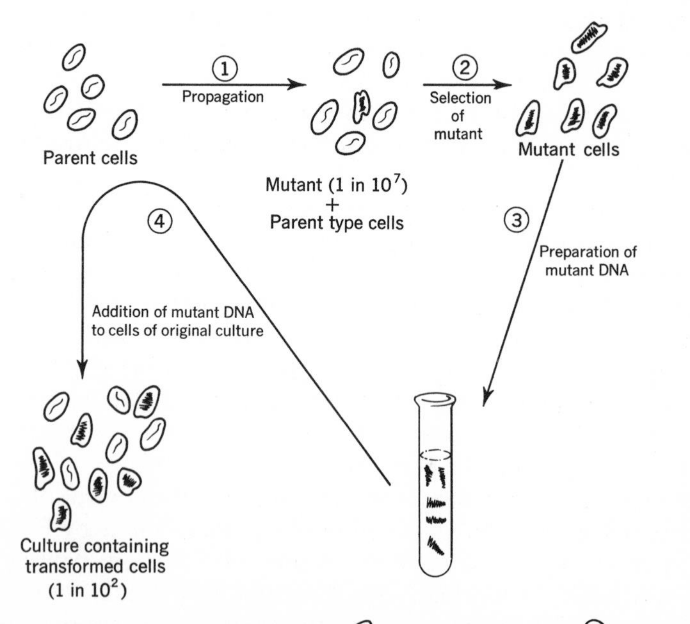

Figure 9–10. Transformation of bacterial cells into a mutant type with DNA from the mutant type.

stood (page 155). The way DNA exerts control on other metabolic processes is the exciting chapter of biochemistry which has begun to unfold in the 1960's (see page 152).

Biological Role of RNA

The various cellular forms of RNA (transfer, messenger, ribosomal) all appear to have a role in the translation of genetic information inherent in DNA into protein structure Figure 9–9.

Transfer RNA serves as an *adapter molecule* in protein biosynthesis. That is, its function is to adapt an amino acid to a polynucleotide template (messenger RNA). This occurs as follows. A specific enzyme attaches an amino acid, for example, leucine, to a transfer RNA molecule. Each molecule of transfer RNA contains an *anticodon,* in the form of a short sequence of bases, which enables it to recognize and pair with, a sequence of complementary bases, a *codon,* in *m*RNA. The *t*RNA base pairs with template or messenger RNA, thus bringing reactive amino acids to the template. By a series of chemical reactions the amino acids which are becoming lined up on the template polymerize to form polypeptide or protein.

Messenger, or template, RNA has been assigned a major role in protein synthesis. This RNA is synthesized on a DNA template in the cell nucleus and becomes associated with cytoplasmic ribosomes where it serves as a template for the lining up of amino acyl-*t*RNA molecules, just prior to polypeptide formation. Thus, messenger RNA directs the arrangement of amino acids in the polypeptide chain (page 160).

High molecular weight RNA, *r*RNA, occurs throughout the cell concentrated in the ribosomes (page 175). Since it is a structural component of the ribosome, a role in protein biosynthesis is suggested. The specific function of the RNA in these processes, however, has not been established.

Viral RNA serves the dual function of being the hereditary material of some viruses as well as the instruction sheet for subverting host metabolism toward production of virus particles. These functions have been deduced from studies on *infectious RNA* and virus *messenger RNA.* A major advance in our understanding of nucleic acid biology was the demonstration that free RNA isolated from TMV is infective in the absence of TMV protein. That is, purified RNA from TMV can induce lesions on tobacco leaves. The infectivity is destroyed by the nucleic acid hydrolyzing enzyme RNAse, but is not affected by anti-TMV serum, which reacts only with the protein coat, not RNA. TMV on the other hand is inactivated by antiserum but not by RNAse. Further, the RNA from a bacterial virus has been demonstrated to direct the synthesis of virus coat protein in an *in vitro* system. When RNA from bacteriophage f2 was used as messenger RNA in a protein-synthesizing system, virus coat protein was produced. In addition to its function as messenger RNA for coat protein synthesis, virus RNA also carries information for the formation of an RNA polymerase (page 157) which is responsible for the production of new virus RNA.

SUGGESTED READING

Brachet, J., *The Biological Role of Nucleic Acids,* Elsevier Publishing Co., New York, 1960.

Chargaff, E., *Essays on Nucleic Acids,* Elsevier Publishing Co., New York, 1963.

Crick, F. H. C., "The Structure of the Hereditary Material" in *The Physics and Chemistry of Life,* Scientific American (ed.), Simon and Schuster, Inc., New York, 1955.

Davidson, J. N., *The Biochemistry of the Nucleic Acids,* John Wiley & Sons, Inc., New York, 1960.

Doty, P., "Inside Nucleic Acids" in *The Harvey Lectures, 1959–1960,* Academic Press, Inc., New York, 1961.

Holley, R. W., "The Nucleotide Sequence of a Nucleic Acid," *Scientific American,* February, 1966.

Holley, R. W., *et al.,* "Structure of a Nucleic Acid" *Science, 147,* 1462 (1965).

Perutz, M. F., *Proteins and Nucleic Acids,* Elsevier Publishing Co., New York, 1962.

Stent, G. S., *Molecular Biology of Bacterial Viruses,* W. H. Freeman, Co., San Francisco, 1963.

Taylor, J. H., *Selected Papers on Molecular Genetics,* Academic Press, Inc., New York, 1965.

Watson, J. D., *Molecular Biology of the Gene,* W. A. Benjamin, Inc., New York, 1965.

Watson, J. D., and F. H. C. Crick, "Molecular Structure of Nucleic Acids" *Nature, 171,* 737 (1953).

Wilkins, M. H. F., "Molecular Configuration of Nucleic Acids" *Science, 140,* 941, (1963).

"It seems that in the field of biosynthesis we have a rare example of progress leading to simplification."

F. Lipmann, 1949

TEN

Principles of Biosynthesis

Introduction

Biosynthetic reactions account for formation of the many biochemical metabolites and biological macromolecules that are essential for life functions. The synthesis of citrate from oxaloacetate and acetyl CoA, Eq. (1), and carbamyl phosphate from CO_2, ATP, and ammonia, Eq. (2), are but

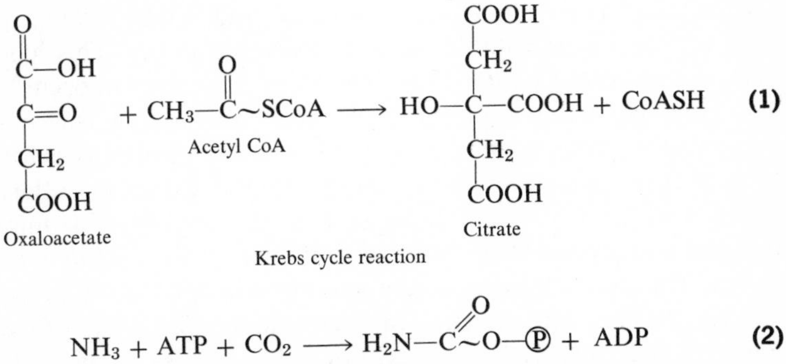

two of numerous biosynthetic reactions that result in the formation of simple metabolites. The formation of biological macromolecules from their simple constituents include: (1) DNA from deoxyribonucleotides,

(2) RNA from ribonucleotides, (3) proteins from amino acids, (4) glycogen from glucose, (5) fatty acids and fat from acetate.*

Although specific biosynthetic reactions are unique in their starting materials and products, it is, however, possible to generalize processes once considered hopelessly complex. All biosyntheses involve: (1) *group activation and transfer*—the energy problem, (2) *chain elongation,* (3) *patternization.*

A simple example that illustrates these points is the biosynthesis of glutathione, a tripeptide, from glutamic acid, cysteine, and glycine, Eq. (3).

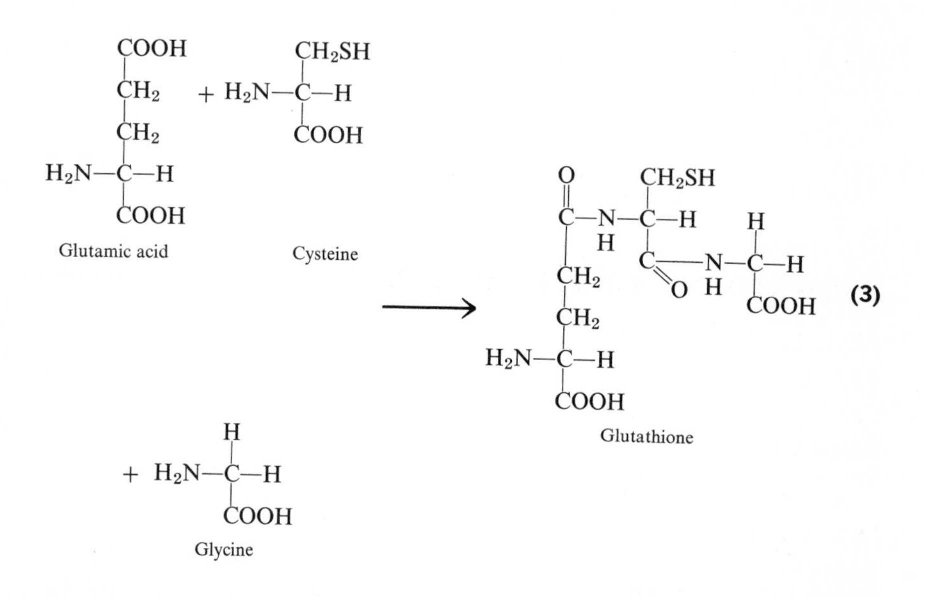

This reaction as written has a positive ΔG and is thus thermodynamically unfavorable. The inevitable *energy problem* has arisen. This has been partially discussed in Chapter Five. How does chain growth occur? The chain can grow beginning with glutamic acid and adding, successively and sequentially, cysteine and then glycine. Another possibility is for the chain to grow from glycine toward glutamic acid. Or, rather than the sequential addition of the subunits, a dimer such as glutamyl cysteine might be synthesized and glycine then attached to it. The chain *elongation problem* has arisen. The establishment of the specific sequential arrangement of glutamic, cysteine, and glycine in glutathione, Glu—Cys—Gly, involves *patternization.* The cell has ways for solving these three problems. The biochemical principles used by the cell will be described and illustrated in the following sections.

* Strictly speaking, fatty acids and fats are not in the *macro* structural class with DNA, protein, etc., but for biosynthetic parallels we have included fatty acids and fats with this group.

The Energy Problem

Anabolic processes might seem to be little more than the reversal of catabolic procedures since a biochemical reaction is catalyzed by an enzyme equally well in either direction, Eq. (4).

$$A \xrightleftharpoons{\text{enzyme}} B \qquad \textbf{(4)}$$

If the breakdown or hydrolysis of a macromolecule, for example, protein, is an enzymatic reaction, Eq. (5),

$$\text{Protein} \xrightarrow{\text{protease}} \text{Amino acids} + \text{Peptides} \qquad \textbf{(5)}$$

the formation of protein might be considered to occur by simply the reverse process, Eq. (6):

$$\text{Amino acids} + \text{Peptides} \xrightarrow{\text{protease}} \text{Protein} \qquad \textbf{(6)}$$

It is clear, however, that this does not occur; proteases are not responsible for protein synthesis. Furthermore, nucleic acid synthesis is not a reversal of nuclease action, and fats, carbohydrates, amino acids, steroids, etc., are not synthesized by the reverse of their breakdown pathways. A consideration of biochemical thermodynamics suggests why this is so. If the degradative reaction has a negative ΔG, it follows that a biosynthetic reaction, if it were a simple reverse process, would have a positive ΔG. As we have pointed out in Chapter Five, however, a reaction which has a positive ΔG is endergonic and can occur only with the input of energy. We must, therefore, consider coupling an exergonic reaction, e.g.,

$$\text{ATP} \longrightarrow \text{AMP} + \text{Ⓟ—O}\sim\text{Ⓟ}$$

with the endergonic reactions of synthesis. The parallel (Figure 10–1) between the technique the organic chemist uses to drive reactions and the

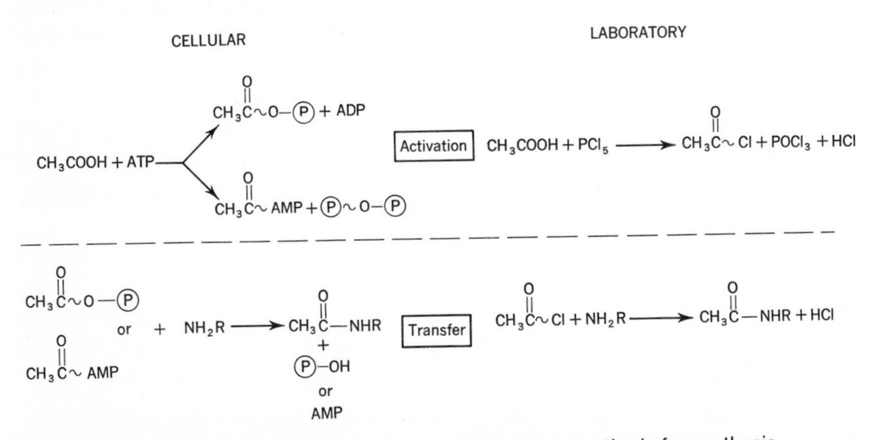

Figure 10–1. Similarities of cellular and laboratory methods for synthesis.

method of the cell was discussed on page 69. The reagents, for example, PCl_5, and conditions used by the chemist are less mild and less specific than those employed by the cell. The procedures, however, are analogous in that they both involve the formation of an *activated intermediate.*

Group Activation

A molecule containing a carboxyl (—COOH), phosphoryl ($—PO_3H_2$), or sulfuryl ($—SO_3H$) group is usually initially prepared for a reaction in cellular biosynthesis by formation of its phosphate or nucleoside monophosphate (NMP) derivative. This preparation occurs by the interaction of the molecule with a nucleoside triphosphate, such as ATP, UTP, etc. Two reactions of biological importance that occur between such a molecule and a nucleoside triphosphate are:

1. Pyrophosphate (Ⓟ—O~Ⓟ) elimination with R~nucleoside monophosphate formation.
2. Nucleoside diphosphate (NDP) elimination with R~phosphate formation.

This is termed *group activation.* A compound with a high potential for group transfer, i.e., an *activated compound,* is formed. Biosynthetic reactions, as a general rule, result in pyrophosphate elimination. As soon as it is made, the pyrophosphate is enzymatically broken-down to two moles of phosphate thereby making impossible a reversal of the biosynthetic reactions.

The similarities of the diverse group activation reactions are shown in Figure 10–2. At the top is the energy source, a nucleoside triphosphate. The pyrophosphate or nucleoside diphosphate elimination reaction results in the *active intermediate* located in the center. *Acceptor molecules* are compounds to which the activated R-group becomes attached during subsequent synthetic reactions. For example, acceptors can be growing chains of macromolecules, e.g., protein and carbohydrates, in addition to molecules that are direct acceptors, such as steroids and polysaccharides, which accept sulfate.

The biochemical value of the activated forms of R is that these activated intermediates have a greater tendency to interact with an acceptor compound, Y, than would R alone. That is, the ΔG of Eq. (7) is more negative,

$$R{\sim}O{-}Ⓟ + Y^- \longrightarrow R{-}Y + Ⓟ{-}O^- \qquad (7)$$

than that of Eq. (8),

$$R + Y \longrightarrow R{-}Y \qquad (8)$$

Activation reactions that release pyrophosphate, Ⓟ~O—Ⓟ, are key reactions in the synthesis of macromolecules. These reactions are rendered

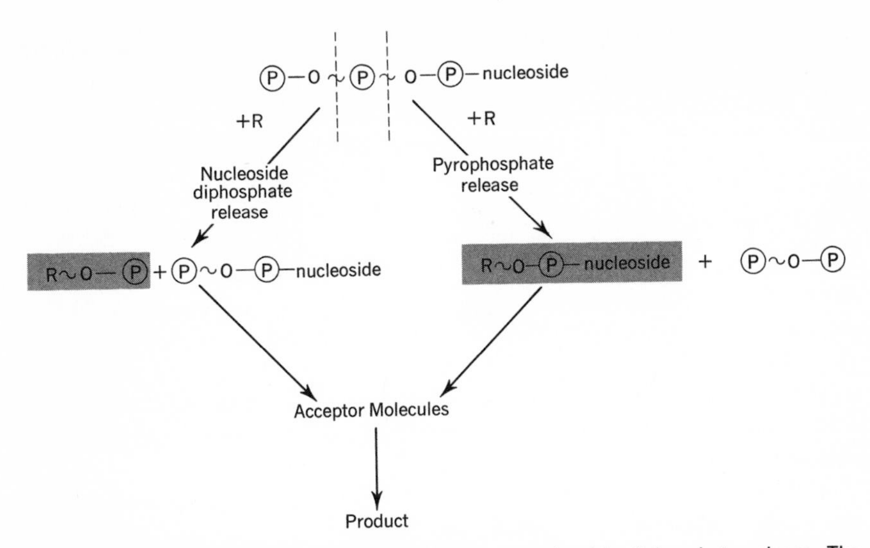

Figure 10–2. Group activation by pyrophosphate or nucleoside diphosphate release. The group R generally contains a carboxyl, phosphoryl, or sulfuryl group which becomes linked to Ⓟ by a ~ bond. R reacts with a nucleoside triphosphate to form a phosphate or nucleotide derivative, the activated intermediate which is shaded. Subsequently, transfer to an acceptor molecule occurs and product is formed.

irreversible and thus thermodynamically more favorable by the widespread occurrence of pyrophosphatase. Essentially, pyrophosphatase breaks down pyrophosphate, Eq. (9),

$$\underset{\text{Pyrophosphate}}{\text{HOH} + \text{Ⓟ}\sim\text{O}\text{—Ⓟ}} \xrightarrow{\text{pyrophosphatase}} \underset{\text{Inorganic phosphate}}{2\text{Ⓟ—OH}} \quad (9)$$

making a pyrophosphate dependent reversal of synthetic reactions impossible. This reaction has a large negative ΔG; -8 kcal/mole.

Chain Elongation

The formation of larger molecules by the addition of small activated units to pre-existing molecules is the second basic step in biosynthesis. This build-up of larger molecules may occur by one of two basic procedures:

1. Coenzymes function as *carriers* of activated molecular subunits.
2. Carriers are not involved; chain growth occurs by condensation or addition of similar molecular units to form more complex molecules.

Figure 10–3 summarizes some of the important coenzymes and the biosynthetic reactions in which they are involved. Although detailed

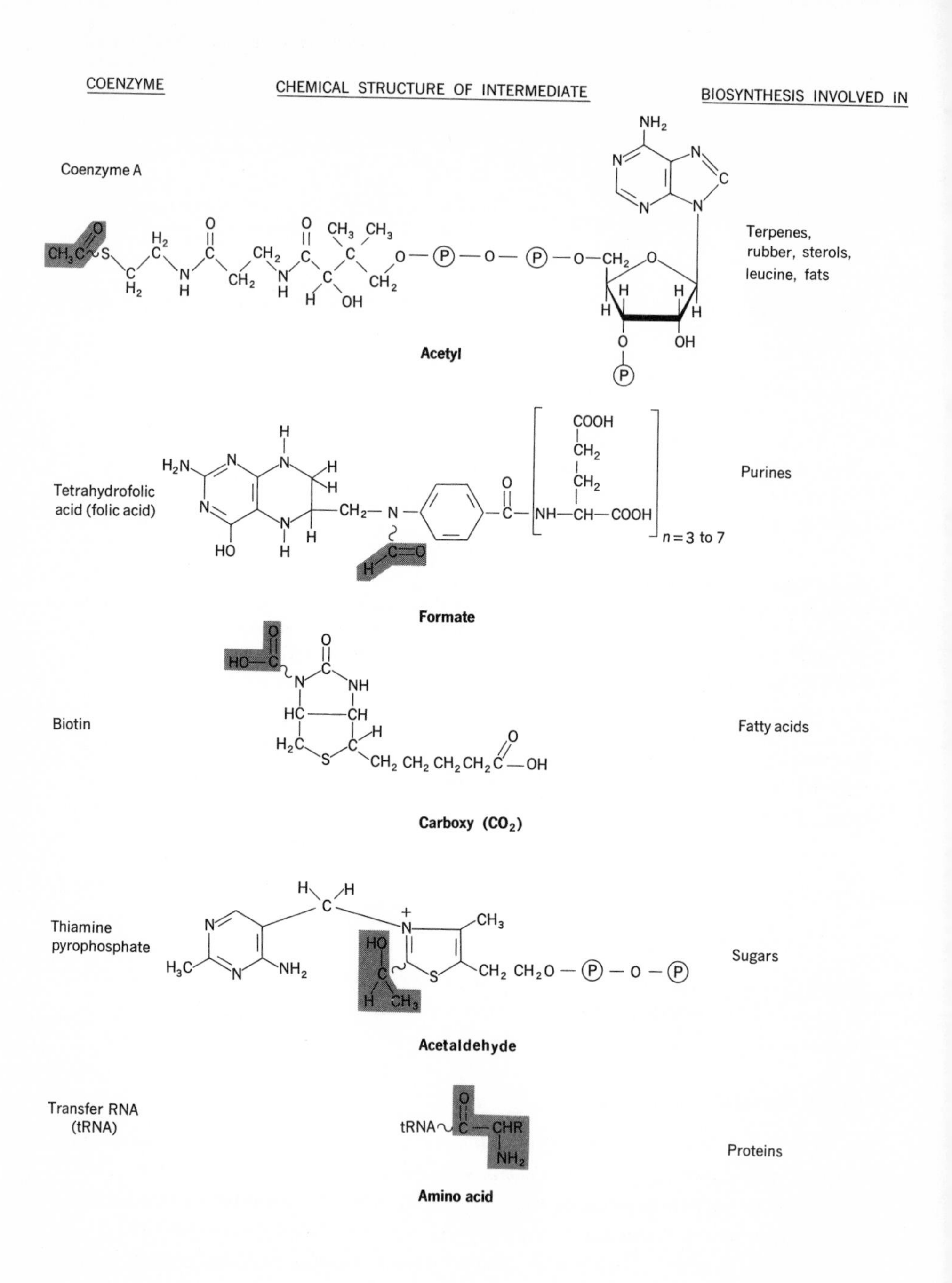
COENZYME
CHEMICAL STRUCTURE OF INTERMEDIATE
BIOSYNTHESIS INVOLVED IN
Coenzyme A
Acetyl
Terpenes, rubber, sterols, leucine, fats
Tetrahydrofolic acid (folic acid)
Formate
n=3 to 7
Purines
Biotin
Carboxy (CO2)
Fatty acids
Thiamine pyrophosphate
Acetaldehyde
Sugars
Transfer RNA (tRNA)
Amino acid
Proteins

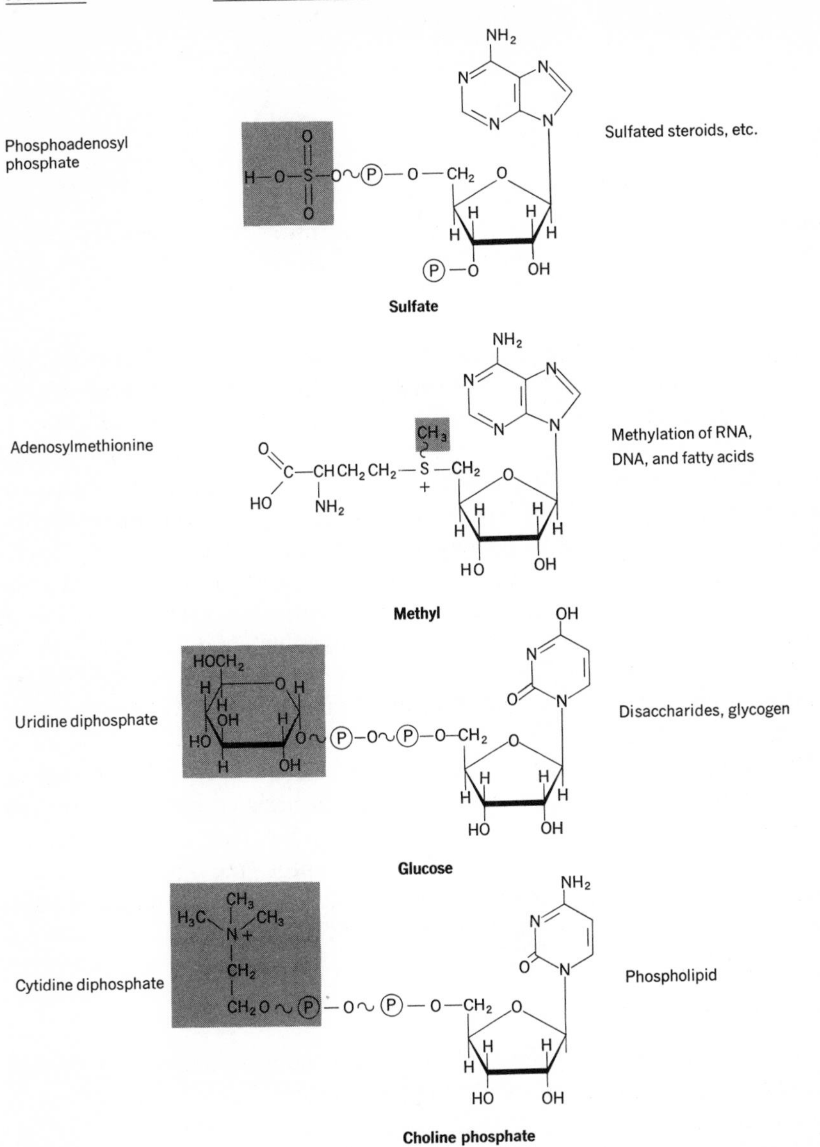

Figure 10–3. Coenzymes in biosynthesis. The "active" group is indicated by shading and bold-face.

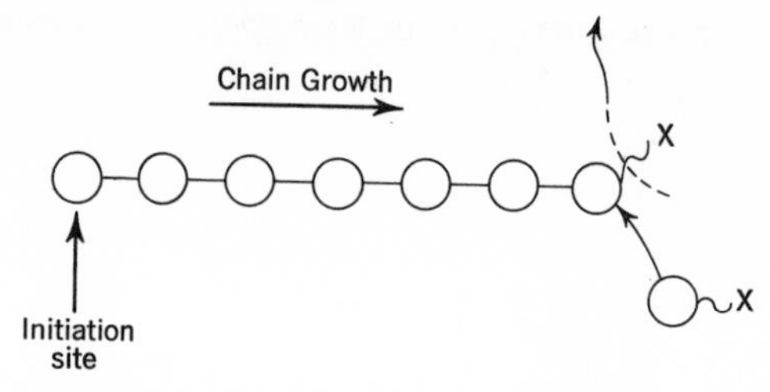

Figure 10–4. Essential aspects of chain growth. Growth begins at an initiation site and activated subunits, ◯∿X, add linearly.

discussion of the roles these coenzymes play in biosynthesis is beyond the scope of this book, several must be briefly mentioned in connection with the chain elongation mechanism. The *active methyl* of adenosylmethionine is used in the methylation of amino groups, for example, the amino groups in the bases of some nucleic acids. *Active carbon* fragments, C_1 units, are transferred by folic acid and are used, for example, in purine biosynthesis. Two carbon units carried by coenzyme A are used in building up the backbone of long chain carbon molecules, such as carotenoids, terpenes, rubber, sterols, and steroid hormones. The *active* CO_2 attached to biotin participates in numerous carboxylation reactions (e.g., acetyl CoA to malonyl CoA, Chapter Eleven). The roles of uridine diphosphate and cytidine diphosphate derivatives and also transfer RNA will be discussed in Chapter Eleven.

Biosynthesis without the involvement of carriers occurs in the case of many simple metabolites as well as in the synthesis of bacterial cell wall peptides, and in the synthesis of DNA and RNA (see Chapter Eleven). Activated groups are transferred to an acceptor, the growing polymer chain (Figure 10–4). The macromolecule is formed by the terminal addition of monomers and is synthesized linearly.

Patternization

The building up of specific and unique molecular structures, by joining a number of dissimilar units through a uniform linking mechanism is *patternization.*

All cellular macromolecules have particular surface and structural patterns that give proteins, nucleic acids, and polysaccharides their individualities. The basis of these features is the fixed sequential arrangement of the constituent subunits. For example, the biological and chemical properties of the simple tripeptide glutathione depend on the arrangement of three amino acids in a definite sequence, namely:

Glutamic—Cysteine—Glycine.

No other sequential arrangement results in a molecule with the unique biological activity of glutathione. Such simple molecular structures, as well as those of complex macromolecules, are biologically formed, with only occasional variance. Little is known about the detailed way this occurs. There are, however, general concepts about patternization which have received experimental support and can now be presented (Figure 10–5).

Deoxyribonucleic acid—the genetic material—is the primary determinant of the pattern for all biosynthetic processes and their products. Thus, DNA of the cell nucleus appears to be capable of determining the pattern of all new DNA as well as RNA synthesized intracellularly. The pattern written in *m*RNA (the *code*) is translated into the primary amino acid sequence of proteins.

At present there appears to be no way of directly translating the nucleotide sequence in DNA into the structural sequence of a fat or polysaccharide. Presumably, the structures of fats and polysaccharides are dependent on the availability of precursors (fatty acids and sugars) and the presence of the enzymes involved in fat and polysaccharide synthesis. It is the composition of these protein enzymes that corresponds to the DNA nucleotide sequence, and it is through these enzymes that genetic control is exerted on fat and polysaccharide structure.

The flow of patternization information can be summarized as shown in Eq. (10).

$$\text{DNA} \longrightarrow \text{RNA} \longrightarrow \text{Protein} \begin{cases} \nearrow \text{Fats} \\ \searrow \text{Carbohydrates} \end{cases} \qquad (10)$$

Two general mechanisms employed by the cell for patternization are: (1) *assembly line mechanism* and (2) *template mechanism.* The assembly line procedure is definitely of importance for the synthesis of small molecules, and it is also of importance in determining larger molecular organization, for example, sterols and bacterial cell walls.

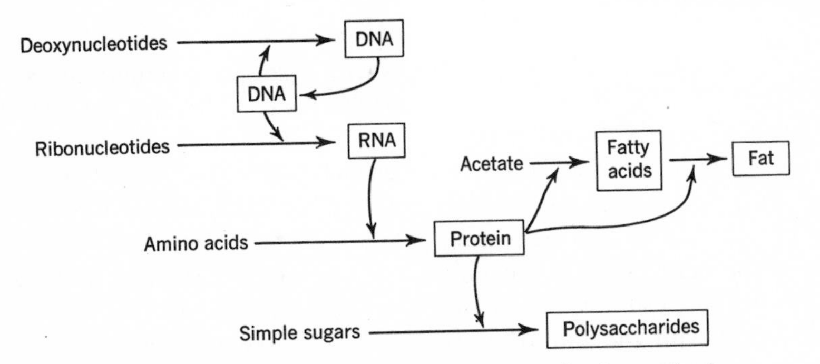

Figure 10–5. Patternization control of macromolecular synthesis.

The template process of regulating patternization has been implicated in the biosynthesis of nucleic acids and, indirectly, proteins (Chapter Eleven). The characteristics of these two mechanisms are illustrated in Figures 10–6 and 10–7.

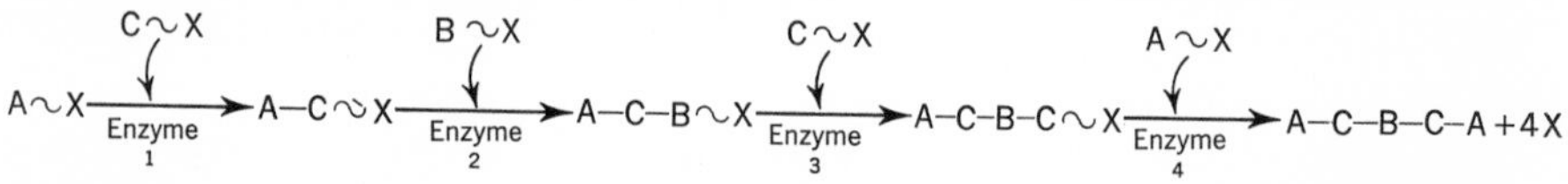

$$A\sim X \xrightarrow[\text{Enzyme 1}]{C\sim X} A{-}C\sim X \xrightarrow[\text{Enzyme 2}]{B\sim X} A{-}C{-}B\sim X \xrightarrow[\text{Enzyme 3}]{C\sim X} A{-}C{-}B{-}C\sim X \xrightarrow[\text{Enzyme 4}]{A\sim X} A{-}C{-}B{-}C{-}A + 4X$$

Figure 10–6. Assembly line patternization mechanism. Enzymes 1, 2, 3, and 4 operate sequentially and have specificity for A ~ X, A—C ~ X, etc., and the unit to be added. Many different polymerizing enzymes are involved.

Biological assembly line mechanisms operate as do their industrial analogs. At points along the biochemical assembly line a specific enzyme adds a subunit in a definite manner to a molecule which grows more complex as it proceeds from one enzyme to the next. Generally, the number of different enzymes involved is equal to the number of linkages formed. No subunit addition is made unless the preceding enzyme has performed its role. These multienzyme systems are of great importance in establishing a pattern or sequential arrangement on a relatively small scale, e.g., glutathione.

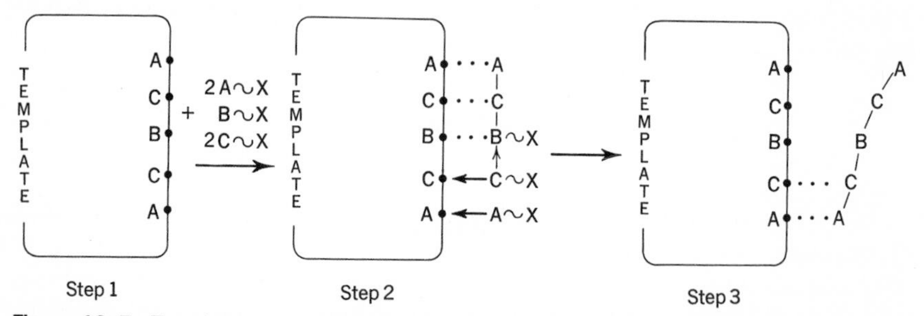

Figure 10–7. Template patternization mechanism. In step 2 the reactants line up on the template and polymerization begins. Release from the template occurs in step 3. One polymerizing enzyme is involved.

In the template mechanism, residues with high group potentials (R∼X) are lined up by specific units or by a specific space pattern of the template. A chemical reaction, usually beginning at one end of the template, occurs with the formation of a linkage between each successive activated residue. The same polymerizing enzyme is involved for each linkage formed, and the elimination of the activating group, X, occurs concomitantly. This over-all process results in the addition of subunits in a definite sequence to a growing macromolecular chain. Specific examples will be presented in connection with the biosynthesis of DNA, RNA, and protein, Chapter Eleven.

Biosynthesis of Several Micromolecules

Pyrimidine rings (page 122) are synthesized from NH_3, CO_2, and aspartic acid by a series of complicated reactions.

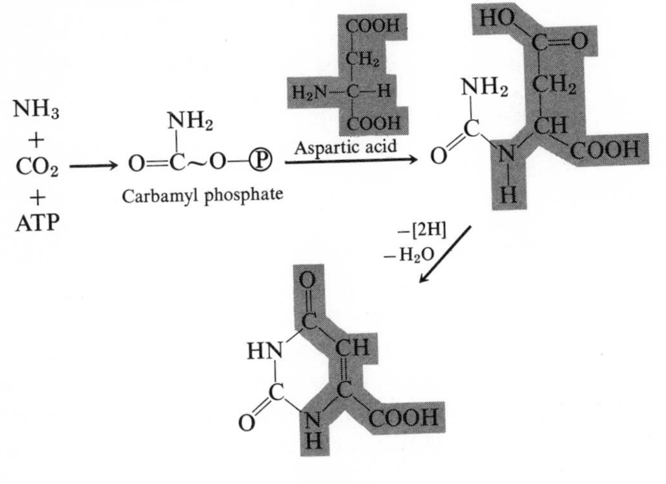

Orotic acid

The family of pyrimidine ribonucleotides (UMP, UTP, CTP, etc.) is derived from orotic acid through a series of further reactions.

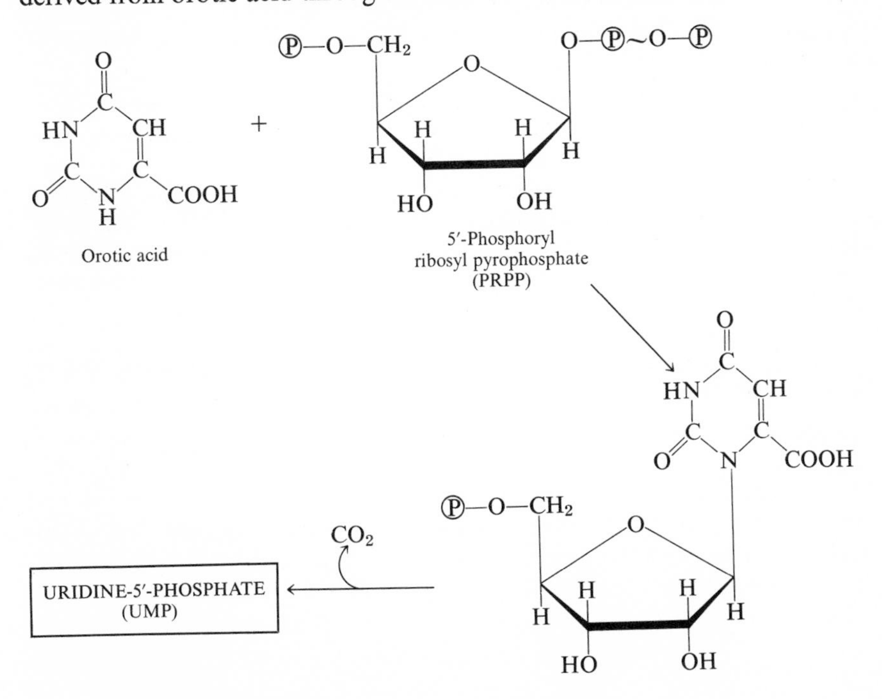

Purine biosynthesis is considerably more involved, and purine rings are derived from smaller fragments of aspartic acid, glycine, glutamine, formate, and CO_2.

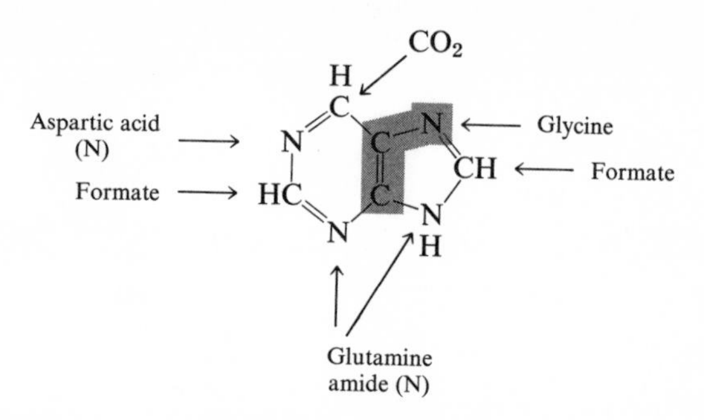

This biosynthesis is considerably more complicated than pyrimidine synthesis and differs in one particular aspect, namely, the purine ring is synthesized on the sugar-phosphate component. The 5′-phosphorylribosyl-1-pyrophosphate, which is an intermediate in pyrimidine synthesis, is the starting molecule on which the build-up of the purine ring occurs.

SUGGESTED READING

Buchanan, J. M., "The Enzymatic Synthesis of the Purine Nucleotides" in *The Harvey Lectures,* 1958–1959, Academic Press, Inc., New York, 1960.

Kalckar, H., "The Nature of Energetic Coupling in Biological Syntheses" *Chemical Reviews, 28,* 71 (1941).

Lipmann, F., "Attempts at the Formulation of Some Basic Biochemical Questions" in *Currents in Biochemical Research 1956,* D. E. Green (ed.), Interscience Publisher, Inc., New York, 1956, pp. 241–250.

Lipmann, F., "Biosynthetic Mechanisms" in *The Harvey Lectures,* 1948–1949, Charles C Thomas, Publisher, Springfield, Ill., 1949.

"... it has become clear during the past decade that proteases are not responsible for protein synthesis, that nucleic acid synthesis is not a reversal of nuclease action, that the paths of fatty acid synthesis and breakdowns are quite distinct."

A. Kornberg, 1962

ELEVEN

Macromolecular Biosynthesis

A variety of macromolecules are synthesized by the cell: the so-called informational molecules (DNA, RNA, and protein) and also the structurally and functionally important fats, starches, and glycogens.

DNA Makes RNA Makes Protein

The biosynthetic relationships among DNA, RNA, and protein are summarized in Figure 11–1. These interrelations were mentioned briefly on page 147 and also in the preceding chapter during the discussion of patternization.

Figure 11–1 shows the flow of genetic information from DNA terminating in new DNA, or from DNA to RNA, culminating in the production of a protein molecule. Three groups of reactions are diagrammed here:

Replication	↻ DNA
Transcription	DNA ⟶ RNA
Translation	RNA ⟶ Protein

In *replication,* free deoxyribonucleotides are assembled linearly to form an identical sequence or replica of the original DNA structure for hereditary transmission.

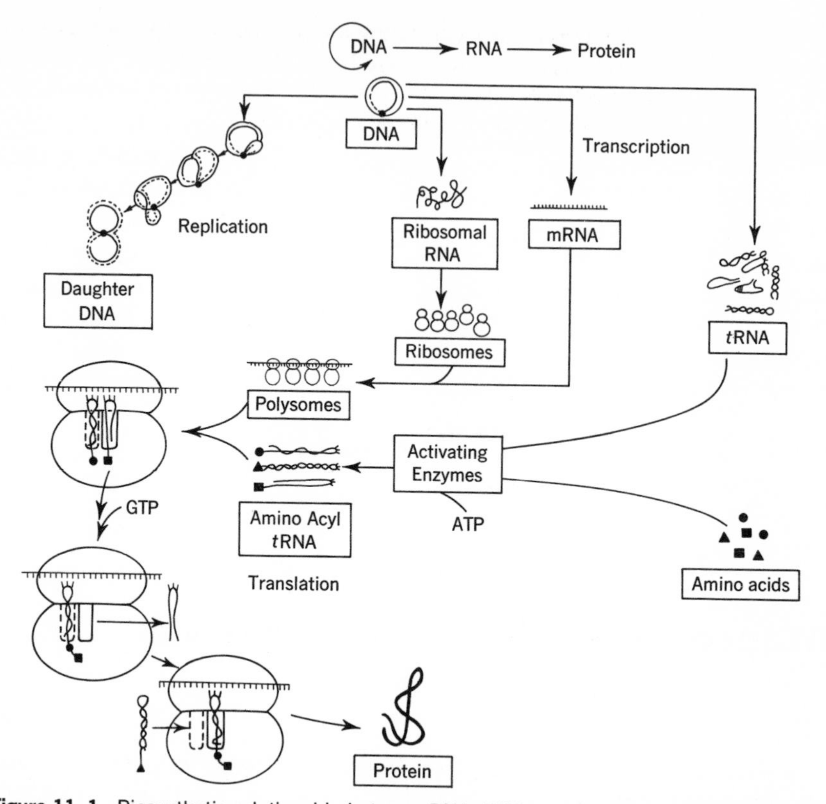

Figure 11–1. Biosynthetic relationship between DNA, RNA, and Protein. In this diagram the relationships that exist in the bacterial cell are outlined. A circular chromosome of DNA is shown and its replication diagrammed. The same relations are presumed to be true for other organisms although the chromosomal DNA may not be circular in its replicative form.

The first process in the over-all information transfer from DNA into protein structure is a *transcription.* The four unit (thymine, adenine, cytosine, and guanine) language of DNA is transcribed into the similar four symbol system (uracil, adenine, etc.) of the RNA's; the ribosomal (*r*RNA), messenger (*m*RNA), and transfer (*t*RNA) RNA's which are complementary to particular regions on DNA. Although all these RNA's are functional constituents of the final *translation* mechanism, it is the *m*RNA that carries the information specifying amino acid sequence in protein product.

In the *translation* process, the coded information coming originally from DNA, contained in *m*RNA, programs the ribosomes for synthesis of protein molecules. The step from messenger RNA to protein is a complex of reactions, all involved in the translation of the four unit nucleotide language of RNA into the twenty unit amino acid language of amino acid sequence in protein.

The synthesis of other macromolecules (fats, carbohydrates, etc.) is directly dependent on protein enzymes with specific structures and thus more indirectly related to the cell's hereditary material, DNA.

Replication—DNA Biosynthesis

The pattern of DNA replication and biosynthesis was proposed in outline form by Watson and Crick and was a direct consequence of their model for DNA (page 129). They suggested that the paired molecules of a DNA helix separated from one another (Figure 11–2). Free deoxyribonucleotides in the cell then became attached by hydrogen bonds to the nucleotide bases of these two DNA molecules. Adenine deoxyribonucleotide paired with thymine nucleotides in the DNA and guanine with cytosine. These lined-up

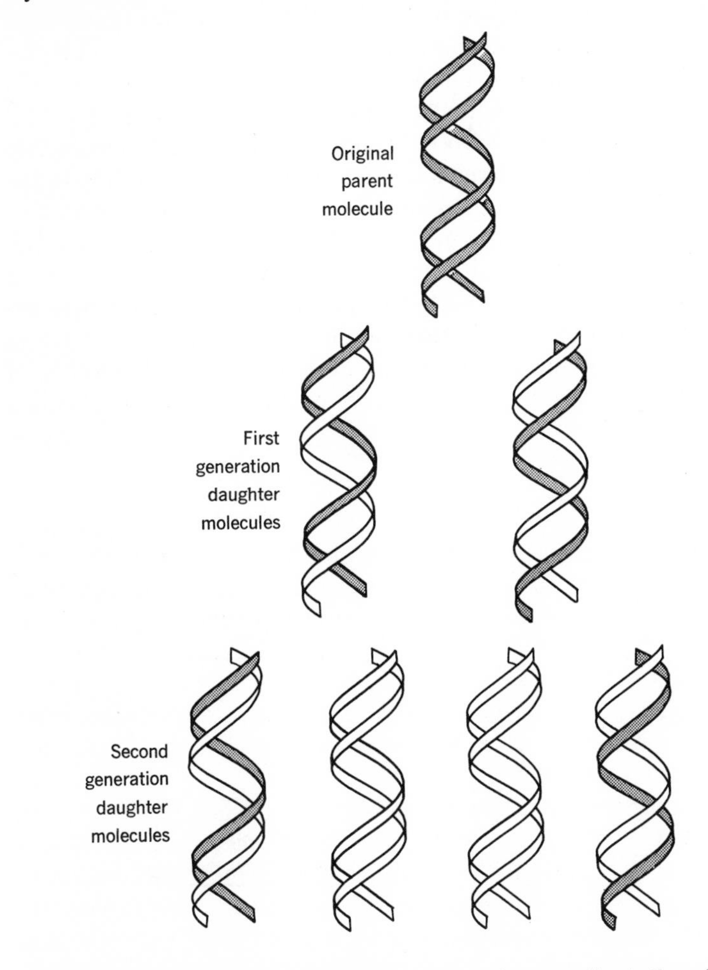

Figure 11–2. Illustration of the replication of DNA chains according to the scheme proposed by Watson and Crick. The white strands represent newly synthesized DNA.

nucleotides were then linked together by a polymerizing enzyme, and a new DNA strand formed which was the identical image of the strand that had separated from the molecule actually acting as a template.

Direct support for the scheme outlined in Figure 11–2 has been obtained by Meselson and Stahl and can be briefly summarized. When *Escherichia coli* bacteria were grown in a medium containing heavy nitrogen (N^{15}) as the sole nitrogen source, all the nucleotide bases of the bacterial DNA became isotopically labeled (Figure 11–3). The DNA could be isolated from the bacteria and, when centrifuged, this heavy DNA (N^{15}-DNA) sedimented faster than DNA (N^{14}-DNA) containing the lighter and normal isotope of nitrogen N^{14} (Figure 11–3). In this way the DNA's could be distinguished.

When bacteria containing the heavy N^{15}-DNA were transferred to a normal nitrogen-containing medium (N^{14} medium), they grew and reproduced using N^{14} to make their DNA. The DNA isolated after time for a doubling of bacteria to occur (first generation) was heavier than normal N^{14}-DNA but lighter than N^{15}-DNA. It appeared that the DNA molecules in these first generation bacteria were composed of a heavy N^{15} strand and a newly formed light N^{14}-DNA strand (Figure 11–3). The second generation of bacteria continuously grown on N^{14} medium had some DNA molecules which contained only N^{14}. These DNA molecules could have originated from replication of the N^{14} strand of DNA in first generation bacteria. Also present in second generation bacteria were N^{14}-N^{15} hybrid DNA molecules containing one strand of N^{14}-DNA and another of N^{15}-DNA. These N^{14}-N^{15}-DNA molecules could arise from replication

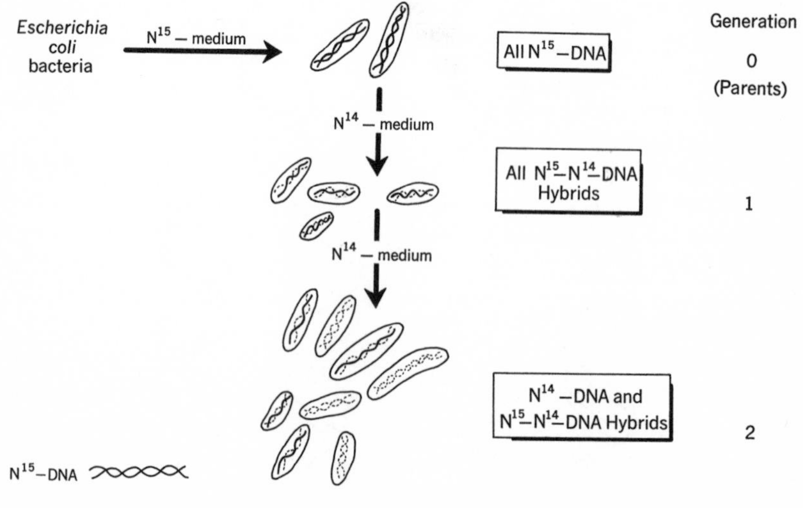

Figure 11–3. DNA replication in bacteria. Meselson and Stahl experiment.

of the N^{15}-DNA strands in first generation bacteria with N^{14} nucleotides. In successive generations the proportion of light N^{14} molecules progressively increased.

The mechanism of DNA biosynthesis has been worked out primarily by A. Kornberg and his associates. The equation for the enzymatic synthesis of DNA is:

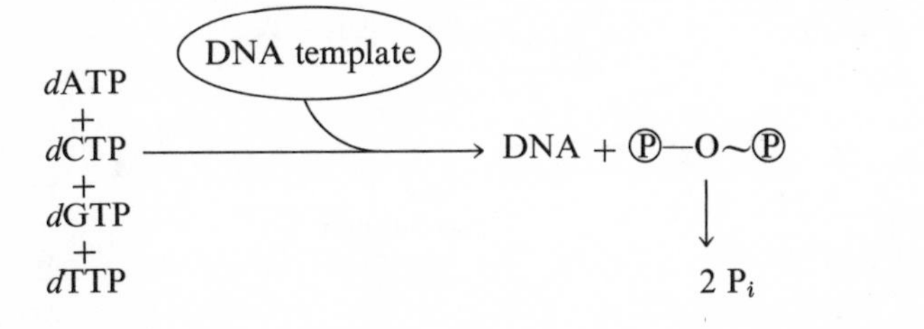

An enzyme called *DNA polymerase* catalyzes a reaction in which deoxyribonucleotides are linked together. Deoxyribonucleoside triphosphates are precursors for synthesis, and pyrophosphate, which increases the group potential of *d*Tp, *d*Ap, *d*Cp, and *d*Gp, is eliminated during the reaction. The characteristics of the DNA product are determined by the DNA template present. For example, if the DNA template contains adenine, thymine, guanine, and cytosine deoxyribonucleotides in the ratio 1.39 to 1.38 to 0.66 to 0.65, the DNA product contains them in the ratio 1.39 to 1.38 to 0.66 to 0.65. Further, the sequential arrangement of bases in the product is identical to that in the template or parent DNA.

The DNA biosynthetic sequence is shown in more detail in Figure 11–4. The reaction between a deoxyribonucleoside triphosphate and a partially completed DNA strand is shown at stage 3. The new DNA is thus built up one nucleotide at a time.

Although the group activation, chain elongation, and patternization problems seem to have been generally resolved for DNA synthesis, there is uncertainty about certain aspects of replication, the foremost being that it is not clear to what extent parent DNA molecules must actually separate into strands before replication occurs.

Transcription and RNA Biosynthesis

The first process along the path of information flow from DNA to protein is transcription of the four unit nucleotide language of DNA into the similar four symbol system of the RNA's (messenger, ribosomal, and transfer RNA's) which are complementary to particular regions on DNA. These RNA's are all functional constituents of the final translation mechanism; however, it appears that *m*RNA carries the information specifying amino acid sequence in the protein product.

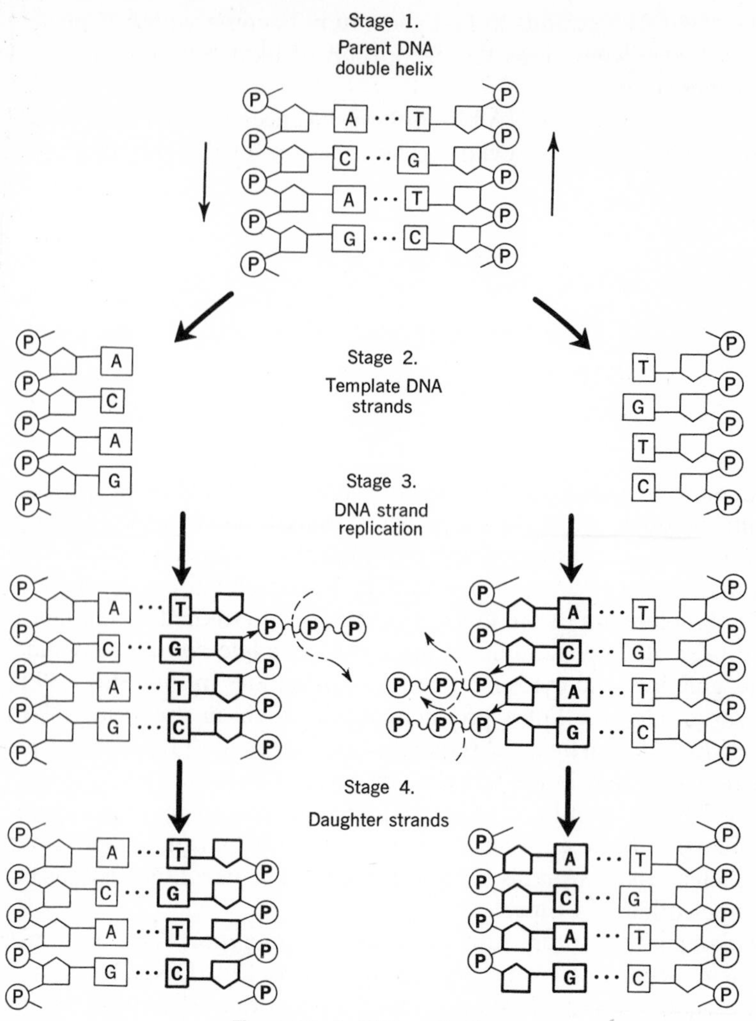

Figure 11–4. DNA replication.

Two lines of experimentation support the notion that the RNA's of the cell are synthesized on a DNA template. First, studies have shown that regions of the DNA base pair with ribosomal, transfer, and messenger RNA's and form so-called DNA-RNA hybrids. This can occur only when there are regions in the DNA that are complementary to regions in the RNA's (e.g., A—T—T—G—C in the DNA pairs with U—A—A—C—G in RNA). This implies that specific regions on the DNA direct the synthesis of specific types of RNA. Second, DNA has been shown to be a template for *in vitro* synthesis of RNA. The RNA formed has a composition and sequence complementary to that of DNA. Studies on *in vitro* biosynthesis of RNA mediated by a DNA template also support the role of DNA in directing RNA synthesis.

DNA-directed RNA biosynthesis occurs as follows:

$$\begin{matrix} \text{ATP} \\ + \\ \text{GTP} \\ + \\ \text{CTP} \\ + \\ \text{UTP} \end{matrix} + \text{DNA template} \xrightarrow{\text{RNA polymerase}} \text{RNA} + \text{DNA template} + \text{Ⓟ}{\sim}\text{O—Ⓟ} \qquad (2)$$

$$\text{Ⓟ}{\sim}\text{O—Ⓟ} \rightarrow 2\ P_i$$

The four nucleoside triphosphates, Mg^{II}, a DNA template, and an enzyme (RNA polymerase) are needed for RNA synthesis. Either single- or double-stranded DNA can act as a template for this reaction.

RNA synthesis is a copying reaction similiar to DNA synthesis and proceeds by base pairing: A to T, G to C, and U to A. The base composition and the base sequence of a double-stranded DNA template is reproduced in the RNA synthesized *in vitro.* This suggests that both DNA strands are copied *in vitro* (page 177), in contrast to evidence which indicates that only one DNA strand is copied *in vivo.* Thus when double-stranded DNA is added, each strand will act as a template for the synthesis of an RNA molecule. Where there is thymidylic acid in DNA, there will be adenylic acid in RNA; where there is deoxycytidylic acid in the DNA, there will be guanylic acid in RNA. Although it is clear that only one strand of DNA acts as template during *in vivo* RNA synthesis, it is not at all clear how regulation of RNA synthesis on a DNA template occurs so that only the specific messenger, ribosomal, and transfer RNA's needed by the cell are synthesized.

The patternization of RNA can also be determined by RNA under certain circumstances. For example, cells infected with an RNA virus produce an RNA polymerase (or RNA replicase) which requires an RNA template for activity.

$$\begin{matrix} \text{ATP} \\ + \\ \text{GTP} \\ + \\ \text{CTP} \\ + \\ \text{UTP} \end{matrix} + \text{RNA template} \xrightarrow{\text{RNA replicase}} \text{RNA} + \text{Ⓟ}{\sim}\text{O—Ⓟ} \qquad (3)$$

$$\text{Ⓟ}{\sim}\text{O—Ⓟ} \rightarrow 2\ P_i$$

The biosynthesis of RNA directed by RNA is similar to RNA synthesis in Eq. (2). In Eq. (3) as before, the base composition and sequence are established by the template: DNA in Eq. (2), RNA in Eq. (3).

The mechanism in Eq. (3) makes it possible for the RNA in RNA-containing viruses to function as genetic material. Many RNA viruses do not use the DNA → RNA → protein pathway of information flow but have an RNA → RNA → protein pathway.

Translation and Protein Biosynthesis

The translation process can be briefly summarized. First, there is activation of amino acids by the so-called activating enzymes, making use of ATP energy. These enzymes also attach the amino acid to transfer RNA to form amino acyl *t*RNA. This amino acyl~*t*RNA becomes associated with a complex composed of a ribosome (page 175) and *m*RNA, and it is presumed that three nucleotide bases (the triplet *anticodon*) in the *t*RNA base pair (A to U and G to C) specifically with a nucleotide triplet (the *codon*) in messenger RNA. Polypeptide chain initiation and growth then occur by a series of reactions which have thus far only been vaguely glimpsed. Protein is the end product. The giant translation step can be broken down into simple steps that involve the energetic, chain elongation, and patternization problems discussed in Chapter Ten.

The initial energy problem is solved by ATP and activating enzymes, so called because they catalyze a reaction that elevates the group potential of an amino acid or simply activate an amino acid. These enzymes have two other names which refer to the fact that they attach this activated amino acid to *t*RNA, i.e., amino acyl *t*RNA synthetase and amino acyl *t*RNA ligase. A number of the activating enzymes have been separated and highly purified, and it is now apparent that there is at least one enzyme for each amino acid-*t*RNA pair. Further, the same enzyme is involved in both the activation reaction, Eq. (4) as well as in Eq. (5), the reaction in which amino acid becomes attached to *t*RNA:

$$\text{Enzyme} + \text{Amino acid} + \text{ATP} \longrightarrow (\text{Enzyme—amino acyl}\sim\text{AMP}) + \text{Ⓟ—O}\sim\text{Ⓟ} \quad \textbf{(4)}$$

$$(\text{Enzyme—amino acyl}\sim\text{AMP}) + t\text{RNA} \longrightarrow \text{Amino acyl}\sim t\text{RNA} + \text{AMP} + \text{Enzyme} \quad \textbf{(5)}$$

There is at least one unique *t*RNA for each amino acid; different amino acids do not become attached to the same *t*RNA molecule. In some cases, however, there is more than one unique *t*RNA for each amino acid. For example, four or five different *t*RNA's correspond to leucine. Each *t*RNA molecule has an individual primary structure (page 129) of about 80 nucleotide bases terminating in a sequence general to all *t*RNA's (the cytidylyl—cytidylyl—adenosine sequence), and an activated amino acid becomes attached to either the 2′- or 3′-hydroxyl of this terminal adenosine.

Our understanding of the subsequent steps in protein synthesis has come largely from studies on a cell-free system obtained from the bacteria *E. coli.* This system contains the components necessary for protein synthesis:

Ribosomes
*t*RNA
Activating and polymerizing enzymes (the *supernatant* fraction)
GTP, ATP, Mg^{II}, and amino acids

Little net protein synthesis takes place in this *in vitro* system, and, to study amino acid polymerization, one or more radioactive amino acids must be used. The components listed are incubated with C^{14} amino acids for 30 minutes at 37°C; then the protein product is precipitated and its content of radioactive amino acids determined.

Ribosomes (page 175), or more probably a cluster of two or more ribosomes (polyribosomes or polysomes), are the sites of protein synthesis. In many tissues ribosomes are attached to one side of a double membrane system, the endoplasmic reticulum (page 175), in an orderly and linear arrangement. In microorganisms, however, the ribosomes appear as particles after disruption of the cell and are not attached to membranes. Structural analysis of ribosomes from many organisms has revealed that they are always constructed from two subunits, one approximately twice the size of the other (Figure 11–1). There are particular binding sites on each subunit for the amino acid adapter (*t*RNA), genetic information (*m*RNA), and the growing polypeptide chain. Amino acyl *t*RNA and the extending protein chain seem to be attached to the larger of the subunits, whereas *m*RNA binds to the smaller subunit. Ribosomes essentially bring together the components involved in the later steps of translation and appear to function as the site of synthesis of any protein if the proper *t*RNAs, *m*RNA, and enzymes are present.

Considerable evidence has been accumulated to support the hypothesis of F. Jacob and J. Monod that a short-lived RNA, messenger RNA, is the intermediary that conveys genetic information to the sites of protein synthesis, the ribosomes. The *m*RNA is formed on a DNA template and is a complementary copy of single DNA strands. The *m*RNA attaches to ribosomes and links them together to form polysomes with single *m*RNA molecules simultaneously functioning on several ribosomes. In contrast to *t*RNA and ribosomal RNA, *m*RNA is metabolically unstable in many types of cells. This is not true in all cells, however; for example, in reticulocytes, which continuously synthesize hemoglobin, the *m*RNA templates appear to be relatively stable.

Most of the basic facts about protein synthesis are brought together in the diagram shown in Figure 11–1. Although the details are yet to be worked out, it seems unlikely that these general relations will be found wrong; all have considerable experimental support.

The initiation and the biosynthetic growth of protein molecules is little understood. It is known that the polypeptide chain begins and grows from the N-terminal amino acid in a sequential manner. Since more than one protein molecule is often coded in a single large *m*RNA, it is clear, if the complete *m*RNA is translated, that each protein must be started and then terminated before a new protein begins. The current notion is that specific base sequences in the *m*RNA signal a start or a stop of protein chain growth. The general scheme for the events that occur during chain growth are shown in Figure 11–1 and a more hypothetical scheme is detailed in Figure 11–5.

The starting amino acyl *t*RNA (N-terminal amino acid) binds to the ribosome, and base pairs form between its anticodon and the beginning codon in *m*RNA. A second amino acyl *t*RNA becomes associated with the ribosome and the second codon of the *m*RNA. Polypeptide chain growth begins and the *m*RNA moves so that a new codon, the third, is in position for association with an incoming *t*RNA, which carries the third amino acid residue for the growing polypeptide chain. As each subunit is added the ribosome moves relative to the *m*RNA, in a fixed direction. Every time the ribosome moves over a group of three nucleotides a new amino acyl *t*RNA moves into position. The forming polypeptide chain is transferred from its *t*RNA of attachment to the amino group of the newly arrived amino acyl *t*RNA. This process repeats until all the codons in the *m*RNA, beginning at the 5′ end, have been "read". At least two different enzymes and the energy of GTP are required for this complicated process.

The patternization of protein molecules has been a subject of considerable speculation; namely, how does DNA determine the amino acid sequence in protein? The messenger RNA hypothesis of Jacob and Monod stimulated much experimental work, and largely through the research of M. Nirenberg and also S. Ochoa and their coworkers the patternization mechanism in protein synthesis is becoming well understood.

Using a slightly refined version of the bacterial system mentioned above, M. Nirenberg and H. Matthaei, in 1961, made the dramatic discovery that synthetic polynucleotides can serve as artificial messenger RNA. The system they developed had a strict dependence on added polynucleotide templates. In fact, the amino acid composition of the protein product was determined by the nucleotide composition of the template polynucleotides added. In their first experiments, Nirenberg and Matthaei found that polyuridylic acid stimulated polyphenylalanine synthesis. Coupling their biochemical evidence with genetic evidence provided by Crick, which suggested a code based on triplets (i.e. three bases code one amino acid),

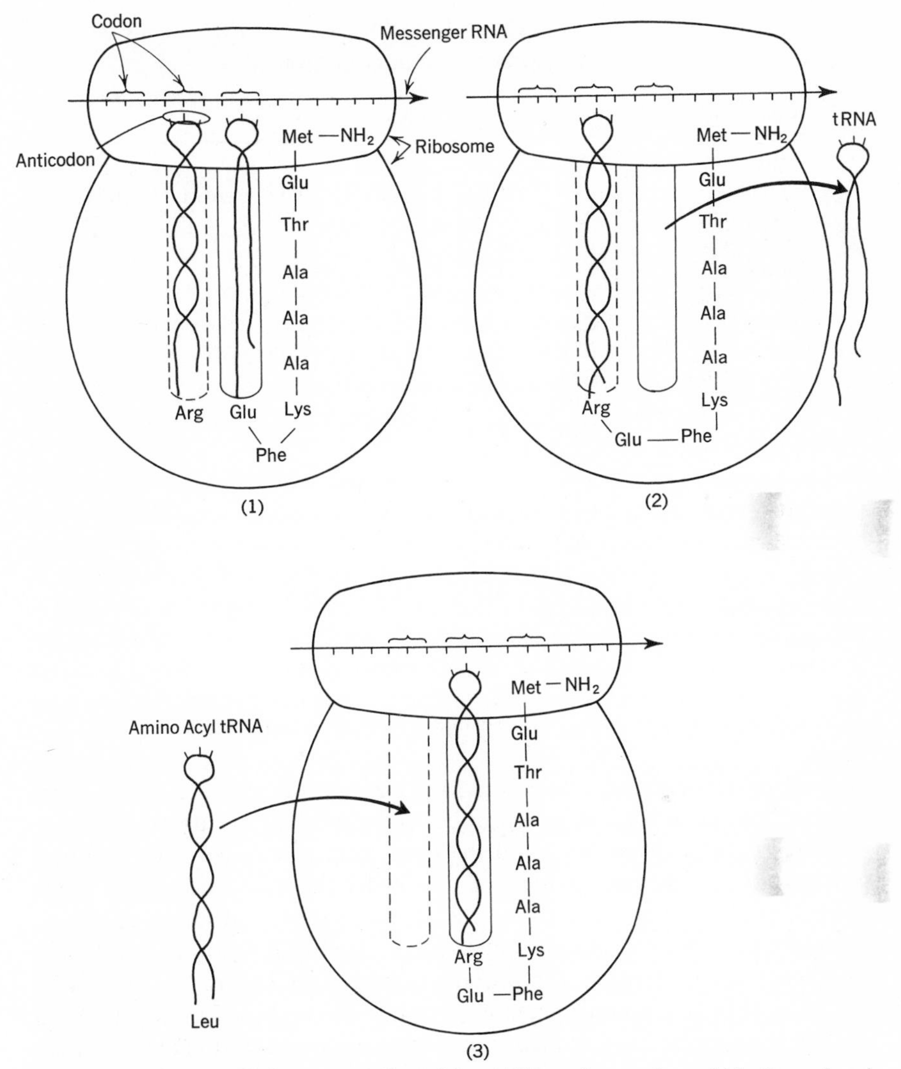

Figure 11–5. Hypothetical representation of the addition of an amino acid to the carboxyl end of a growing polypeptide chain. The messenger RNA moves to the right.

Nirenberg and Matthaei postulated UUU as the triplet codon in *m*RNA that specified phenylalanine; the ultimate DNA codon would be AAA.

Further studies by Nirenberg's group and also by S. Ochoa and his associates have made use of copolynucleotides with varying base composition (e.g., poly UG, UC, etc.) to establish a codon map for all the amino acids (Table 11–1). For example, poly UC stimulates the synthesis of protein containing only leucine, serine, phenylalanine, and proline. By rather elegant correlation of the amount of amino acids incorporated with the

TABLE 11-1

SUMMARY OF *m*RNA CODONS*

Amino Acid	*m*RNA Code Words					
Alanine	GCU	GCC	GCA			
Arginine	CGU	CGC	CGA	CGG	**AGA**	GCG
Asparagine	AAU	AAC				
Aspartic acid	GAU	GAC				
Cysteine	**UGU**	UGC				
Glutamic acid	**GAA**	**GAG**				
Glutamine	CAA	CAG				
Glycine	GGU	GGC	GGA	GGG		
Histidine	CAU	**CAC**				
Isoleucine	AUU	AUC				
Leucine	UUG	**CUC**	CUG			
Lysine	**AAA**	**AAG**				
Methionine	AUG					
Phenylalanine	**UUU**	UUC				
Proline	CCU	**CCC**	CCA	CCG		
Serine	UCU	UCC	UCA	UCG	AGU	AGC
Threonine	ACU	ACC	**ACA**	ACG		
Tryptophan	UGG					
Tyrosine	UAU	UAC				
Valine	GUU	GUC	GUA	**GUG**		

* Codons for which the specific sequence of bases is known are indicated by bold face.

amount of a particular nucleotide in a synthetic messenger RNA, these investigators have been able to propose codons for all twenty amino acids.

More recently, Nirenberg and his coworkers have used a refined procedure and system that enables them to order the nucleotide bases in the *m*RNA codon. They have found that trinucleotides, although unable to bring about protein synthesis, cause amino acyl *t*RNA to become bound to ribosomes as if ready for protein synthesis to occur. The particular amino acyl *t*RNA bound depends not only on the base composition but also on the specific base sequence in the trinucleotide. For example, GUU causes valyl-*t*RNA to be bound to ribosomes; UGU causes cysteinyl-*t*RNA binding, and UUG, leucyl-*t*RNA binding. These then are most probably the specific codons containing two U's and one G.

There are several features of the biochemically determined genetic code that should be noted. First, there is considerable redundance or *degeneracy* in the code, i.e., situations where more than one codon exists for an amino acid. For example, alanine has three codons, arginine has four, and leucine has at least four. Ambiguity also exists in the code in the case of UUU coding for both leucine and phenylalanine. The codons listed in Table 11-1 for *E. coli* have also been found for other organisms as well, evidence for a universal code.

Polysaccharide Biosynthesis

Glycogen, the storage form of glucose, was assumed to be synthesized by the reversal of the glycogen breakdown pathway, Eq. (6). That is,

$$\text{Glucose-1-phosphate} \xrightarrow{\text{phosphorylase}} \text{Glycogen} + P_i \qquad \textbf{(6)}$$

Accumulated data cast doubt on this as the major path of synthesis, and in 1957 evidence was presented by L. Leloir for a new pathway of glycogen biosynthesis. An enzyme catalyzing glycogen formation from uridine diphosphoglucose UDPG (I) was detected in rat liver and has subsequently been found to be widespread throughout plant and animal tissues.

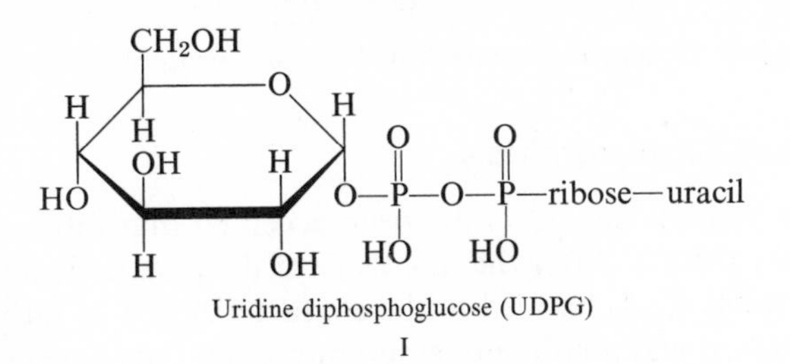

Uridine diphosphoglucose (UDPG)
I

The UDPG involved in glycogen synthesis is synthesized through reactions of glucose-1-phosphate with UTP. The enzymic reaction for glycogen formation is:

$$\text{Uridine diphosphoglucose} \xrightarrow{\text{glycogen synthetase}} \text{UDP} + \text{Glycogen} \qquad \textbf{(7)}$$

in which glycogen serves as an acceptor for a glucosyl unit with a high group potential. The enzyme which catalyzes the reaction has been termed glycogen synthetase (for brevity). Many of the properties of glycogen synthetase are similar to those of phosphorylase. The fundamental difference, however, between glycogen formation from glucose-1-phosphate and UDPG resides in the equilibria of the reactions. If the ratio of inorganic phosphate is changed (*in vitro*), the phosphorylase reaction can easily be made to go forward or backward according to the mass action law. In the cell, the concentration of phosphate is such that this reaction would be oriented toward glycogen breakdown. In the case of glycogen synthetase, the reaction is completely displaced in favor of glycogen synthesis, with little chance of reversal. The evidence that glycogen synthesis proceeds exclusively by the mechanism involving UDPG is now overwhelming. The biosynthesis of glycogen is illustrated in Figure 11–6.

Starch is synthesized in plant tissues by a series of reactions similar to those for glycogen in Figure 11–6. The activated form of glucose, however, is adenosine diphosphoglucose.

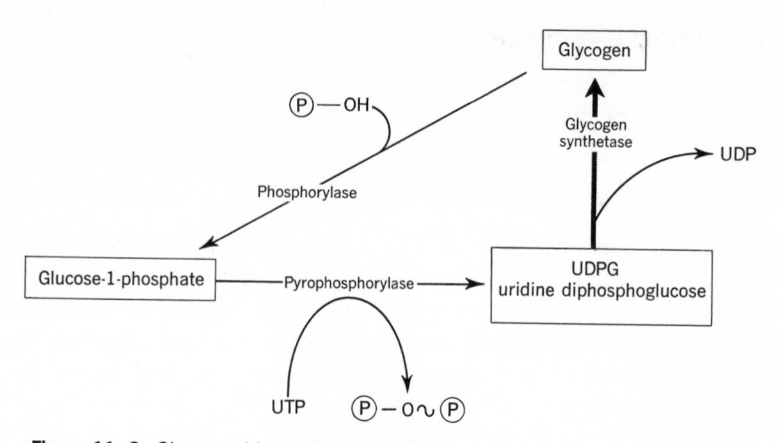

Figure 11–6. Glycogen biosynthesis via UDPG and phosphorolytic breakdown.

Fatty Acid and Fat Biosynthesis

For many years it has generally been accepted that fatty acids are synthesized from acetate. After the discovery of the metabolically active form of acetate, acetyl CoA, had led to the characterization of fatty acid oxidation (page 115), it was an obvious assumption that fatty acid synthesis from acetyl CoA could be achieved by the same enzymes, since each step in fatty acid degradation is reversible. This, however, is not the path of fatty acid synthesis. Experimental evidence supporting fatty acid synthesis via a pathway independent of the enzymes of the β-oxidation sequence has recently been presented by F. Lynen and his coworkers.

The difficulty underlying the assumption that synthesis proceeded by a reversal of breakdown was the inevitable thermodynamic difficulty, not unlike that for other biosynthetic processes. Under physiological conditions the thiolase reaction that catalyzes the condensation of acyl CoA with acetyl CoA, to form the homologous β-ketoacyl CoA, does not favor the synthetic process.

In the first step of fatty acid synthesis, acetyl CoA adds CO_2 with the aid of a biotin-containing enzyme to form malonyl CoA, Eq. (8):

$$\underset{\text{Acetyl CoA}}{CH_3\overset{\overset{O}{\|}}{C}\sim SCoA} + CO_2 + ATP \xrightarrow{\text{Biotin}} \underset{\text{Malonyl CoA}}{\overset{\overset{COOH}{|}}{CH_2}-\overset{O}{\overset{/\!/}{C}}\sim SCoA} + ADP + P_i \quad \textbf{(8)}$$

The reaction is ATP dependent and passes through an intermediate active carboxyl, namely, carboxybiotin (page 144). Malonyl CoA is readily converted to fatty acids in the presence of acetyl CoA, $NADPH_2$, and enzymes, Figure 11–7.

The thermodynamic advantage gained in using malonyl CoA instead of simply acetyl CoA in fatty acid synthesis is considerable. The condensation of an acyl CoA (acetyl or higher fatty acyl CoA) with malonyl CoA results in the simultaneous liberation of CO_2, a process that shifts the over-all reaction equilibrium toward synthesis and results in a more negative ΔG of reaction.

Acetyl CoA provides the building block or *primer* onto which the C_2 units derived from malonyl CoA are attached. CO_2 is released during this condensation, and $NADPH_2$ provides electrons needed for the complete reduction of the carbonyl

$$\overset{\text{O}}{\overset{\|}{-\text{C}-}}$$

to the methylene

$$-CH_2-$$

group. When $NADH_2$ is substituted for $NADPH_2$, the rate of fatty acid synthesis decreases by 75 per cent. For palmitic acid synthesis (C_{16}),

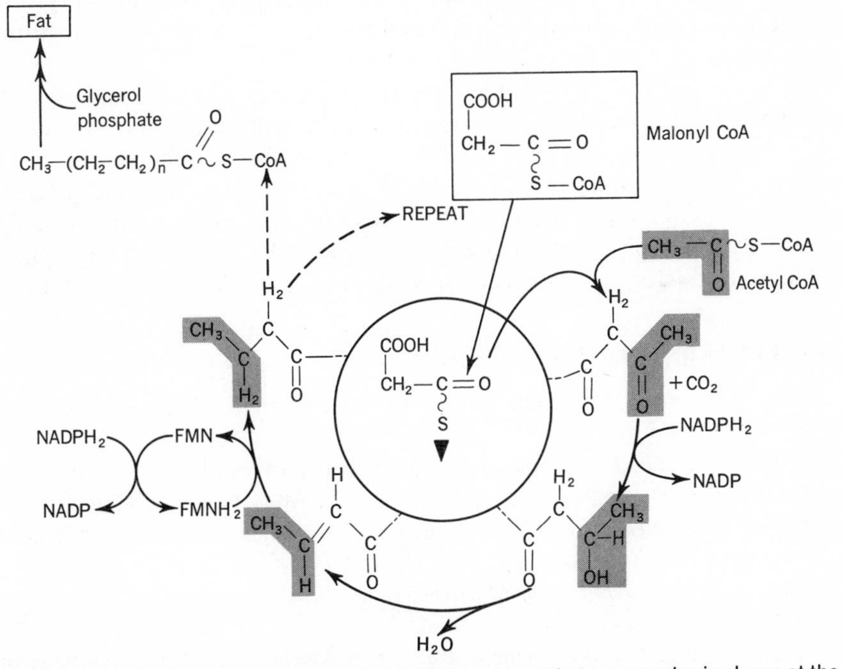

Figure 11–7. Fatty acid and fat synthesis. The fatty acid synthetase complex is shown at the center. The initial reactant, malonyl CoA, is transferred to the complex, and subsequent reactions occur with substrates bound to the multienzyme complex. Overall Reaction:

$$CH_3\overset{O}{\overset{\|}{C}}\sim SCoA + n \text{ Malonyl CoA} + n \text{ NADPH} + n \text{ FMNH}_2 \longrightarrow$$

$$CH_3(CH_2)_n\overset{O}{\overset{\|}{C}}\sim SCoA + n \text{ NADP} + n \text{ FMN} + n \text{ CO}_2$$

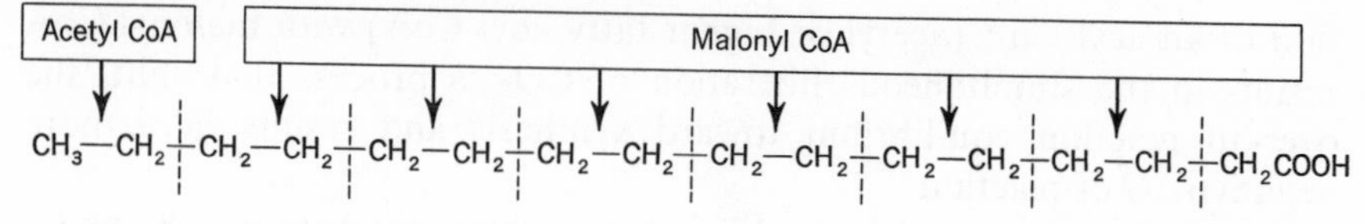

Figure 11–8. Origin of the carbon atoms of palmitic acid.

acetyl CoA is incorporated into the tail end of the fatty acid, whereas malonyl CoA provides the C_2 units for condensation and therefore carbon atoms 1 to 14.

The finer details of the transfer mechanism, whereby the C_2 units are added to primer acyl CoA, are still somewhat obscure. Certain details, however, of the over-all process are known (Figures 11–7 and 11–8).

The synthetic pathway differs from the reversal of the degradative cycle (page 115) in several regards: (1) although the same acid intermediates occur they are always enzyme bound; (2) the condensing unit is a thiol ester of malonate rather than of acetate; (3) the driving force of the reaction is supplied by decarboxylation of the malonyl derivative; (4) NADP and FMN are substituted for NAD and FAD; (5) a protein may substitute for CoA as an acyl carrier.

Fats are synthesized from the fatty acyl CoA formed above and glycerol phosphate, which could have arisen via carbohydrate metabolism. There is a rather non-specific enzyme that is responsible for the formation of diglyceride phosphate from 2 moles of activated fatty acid and glycerol phosphate. C_{16}-, C_{17}-, and C_{18}-fatty acids are used preferentially. Finally, the diglyceride phosphate is dephosphorylated by the action of a phosphatase and is brought to reaction with another mole of fatty acyl CoA.

SUGGESTED READING

Allfrey, V. G., and A. E. Mirsky, "How Cells Make Molecules," *Scientific American,* September, 1961.

Chantrenne, H., *The Biosynthesis of Proteins,* Pergamon Press, Inc., New York, 1961.

Crick, F. H. C., "The Recent Excitement in the Coding Problem" in *Progress in Nucleic Acid Research,* J. N. Davidson and W. E. Cohen (eds.), vol. I, Academic Press, Inc., New York, 1963, pp. 164–215.

Ingram, V., *The Biosynthesis of Macromolecules,* W. A. Benjamin, Inc., New York, 1965.

Jacob, F., and J. Monod, "Genetic Regulatory Mechanisms in the Synthesis of Protein," *Journal of Molecular Biology, 3,* 318 (1961).

Kornberg, A., *Enzymatic Synthesis of DNA,* John Wiley & Sons, Inc., New York, 1962.

Leloir, L., "The Biosynthesis of Glycogen, Starch and Other Polysaccharides" in *The Harvey Lectures,* 1960–1961, Academic Press, Inc., New York, 1961.

Lipmann, F., "Biosynthetic Mechanisms" in *The Harvey Lectures, 1948–1949,* Charles C Thomas, Publisher, Springfield, Ill., 1949.

Lynen, F., "Biosynthesis of Saturated Fatty Acids," *Federation Proceedings, 20,* 941–951 (1961).

Nirenberg, M., "The Genetic Code, II," *Scientific American,* March, 1963.

Nirenberg, M. W., and J. H. Matthaei, "The Dependence of Cell-free Protein Synthesis in *E. coli* upon Naturally Occurring or Synthetic Polyribonucleotides," *Proceedings of the National Academy of Sciences, U.S.A., 47,* 1588 (1961).

Ochoa, S., "Synthetic Polynucleotides and the Genetic Code" in *Informational Macromolecules,* H. Vogel, H. Bryson, and J. O. Lampen (eds.), Academic Press, Inc., New York, 1963.

Watson, J. D., "Involvement of RNA in the Synthesis of Proteins" *Science, 140,* 17, (1963).

"All the physiological activities of animals and plants—assimilation, secretion, excretion, motion, generation—are expressions of the activities of the cells considered as physiological units."

T. H. Huxley, 1887

TWELVE

Biochemical Cytology

The beginning of cell biology antedates Huxley's statement and is generally associated with the proposal of the cell theory in the late 1830's by Mathias Jakob Schleiden and Theodor Schwann. This theory characterized the cell as the structural unit of organization of living systems. Just as atoms comprise the component parts of the molecule, the cell came to be regarded as the fundamental unit of organisms. When increasingly powerful microscopes were developed and used by cell biologists to describe the anatomy of the cell, the notion of a cell progressively changed from that of a membrane containing a blob of jelly-like cytoplasm and nucleus to a richly differentiated cytoplasmic matrix with specialized subcellular bodies or organelles. The further development of microscopic techniques, and particularly electron microscopy, has made it possible for biologists to discern the intricacies and the functions of the subcellular bodies. Recently, biochemists have directed their attention to the molecular ecology of these particles. By a different route from that of the cell biologists, biochemists have approached the question: "What is the biochemical composition, structure, and function of these subcellular organelles?" The biochemist has disrupted the cell and proceeded to isolate intracellular bodies, e.g., nuclei, and to trace some of the biochemical pathways localized in these structures.

The cell is an exceedingly complex object, and our knowledge of cell

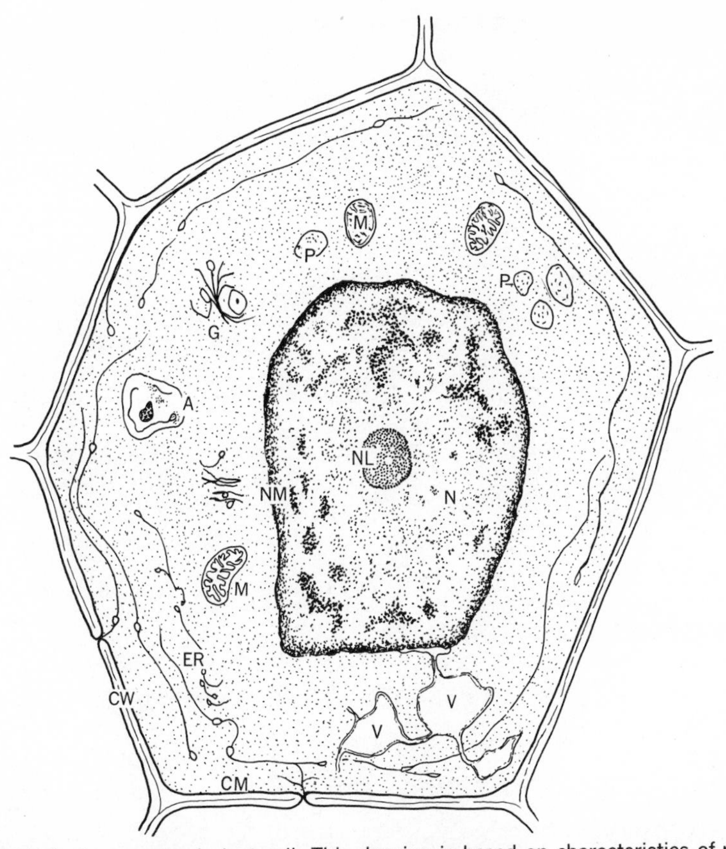

Figure 12–1. A generalized plant cell. This drawing is based on characteristics of rapidly growing meristematic cells of the plant. The intracellular contents are similar to those in mature plant cells. The vacuoles, however, in the mature cell are larger than in the growing cell and mature chloroplasts are also present in the former. Representative cellular structures are shown: N—nucleus, NM—nuclear membrane, M—mitochondria, ER—endoplasmic reticulum, CW—cell wall, V—vacuole, P—proplastid, C—chloroplast, G—golgi, A—amyloplast (starch body), CM—cell membrane, NL—nucleolus.

structure is still somewhat rudimentary. At the outset, one should realize that there is no "typical" cell and that the discussion which follows is about the *generalized* cell. The generalized cell will refer to a composite of the features which cells have in common. Figures 12–1, 12–2, and 12–3, for example, illustrate the anatomical features of a generalized plant, animal, and bacterial cell, whereas, Figures 12–4, 12–5, and 12–6 are actual photomicrographs of cells. In the sections that follow, we will discuss briefly some of the basic anatomical and biochemical features of cells.

Intracellular Organization

Cells differ greatly in shape, size, and function; indeed, the same intracellular structures are not found in all cells, or may vary in distribution and

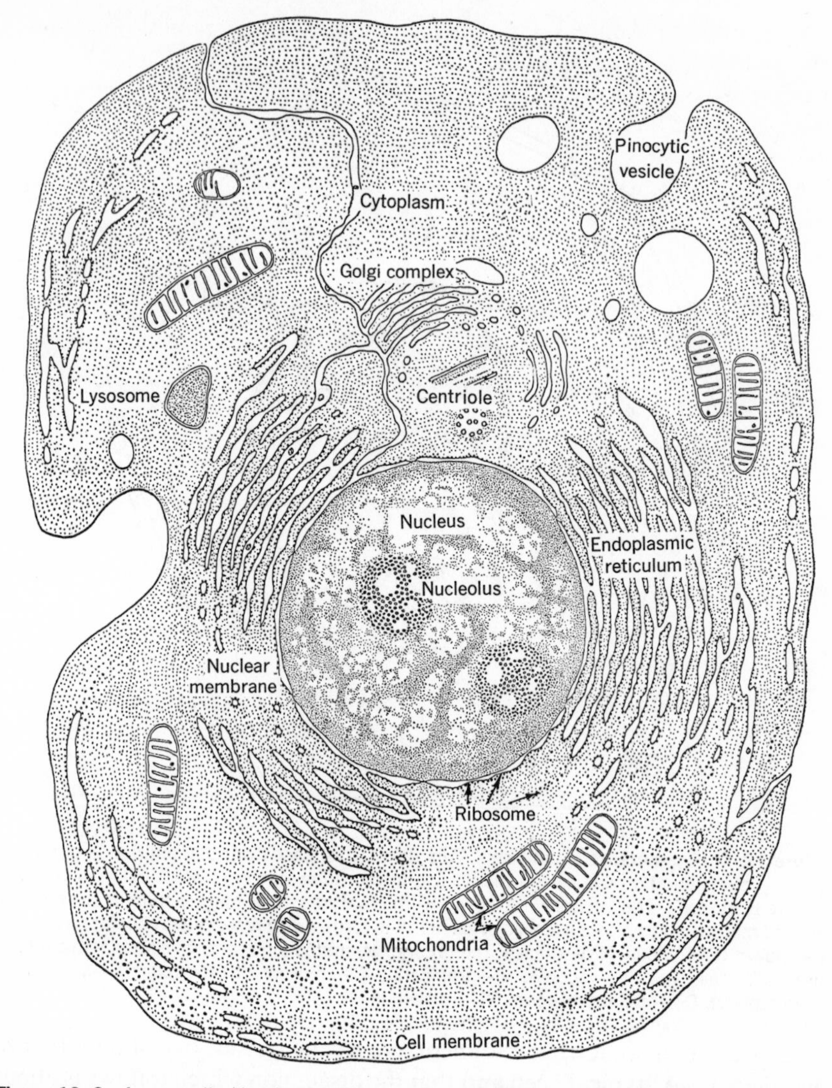

Figure 12–2. A generalized animal cell based on what is seen in electron micrographs such as the one reproduced in Figure 12–5. The mitochondria are the sites of the oxidative reactions that provide the cell with energy. The dots that line the endoplasmic reticulum are ribosomes: the sites of protein synthesis. In cell division the pair of centrioles, one shown in longitudinal section (rods), other in cross section (circles), part to form poles of the apparatus that separates two duplicate sets of chromosomes. (Redrawn from Brachet, 1961.)

amount. Most cells, however, have common features which can be simply summarized.

The cellular contents are enclosed by a *cell membrane,* which is responsible for the influx and extrusion of biochemical substances. This membrane is an essential feature of every cell and is found even in bacteria and fungi.

The membrane is only about 0.010 microns thick and cannot be seen with the optical microscope. It consists of proteins and phospholipids arranged in a regular pattern to form a lipoprotein matrix. Plant cells have, in addition, rigid walls that surround and protect the cell membrane. The plant cell wall consists primarily of the polysaccharides cellulose and lignin and is often a comparatively strong and semirigid structure that provides mechanical support for the plant tissues.

The *nucleus* is generally a spherical body enclosed by a double-layered membrane. It becomes readily apparent during certain stages of cell division (prophase) and can be easily seen with the aid of a microscope because of its large size and somewhat greater optical density than the cytoplasm surrounding it. Its higher optical density is due to the presence of particles (chromosomes) rich in DNA. Electron microscopic studies have revealed that the cell nucleus is connected with the cytoplasm through a system of pores in the nuclear membrane which eventually becomes part of the endoplasmic reticulum (page 175). The essential and unique function of the nucleus is to serve as the principal site for the regulation and transmission of hereditary characteristics. This regulatory control involves the chromosomes and their major constituents DNA and basic proteins. The nucleus contains, in addition to the genetic material, one or more dark round bodies called *nucleoli.* These bodies are intermeshed with chromosomal DNA and appear to be involved in protein and RNA synthesis.

The *mitochondria* of animal cells are small, usually rod-shaped, bodies or subcellular particles which are distributed throughout the cytoplasm. They are about 1–3 microns in diameter, about $\frac{1}{50}$ the diameter of a nucleus, and about the same size as many bacteria. The mitochondria can be selectively stained with Janus green and can then be seen with the light microscope as elongated oval bodies. The electron microscope is much more revealing and has shown that mitochondria are enclosed by a double-layered membrane which has projections inward from the inner membrane toward the mitochondrial center; these projections are called cristae.

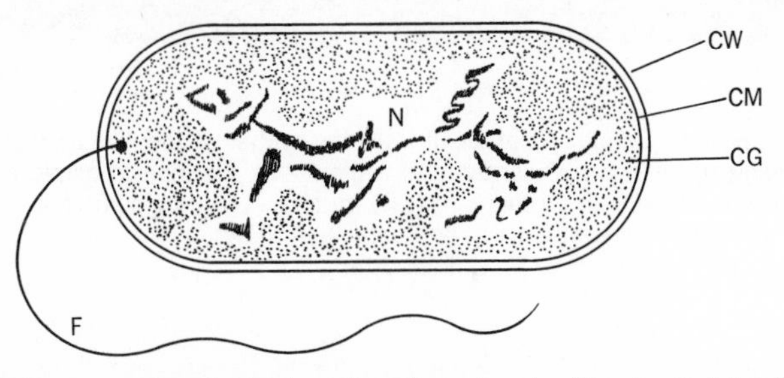

Figure 12–3. Diagram of longitudinal section through a bacillus bacterial cell showing cell wall (CW), cytoplasmic membrane (CM), cytoplasmic granules (CG)—primarily ribosomes—the ramifying nuclear region (N), and the flagellum (F).

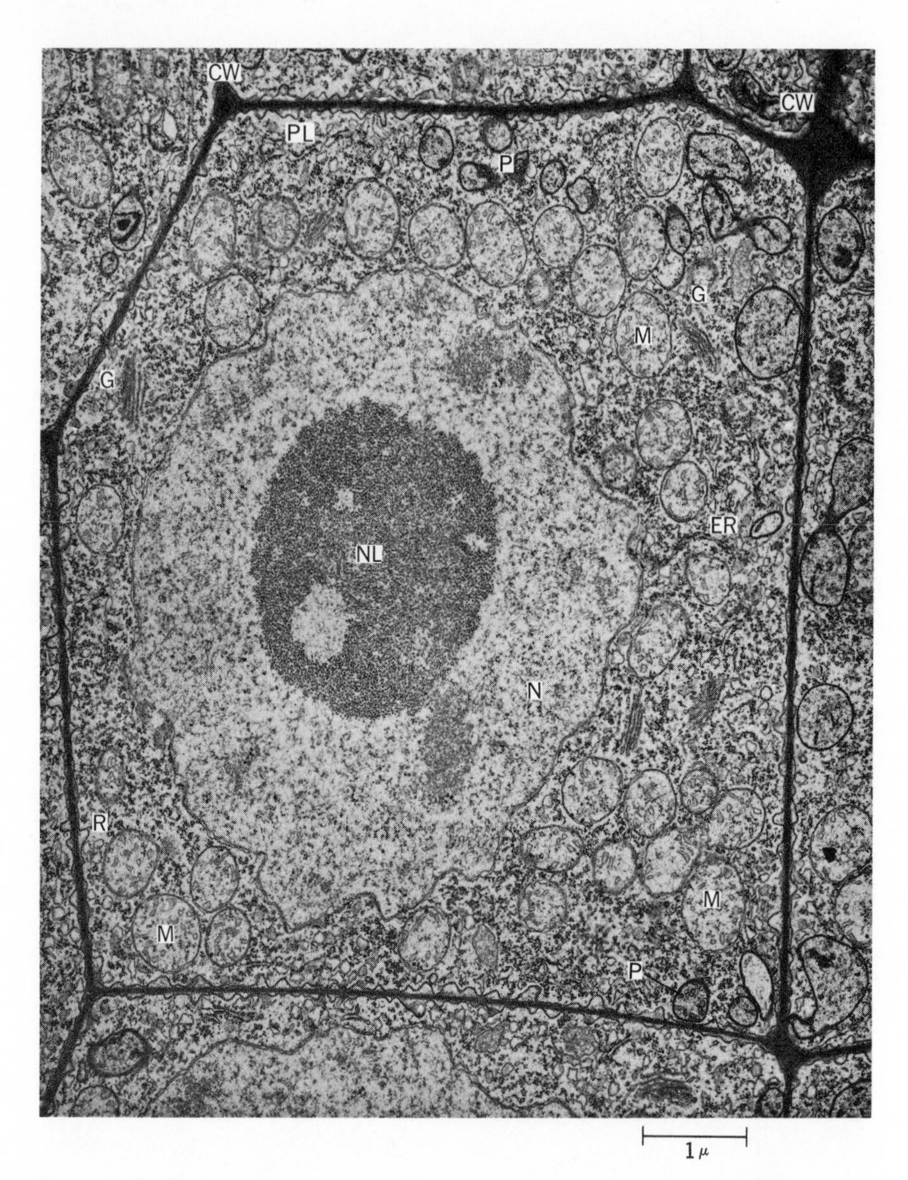

Figure 12–4. Electron micrograph of a cell from the anther of the African violet (*Saintpaulia ionantha*) showing representative contents of a plant cell. Fixation in osmic acid. Mitochondria (M), golgi (G), endoplasmic reticulum (ER), nucleus (N), nucleolus (NL), plasmalemma (PL), ribosomes (R), proplastids (P), and cell wall (CW) are illustrated. Magnification 13,500×. Electron micrograph by M. C. Ledbetter.

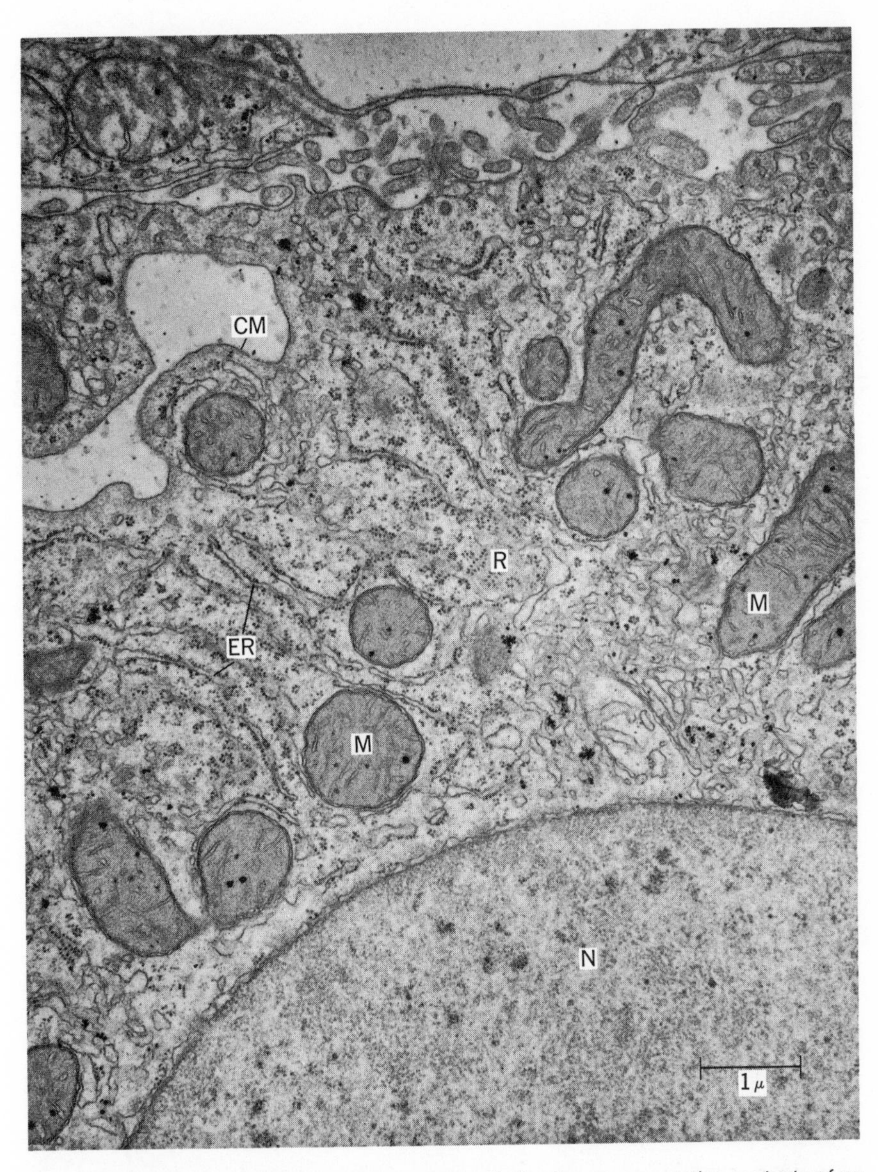

Figure 12–5. Electron micrograph of a rat liver cell showing representative contents of an animal cell. Mitochondria (M), golgi (G), endoplasmic reticulum (ER), nucleus (N), ribosomes (R), cell membrane (CM) are illustrated. Magnification 13,500×. Electron micrograph by J. D. Jamieson.

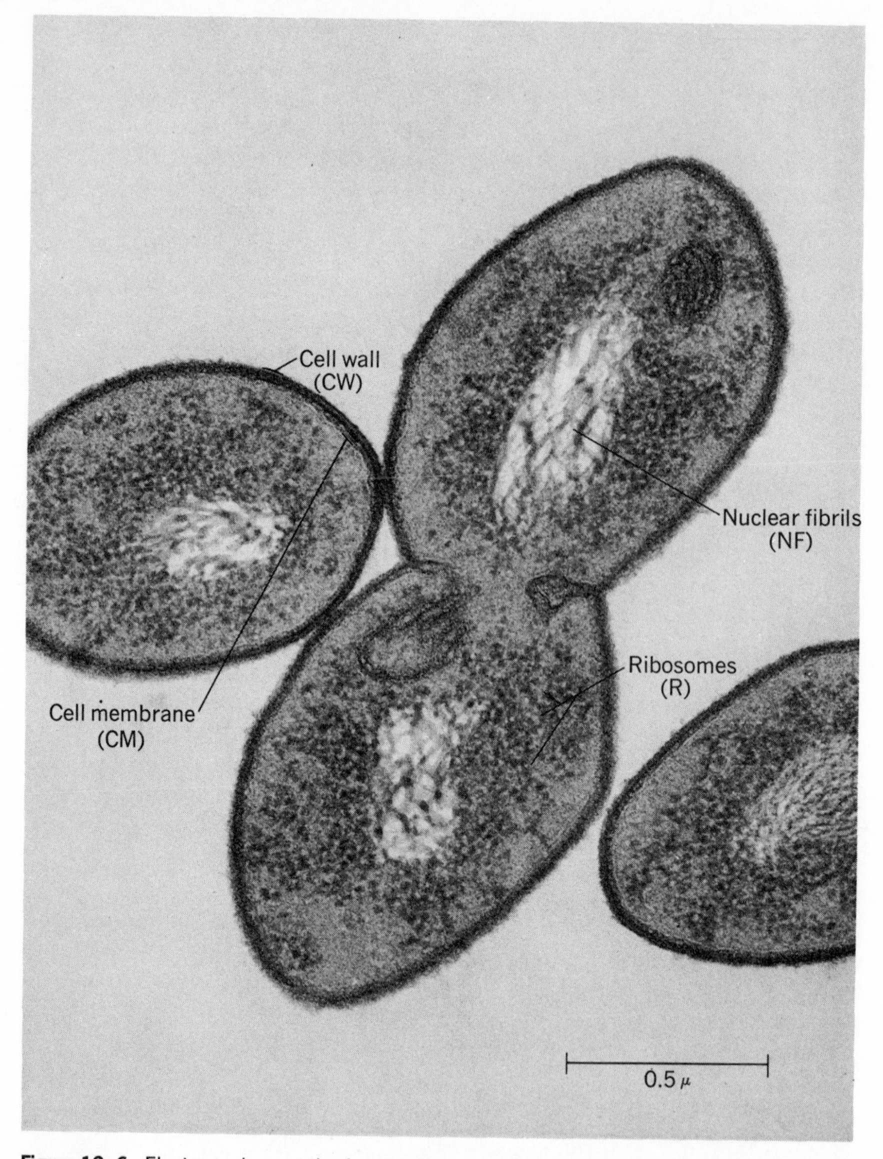

Figure 12–6. Electron micrograph of several bacterial cells (*Diplococcus pneumoniae*) showing cell division (center). The cell wall (CW), cell membrane (CM), ribosomes (R), and nuclear fibrils (NF) can be seen. Electron micrograph by J. D. Jamieson.

Energy for biological processes is generated in the mitochondria, the powerhouses of the cell.

Plant cells contain highly specialized pigmented structures called *chloroplasts.* The chloroplasts contain virtually all the chlorophyll of the plant cell and play a major role in the capture and utilization of light energy. The shape and size of chloroplasts vary widely and are characteristic of the plant species in which they occur, although, in any particular species chloroplasts are not necessarily present in all tissues. The chloroplast particle is enclosed by a membrane and is nearly filled with another membranous structure having many internal folds. Chlorophyll is concentrated in certain of these internal folded areas and appears as flat piles of laminated disks producing units called *grana.* The hydrophilic part of the chlorophyll molecule is bound to the protein portion of the surrounding membrane, whereas its long hydrocarbon chain is associated with lipids.

The *lysosomes* are slightly smaller than mitochondria and contain most of the active degradative or hydrolytic enzymes of the cell; for example, RNAse, β-glucuronidase, phosphatases, cathepsins, etc. The lysosomal membrane is extremely sensitive and is ruptured under a variety of physiological conditions. Its rupture leads to a release of the hydrolytic enzymes and subsequent breakdown of the cell (cytolysis). These bodies aid in removal of dead cells or foreign cells.

Besides these specialized organelles (mitochondria, lysosomes, etc.), the cell sap of many cell types (e.g., liver) contains a system of interconnected membrane-bounded compartments collectively known as the *endoplasmic reticulum* (ER). Some portions of the endoplasmic reticulum have attached to their surface particles of about 0.02 microns diameter known as *ribosomes.* These membranes have a grandular appearance in the electron microscope and, hence their name, the *rough surfaced* endoplasmic reticulum. This rough surfaced membrane is the site of synthesis of proteins for export out of the cell, for example digestive enzymes from the pancreas and albumin from the liver. Other portions of the endoplasmic reticulum are devoid of attached particles and are correspondingly termed *smooth surfaced* endoplasmic reticulum. This smooth membrane system, which includes the *Golgi complex,* is mainly involved in intracellular transfer of materials and preparation of substances for export. Numerous structural and functional continuities can be found between the endoplasmic reticulum and both the nuclear envelope and the cell surface. Thus the endoplasmic reticulum is the means whereby the cell can maintain efficient contact with its environment.

In addition to being attached to the endoplasmic reticulum, ribosomes are also found free in the cell sap. These free ribosomes are the sites where proteins for use within the cell (e.g., enzymes and repair proteins) are formed.

Vacuoles are conspicuous in the cytoplasm of plant cells but less so in animal cells except protozoa. In immature or rapidly dividing cells they are relatively small, but once a cell becomes mature they coalesce and become enlarged. Vacuoles appear, however, not to be a living portion of the cell but a reservoir for essential materials as well as waste products. For example, vacuoles contain some of the pigments that determine flower, leaf, and fruit color, in addition to simple organic acids, salts, and sugars. In protozoa these bodies serve as important elements for digestion.

A large proportion of the remainder of the cell is the *cytoplasm.* This may still include very small intracellular bodies, e.g., the microbodies, whose significance is not fully appreciated, or it may simply be the amorphous "soluble" remainder of the cell. There are an enormous number of large and small molecules not known to be associated with any well-recognized intracellular structures and can therefore be termed cytoplasmic molecules. For example, all of the enzymes involved in the conversion of glucose to pyruvate or lactate (anaerobic glycolysis) remain in the cytoplasm or supernatant after the nuclei, mitochondria, and other particles have been removed. Similarly, many other metabolic systems appear to be soluble. It should be recognized, however, that methods for preparing and separating cell constituents are still very crude, and that destruction or release of molecular components from discrete cell structures may easily occur during isolation.

Specialized Cells

The general morphological characteristics of plant, animal, and bacterial cells have been outlined. As is to be expected, the diversity of nature includes variations on these central themes. When a cell has become highly specialized toward one particular function, this is usually reflected in unique structural features. The cell structure may be specifically changed so that more specialized activities can be performed more efficiently. A few examples are depicted in Figure 12–7. The erythrocyte is a cell which has evolved a very distinctive structure to achieve the purpose of oxygen transport. In most organisms, the erythrocyte is anuclear and contains cytoplasm composed of about 30 per cent of one type of protein, hemoglobin; water (67 per cent) and assorted biological material (3 per cent) comprise the remainder. Nerve cells are specialized and exhibit to a high degree the phenomena of irritability and conductivity. The dendrites, long protoplasmic processes, are specialized features which make possible the functional connections between different nerve cells. Conduction of the nerve impulse occurs along the elongated axons. An example of a plant cell highly specialized toward reproduction is the male gametophyte of the pollen cell of the *Ephedra* genus. This cell is characterized by multiple nuclei destined to participate in the development of the stalk and body of the flower. The spermatozoon is another cell specialized toward reproduction. It has a tail that permits mobility and a nucleus, located in the head, ready for transmission to the ovum and initiation of fertilization. All cells have a certain degree of specialization and are capable of performing functions other cells can not. This is the reason there is no typical cell.

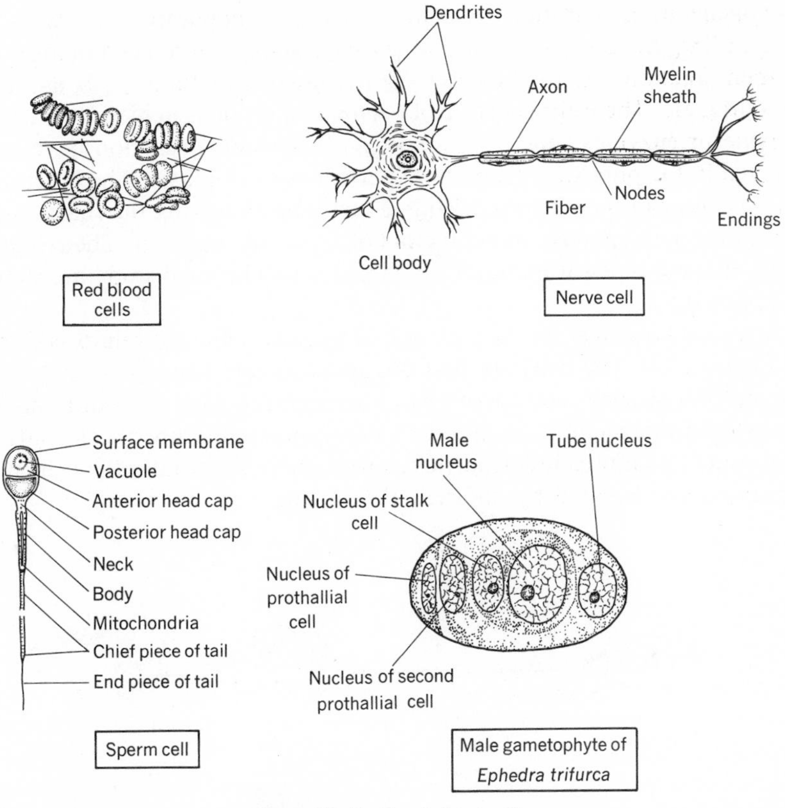

Figure 12–7. Specialized cells.

Isolation of Cellular Components

Although the cell is the basic structural unit of the living organism, only bacteria, protozoa, and some algae exist as single cells. In other animals and plants, the cells are integrated into tissues and organs which are likely to be quite heterogeneous in composition and function. It is thus possible to study biochemical reactions at various levels of supra- or subcellular organization. This has led to a broad classification of biological reactions as being studied on an *in vivo* or *in vitro* basis. *In vivo* refers to an experiment conducted with an intact, whole animal. The *in vitro* study in its extreme is an experiment conducted literally in the test tube. The isolated organ is the first level of disorganization from the intact animal and proves to be a useful *in vitro* approach. A further level of disorganization is achieved when the organ is cut into thin slices for study. Special whole cell preparations are sometimes available, for example, erythrocytes, sperm cells, certain isolated tumor cells and cells from many tissues. As a final step of disorganization, the tissue sample is broken down into a homogeneous preparation by some mechanical apparatus, for example, by grinding the tissue in a glass or plastic homogenizer. The homogenate is then fractionated into discrete intracellular structures such as mitochondria, etc. The ultimate state of *in vitro* resolution is achieved when the enzyme or enzymes catalyzing a specific biochemical reaction have been isolated in the pure state from these particles or cytoplasm. The biochemical reaction can then be observed in a test tube by mixing the reactants or substrates with enzyme and cofactors in a suitable medium. The relationships of some types of material available for biochemical study are shown in Figure 12–8.

A typical flowsheet for the isolation of various cellular subunits is shown in Figure 12–9. The cells are first disrupted in cold isotonic sucrose with the aid of a Waring blender or glass homogenizer. This procedure breaks the cytoplasmic membrane, and the heterogeneous mixture of cell contents spills out. The intracellular particles and soluble supernatant can then be separated and isolated by differential centrifugation.

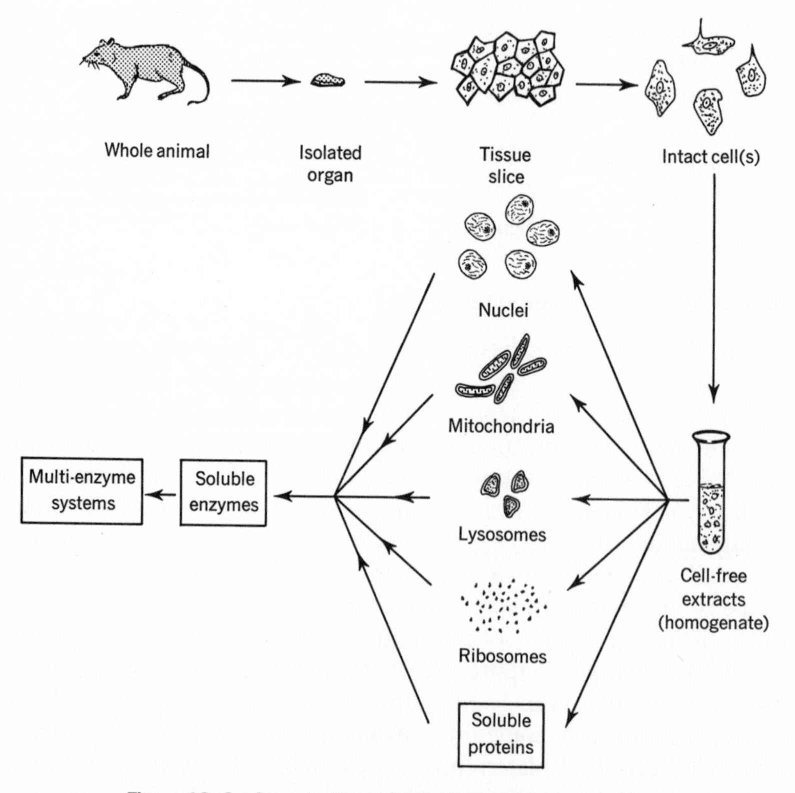

Figure 12–8. Organizational levels for biochemical studies.

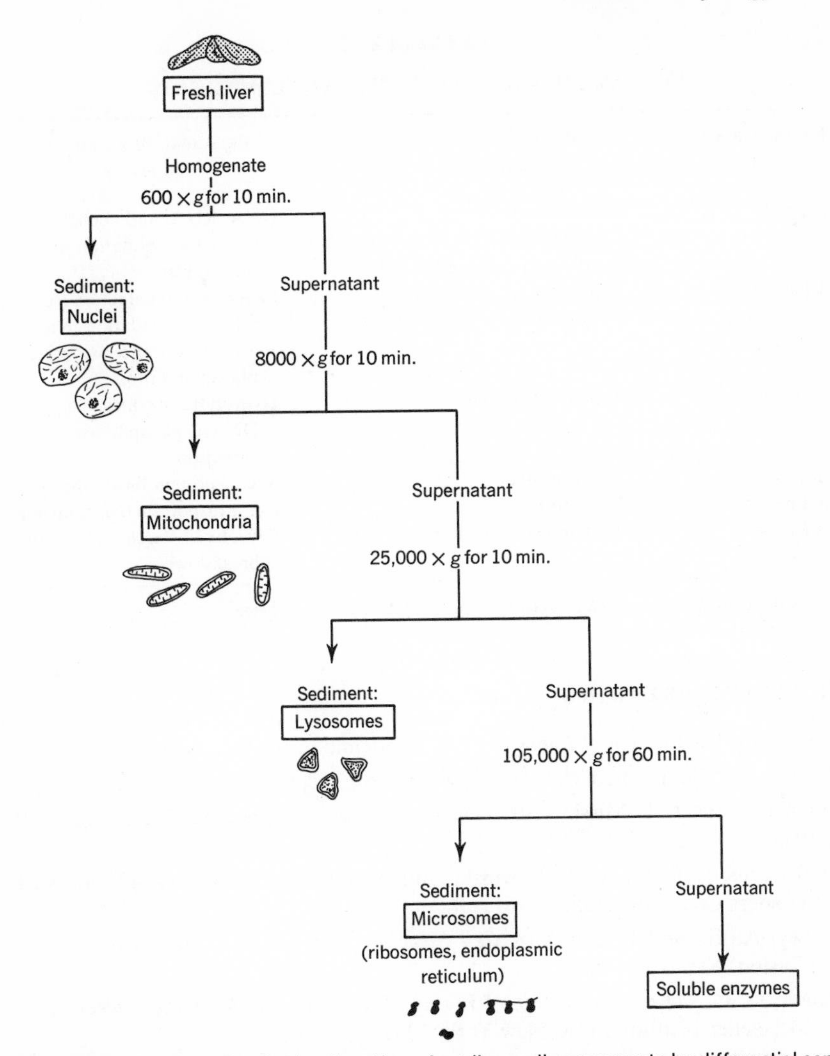

Figure 12–9. Flowsheet for the fractionation of rat liver cell components by differential centrifugation. The gravitational force (*g*) and time of centrifugation (minutes) are indicated.

Biochemical Properties of Cellular Components

Some of the biochemical properties of various intracellular fractions from rat liver cells are summarized in Table 12–1. The information contained in this table has come primarily from investigations on isolated intracellular structures.

In this chapter we have tried to emphasize that the intracellular components and their biochemical activities are integrated into a highly ordered and dynamic state within the cell.

TABLE 12-1

BIOCHEMICAL ACTIVITIES OF CELLULAR COMPONENTS

Cytological Structure	Major Biochemical Constituents	Principal Biochemical Activity
Nuclei	DNA, histones,* other proteins	DNA, RNA, and coenzyme synthesis; regulation of metabolism
Mitochondria	Lipoproteins, phospholipids, cytochromes, flavoproteins	Enzymes and cofactors for: fatty acid oxidation, Kreb's citric acid cycle, oxidative phosphorylation
Lysosomes	Protein (enzymes)	Hydrolytic enzymes, e.g., DNAse, phosphatase, cathepsin
Ribosomes	RNA, protein	Site of protein biosynthesis
Cell membrane	Lipoprotein	Ion transport, active transport
Cytoplasm	Protein (enzymes), salts	Glycolysis, starch and glycogen breakdown

* Histones are proteins containing large amounts of lysine and/or arginine.

SUGGESTED READING

Bourne, G. H., *Division of Labor in Cells,* Academic Press, Inc., New York, 1963.

Brachet, J., "The Living Cell," *Scientific American,* September, 1961.

Brachet, J., and A. E. Mirsky (eds.), *The Cell,* Academic Press, Inc., New York, 1959–1965.

DeRobertis, E. D. P., W. W. Nowinski, and F. A. Saez, *Cell Biology,* 4th ed., W. B. Saunders Co., Philadelphia, 1965.

Loewy, A. G., and P. Siekevitz, *Cell Structure and Function,* Holt, Rinehart and Winston, New York, 1963.

Palade, G. E., "The Organization of Living Matter," in *The Scientific Endeavor,* The Rockefeller Institute Press, New York, 1965.

Porter, K. R., "Submicroscopic Morphology of Protoplasm" in *The Harvey Lectures, 1955–1956,* Academic Press, Inc., New York, 1956.

Swanson, C. P., *The Cell,* Prentice-Hall, Inc., Englewood Cliffs, N.J., 1962.

Weiss, P., "From Cell to Molecule" in *The Molecular Control of Cellular Activity,* J. M. Allen, (ed.), McGraw-Hill Book Co., Inc., New York, 1962.

Index

Abbreviations
  of amino acids, 16–17
  of nucleoside phosphates, 128
Acetyl coenzyme A (acetyl CoA), 64, 144
Acetyl phosphate, energy-rich bond, 64
Acid Anydride, 65
ACTH, *see* Adrenocorticotropic hormone
Activation, in biosynthesis, 140, 142–43
  of acetyl, 64, 144
  of amino acids, 152, 158
  of monosaccharides, 163
Activators of enzymes, 47, 49
Active acetate, *see also* Acetyl CoA
  and coenzyme A, 144
  and Krebs cycle, 96
  key intermediate, 117–19
Active carbon dioxide, 144, 146, 164
Active carboxyl, 142
Active glucose, 145, 163
Active site of enzymes, 54–55
Active sulfate, 145
Acyl coenzyme A, and fatty acid synthesis, 164–66
Adenine, 59, 122, 124
Adenosine, 59, 125
Adenosine triphosphate (ATP), 59, 79
  and amino acid activation, 158
  and biosynthesis, 10, 141
  and coupled reactions, 69
  ΔG of hydrolysis, 64
  energy rich bonds, 57ff.
  formation of, 70–80
    from Krebs cycle, 96–97
    in oxidative phosphorylation, 73–77
    in photosynthesis, 77–79
  formula of, 59
  hydrolysis of, 63–64
Adenosyl methionine, 145
Adenylic acid, 128
Adrenocorticotropic hormones, (ACTH), 21, 39–40
Aerobic glycolysis, 94–99
Amino acids, 14–20
  activation of, 144, 152, 158
  chemical properties of, 19
  classification of, 16, 17
  incorporation into proteins, 158–62
  optical activity, 20
  unusual, 18
Amino acid activating enzymes, 152, 158
Amino acid derived hormones, 41
Amino acid sequence in proteins, 23–30
  and base code, 158–62
Amino acyl-tRNA, 144, 153, 158–62
Anaerobic glycolysis, *see* Embden-Meyerhof Pathway
Anions, 7–8
Anticodon, 137, 158, 161
Apoenzyme, 52
Aromatic amino acids, 16–17
Assembly line method of patternization, 147–48
Asymmetric carbon atoms, 83–85
ATP, *see* Adenosine triphosphate
Autotrophic metabolism, 11
Auxins, 39

Bacterial viruses, *see* Bacteriophage
Bacteriophage, 132, 137
Base code, 12, 151–62, *see also* Genetic code
Base pairing, 129, 131, 160
Base ratios
  in DNA, 121, 132
  in RNA, 134
Base sequence as code for amino acid sequence, 162
Beeswax, 107
Bioenergetics, 57–69
Biosynthesis, 12, 139ff.
  energy for, 57–59, 62–69, 141–43
  group activation, 140, 142–43
  of, carbohydrates, 145
    DNA, 145, 151–55
    fatty acids, 144, 164–66
    polysaccharides, 163–64
    proteins, 144, 158–63
    RNA, 155–58
  patternization, 140, 146–48
Biotin, 144
  and fatty acid synthesis, 164

Caloric value of foodstuffs, 117
Carbamyl phosphate, 139
Carbohydrates, 81–101, *see also* individual mono-, di- and polysaccharides
  and Krebs cycle, 94–97
  and Embden-Meyerhof pathway, 93–94
  and phosphogluconate oxidative pathway, 98–99
  energy from, 94, 97
  glycolysis, 93–94
Carbon fixation, 99–101
Carbon dioxide, 94–97, 99–101
  fixation, 99–101
  formation of, 94–97, 118
  reduction to carbohydrate, 99–101
Carboxybiotin, 144

Carboxypeptidase, 26
and amino acid sequence studies, 26–27
Catalysis, 43–45
Cations, 6–8
Cell membrane, 170
Cell types,
animal, 170, 173
bacterial, 171, 174
plant, 169, 172
specialized, 176–77
Cell walls, 169
Cellular organization, 169–76
Cellulose, 89
Cephalins, 108
Cerebrosides, 108–109
Chain elongation in biosynthesis, 140, 143, 146
Chain initiation in biosynthesis, 146
Chlorophyll, 78–79, 174–75
Chloroplast, 174–75
Cholesterol, 112
Choline, 108
Chromosome, 132
Citric acid, 94–97
Citric acid cycle, *see also* Krebs cycle
and energy yield, 97
diagram of, 95
enzyme reactions of, 94–97
in amino acid metabolism, 118
in fatty acid oxidation, 118
CoA, *see* Coenzyme A
Codehydrogenase I, *see* Nicotinamide adenine dinucleotide
Codon, 137, 158–62
Coenzyme, 45, 143
definition of, 45
table of, 46 144–45
Coenzyme A (CoA), 95–97, 144, 164–66
Coenzyme Q, 73–77
Commission on Enzymes of the International Union of Biochemistry, 55
Comparative biochemistry, 5–13
Competitive inhibition, 51–52
Configuration, 84
Conformation of,
DNA, 129–32
proteins, 23, 30–37
Conjugated proteins, 37
Coupled reactions, 67–69
Creatine phosphate, 64
Cristae of mitochondria, 171
C-terminal amino acid, 25
Cytidine, 125
Cytidine diphosphate, 145
Cytidine monophosphate, 9, 126
Cytochromes, 73–77
Cytoplasm, 169, 176, 180
Cytosine, 122, 124

Dark reaction, 99–101
Dehydrogenases, 73
Deoxyribonucleic acid (DNA), 120ff., 129–37
and protein synthesis, 135, 151–53
and RNA synthesis, 135, 151–53, 155–59
as genetic material, 134–37, 151–55
base constituents, 122–25
biosynthesis of, 151–55
structure of, 122, 129–32
transforming principle, 134–36
Deoxyribose, 82
Depot fat, 113
Dextrose, *see* glucose
Dicarboxylic acid cycle, *see* Krebs cycle
Dihydroxyacetone, 82
Disaccharides, 86–87, *see also* individual sugars
Diversity in the biochemical plan, 12–13
DNA, *see* Deoxyribonucleic acid
Double-stranded
DNA, 129–32
RNA, 134
DPN, *see* Nicotinamide adenine dinucleotide

Electron carrier systems, 72–77
Electron microscopy of an,
animal cell, 173
bacterial cell, 174
plant cell, 172
Electron transport, 71–73
and cytochromes, 76–77
and flavoproteins, 76
and oxidation, 71–73
and phosphorylation of ADP, 74–75
Embden-Meyerhof pathway, 93–94
diagram of, 92
relation to Krebs cycle, 99
Endergonic reactions, 61–62, 141
Endoplasmic reticulum, 175
Energetic coupling of reactions, 67–69
Energetics, 60, 141
Energy of activation, 44
Energy-poor bond, 62–65
Energy-rich compounds, 62–67
table of, 64
Energy yield of aerobic glycolysis, 97
anaerobic glycolysis, 93–94
from fatty acid oxidation, 114–17
Enol phosphate, 64–66
Enthalpy, 60
Enthalpy Change (ΔH), 60–61
Entropy, 60–61
Enzyme(s), 43
Enzyme(s), 43ff.
active center of, 55
definition of, 43
inhibition, 47, 49–52
mechanism of action, 52–55

Enzyme(s), specificity of, 50
  structure, 45
Enzyme activators, 47, 49
Enzyme-substrate complex, 53
Ethanol formation, 92
Exergonic reactions, 61–62
  linked to endergonic reactions, 67, 141

FAD, *see* Flavin adenine dinucleotide
Fat(s), *see also* Lipids
  biological function of, 111–13
  biosynthesis of, 164–66
  chemical composition, 9
  as depot material, 113
  energy content, 114, 117
  metabolism, 113–19
Fatty acids, 103–106
  biosynthesis of, 164–67
  branched chain, 105
  cyclic, 105–106
  β oxidation of, 114–17
  saturated, 103
  unsaturated, 104
Feedback control, 40
Fermentation, *see* Anaerobic glycolysis
Ferredoxin, 78
Fischer's projection formula, 84–85
Flavin, 75–76
Flavin adenine dinucleotide (FAD), 75
Flavin mononucleotide (FMN), 75–76
Flavoprotein, 73–76
FMN, *see* Flavin mononucleotide
Free energy change (ΔG), 60–61
  in biosynthesis, 62–69, 141–42
Fructose, 83
Furanose, 86

Galactose, 83
GDP, *see* Guanosine diphosphate
Gene(s), 120
  and DNA, 120, 135–37
  and protein synthesis, 158–62
Genetic code, 151–53, 159–62
Genetic material, *see* Deoxyribonucleic acid
Globin, 33–36
Glucose, 83–84
  activated, 145, 163
  and glycogen synthesis, 163–64
  breakdown,
    by glycolysis, 92–94
  oxidation, Krebs cycle, 94–97
    Phosphogluconate pathway, 98–99
Glucose-1-phosphate, 91, 163
Glucose-6-phosphate, 93
Glucose-6-phosphate dehydrogenase, 98
Glutathione, 140
Glyceraldehyde, 82
Glyceraldehyde-3-phosphate
  in glycolysis, 92–93
  in photosynthesis, 100
Glycerol, 106
Glycogen, 88, 90
  biosynthesis of, 163–64
  structure of, 88, 90
Glycolipids, 109
Glycolysis
  aerobic, 98–99
  anaerobic, 93–94
Glycoside linkage, 86–87
Glyoxylate cycle, 117–19
Golgi complex, 175
Group activation in biosynthesis, 140, 142
GTP, *see* Guanosine triphosphate
Guanine, 122–24
Guanosine, 125
Guanosine diphosphate (GDP), 127
Guanosine triphosphate, 127, 160

Heat of activation, change of (ΔE), 60–61
Heat of reaction, change of (ΔH), 60–61
Helical structure, 31, 130
α-Helix, 31–33
Helix model of DNA, 129–32, 153
  of proteins, 31
Heme, 30
Hemoglobin 24, 33–37
  helix structure in, 34
  structure of, 24
  tertiary structure of 34–36
Hereditary factors, 120, 132, 134–38
Heterotropic metabolism, 11
Hexoses, 82–83
Hexose monophosphate shunt, *see* Phosphogluconate oxidative pathway
High energy bonds, 57–60, 62–69
High energy compounds, 62–69
Histones, 180
Holoenzyme, 52
Hormones, 38–41, 110
  table of, 40, 41, 112
Hydrogen bond, 32–33, 129, 131, 153
  and base pairing in DNA, 129, 131
  in proteins, 32–33
Hydrogen transfer, 72–77
Hypophyseal hormones, 40–41

Induced-fit of specificity, 54
Information molecule, 134–35
Inhibition of enzyme action, 47–51
Inhibitors, 47, 49–52
  competitive, 50–52
  noncompetitive, 50–52
  table of, 49
Inorganic ions
  and biological function, 5–8
  and enzyme action, 46

Inosine, 129
Insulin, 27–28
Interrelations in glucose metabolism, 99, 118
Intracellular bodies or particulates, 169–75
  biochemical properties of, 179–80
  isolation of, 179
Intracellular organization, 169–76
Iron
  in cytochromes, 76–77
  in hemoglobin, 30
  metabolism, 6–7
Isocitric acid, 95–97
Isomerism, 19–20, 84–85

K_m, 48
Kinetics of enzymic reactions, 46–49
Krebs citric acid cycle, 94–97

Lactic acid, 92–94
Lactose, 87
Lecithin, 108
Light as energy source, 57–58, 77–79
Light reaction in photosynthesis, 77–79
Lipid, *see* Fat
Lipids, 102ff.
  compound, 102, 107–110
  fatty acids from, 103–106
  function of, 111, 113
  simple, 106
Lipoproteins, 109
Liver, 179
Lysosomes, 175, 178–80

Malic acid, 95
Malonate, 52
Malonyl CoA, 164–65
Mechanism of enzyme catalysis, 52–55
Melanocyte stimulating hormone, 40
Messenger RNA, 120, 132–35, 137–38, 152–53, 158–62
  and base code, 162
  chemistry of, 133
  function in protein synthesis, 135, 137, 152–153, 158–62
Metabolic pathways, 58, 93–99, 100, 114–19
Metals in biological systems, 5–8, 46
Michaelis constant (K_m), 48
Microsomal fractions, 179–80
Microsomes, *see also* Ribosomes, 179
Mineral elements essential to life, 5–8
Mitochondria, 171, 178–80
Monosaccharide, 81–86
  definition, 81
  function of, 90–91
  nomenclature, 82
MSH, *see* Melanocyte-stimulating hormone
Mucoprotein, 37
Myoglobin, 30, 34, 36

NAD, *see* Nicotinamide adenine dinucleotide
NADP, *see* Nicotinamide adenine dinucleotide phosphate
Nerve Cell, 176–177
Nicotinamide adenine dinucleotide (NAD), 73–76
  in oxidative-phosphorylation, 73–76
  nomenclature of, 75
Nicotinamide adenine dinucleotide phosphate (NADP), 75
  and photosynthesis, 77–79, 99–101
  and phosphogluconate oxidative pathway, 98–99
Nicotinamide nucleotides, 73–76
Nomenclature of enzymes, 55
Noncompetitive inhibition, 50–52
N-terminal residue, 25
N-terminal amino acid analysis, 26
Nucleic acids, 120ff.
  chemistry of, 120–23, 128–29
  function of, 134–38
  see also RNA and DNA
Nucleolus, 169–71
Nucleoproteins, 37
Nucleosides, 122–23, 125
Nucleotides, 122–23, 126–28
  abbreviations for, 128
Nucleus, 169–73, 178–79

Oleic acid, 104
Oligosaccharide(s), 81, 86–87
Optical activity, 19–20, 84–85
Optimal conditions for enzymatic action, 47–49
Orotic acid, 149
Oxaloacetic acid, 95–97
Oxalosuccinic acid, 95–97
Oxidases, 73
Oxidation, and electron loss, 73
β-Oxidation, 114–17
Oxidation potential, 72
Oxidative metabolism, 71, 94–99
Oxidative phosphorylation, 71–77
  and electron transport, 71–73
  ATP yield, 74
  components involved in, 73–77
Oxygen, 7, 72–73
Oxygenases, 73
Oxytocin, 21, 40

Palmitic acid, 103, 166
Patternization in biosynthesis, 140, 146–48
Pentose nucleic acids, *see* Ribonucleic acid
Pentose phosphate pathway, *see* Phosphogluconate oxidative pathway
Pentoses, 82
Peptide bond or linkage, 20–21
Peptide hormones, 21–22

Peptide, 21–22, 40
pH and enzyme activity, 47
Phage, *see* Bacteriophage
Phosphate, 57–58, 63–67, 70ff.
Phosphate bond energy, 57–60, 62–67, 70ff.
Phosphatidal ethanolamine, 108
Phosphatidal choline, 108
Phosphatidal serine, 108, 110
Phosphatidic acid, 107
Phosphoenol pyruvic acid, 64, 92, 94
Phosphogluconate oxidative pathway, 98–99, 118
Phospholipids, 107–109
Phosphorylase, 163
Phosphorylation, oxidative, 71–77
  and photosynthesis, 58, 77–79
Photolysis of water, 78–79
Photophosphorylation, 58, 77–79
  cyclic, 78
  noncyclic, 78–79
Photosynthesis, 78–79, 99–101
  and carbon fixation, 99–101
  and energy transduction, 77–79
  ATP formation, 58, 77–79
Pituitary hormones, 40–41
Pneumococci, 135–36
Polynucleotide(s), *see also* Nucleic Acids, RNA and DNA
  biosynthesis of, 151–58
  chemistry of, 120–23, 128–34
Polypeptide(s), *see also* Protein, 22
Polysaccharide(s), 81, 87–90
  biosynthesis of, 163–64
  breakdown of, 91
  chemistry of, 87–90
Potassium, 5–7
Primary structure of proteins, 23–30
Progesterone, 112
Prosthetic group, 45, 46
Protein(s), 9, 14, 22ff.
  amino acid sequence, 23
  biochemical function, 37–38
  biosynthesis, 158–62
  conjugated, 37
  C-terminal residues, 25
  determinations of amino acid sequence, 25–30
  end group analysis, 25
  helical structure, 24, 30–32
  molecular weights of, 22–23
  primary structure of, 23–30
  secondary structure of, 30–33
  shape, 33–37
  tertiary structure, 33–37
  x-ray analysis of, 34
Protein biosynthesis, 135, 144, 147, 151–52, 158–62
Purine bases, 124–25
Purine nucleotides, 126–28
Pyranose, 85–86
Pyrimidine bases, 122–24
  biosynthesis of, 149–50
Pyrimidine nucleotides, 126–28
Pyrophosphate, 64, 141–43
Pyruvic acid, 93–99

Quinones and oxidative phosphorylation, 73–77
Quaternary structure, 37

Rate of enzymic reaction, 46–49
Reaction specificity, 50
Reaction kinetics, 46–48
Replication, 151–55
Respiratory chain, *see also* Oxidative phosphorylation, 71–77
Ribonuclease, 23, 28–29
Ribonucleic acid (RNA), 123, 132
  biosynthesis of, 151–53, 155–58
  high molecular weight, 134, 137
  messenger, 132, 152
  ribosomal, 132, 134, 135, 137, 152
  structure of, 132–34
  transfer, 132, 152
  viral, 132
Ribose, 82, 84–85, 124
Ribosomal RNA, 120, 134–35, 137
Ribosomes, 135, 152, 178–80
  and protein synthesis, 135, 152
RNA, *see* Ribonucleic acid

Saccharose, *see* Sucrose
Saturated fatty acids, 103–04
Secondary structure of proteins, 30–33
Sodium, 5–7
Soluble ribonucleic acid, *see* Transfer RNA
Specificity of enzyme action, 50, 54–55
Sperm cell, 177
Sphingolipid, 108–10
Sphingosine, 108
Standard change of free energy (ΔG), 60–61, 63–69
  and biosynthesis, 142–43
Starch, 88–89, 163
Stearic Acid, 104
Stereoisomerism, 19–20, 84–85
Sterospecificity in enzyme action, 50
Steric configuration of carbohydrates, 84–85
Steroid, 110–11
Steroid, hormones, 110–12
Sterols, 112
Structure of cells, 168–76
Structure of DNA, 129–34
Structure of proteins, 23–37
Substrate, 44–48
Substrate-linked phosphorylation, 70–71

Substrate specificity, 50
Sucrose, 87
Sugar(s), *see* individual members, also
 Monosaccharide and Disaccharide
Sulfate, 145
Sulfur, 7
Synthetases,
 amino acyl-tRNA, 158
 for DNA, 155
 for glycogen, 163
 for RNA, 157

Template mechanism for patternization,
 147–48
Template RNA, 132–34
Tertiary structure of proteins, 33–36
Testosterone, 112
Tetrahydro folic acid, 144
Thermodynamics, 60–61
Thiamine pyrophosphate, 144
Thioester, 64
Thymidine, 125
Thymine 122, 124
Thymine deoxyriboside, *see* Thymidine
Thyroxine, 41
TMV, *see* Tobacco mosaic virus
Tobacco mosaic virus, 30, 36, 133–34, 137
TPN, *see* Nicotinamide adenine dinucleotide
 phosphate
Trace elements in organisms, 6–8
Transfer RNA, 129, 132–34, 137, 158–62
 chemistry of, 129, 133
 in protein synthesis, 137, 152, 158–62
Transformation of microorganisms, 135–37
Transcription, 151–52, 155–58
Translation, 151–52, 158–62
Tricarboxylic acid cycle, *see* Krebs cycle
Triglyceride, 106, 110
Trioses, 82
Triphosphopyridine nucleotide (TPN), *see*
 Nicotinamide adenine dinucleotide
 phosphate

Ubiquinone, 73–77
UDPG, *see* Uridine diphosphoglucose
Uracil, 123
Uridine diphosphoglucose (UDPG), 145,
 163–64
Unsaturated fatty acids, 104–105
Unity in the biochemical plan, 8–10, 13

V_{max}, 47–48
Vacuole, 175
Van der Waals interactions, 33
Vasopressin, 21, 40
Viruses,
 DNA of, 132
 RNA of, 132, 137
 structure of, 132–33
Vitamins, 12, 144–45

Water, 5, 95
Wax, 107

Xanthine, 124
X-Ray diffraction analysis of
 DNA, 129–32
 proteins, 34–36